TRAVELS
AND
TRADITIONS OF
WATERFOWL

by H. Albert Hochbaum

THE UNIVERSITY OF MINNESOTA PRESS, Minneapolis

*To James Ford Bell, of Minneapolis
who founded the Delta Waterfowl Research Station in 1931*

*to Arthur Sullivan, of Winnipeg
who established the international breadth of its program*

*and to the everlasting fellowship of
scientist and sportsman upon which hinges
the wildfowling of generations to come*

Foreword

THE migration of birds has doubtless fascinated the mind of man throughout history. Certainly the artists of the Altemira Caves must already have been interested, since their drawings include migratory species. Practically all over the world some favorite winter absentee is welcomed back as the harbinger of spring upon its annual return. To Albert Hochbaum, author of this book, living on his Manitoba marsh, it is the Canada Goose and the Whistling Swan that constitute the first tangible guarantee that spring is on its way back, no matter what the frozen lake may be doing at the time or how belated the weather prospects. Seemingly the birds are as sure of themselves — taking their performance year in and year out — as the devisers of our own calendar. And therein lies a patent mystery, since birds are not equipped with sextants and compasses, mathematical tables or the gift of speech. How do they come to be so wise?

The various aspects of this problem have been a matter of observation for centuries and of scientific research for decades. In more recent years some of the refinements of the experimental method have been applied to certain of its phases, such as the physiological timing mechanisms and reproductive rhythms of migrants or the navigational equipment of homing pigeons. Experiments, however, have to be based on previously acquired knowledge derived from observations, and the days of observation are not yet by any means over. Field records remain as important as they have ever been.

When Albert Hochbaum published his first book, *The Canvasback on a Prairie Marsh*, in 1944, he won for himself an enviable reputation as observer, recorder, and artist from which it is safe to predict that his present volume will detract nothing. It has been a more difficult book to write, since it includes a review of much of the literature and questions some of the theories currently held. With his views one may, of course, agree or disagree as one thinks fit, but much of what he has to say is new and deals with an aspect of migration seldom enough touched upon — the matter of *tradition*. In this respect he has made as definite a contribution to the literature as he did with his *Canvasback*, and is doubtless destined to modify present modes of thinking on numerous aspects of bird migration.

Mr. Hochbaum has had opportunities that come to few people to collect the material he now presents to his readers. For sixteen years he has resided at Delta, Manitoba, on the south shore of Lake Manitoba, on one of the most celebrated wildfowl marshes of the province. Here he has canoed, photographed, hunted, and ruminated, in an environment which, although static in its main features, is perpetually undergoing change. He has seen his marsh almost dried out, as in the forties, and virtually flooded out, as in 1954. He has watched the resident populations rise and fall, flourish and fail. As Director of the Research Station, he has organized and conducted pertinent investigations into the field to which he has devoted his life. This station, sponsored by the North American Wildlife Foundation and the Wildlife Management Institute, and operating in an atmosphere of complete academic freedom, untrammeled by Government restrictions and red tape, moreover has won for itself a reputation that has attracted many ornithological celebrities, each of whom has left some constructive contribution behind him. We shall again be grateful that fate has placed so able an observer in such a favorable setting, the fruits of which we can now ourselves enjoy.

To close without a reference to the excellent illustrations which accompany the text would be to do Mr. Hochbaum an injustice. It has been my privilege to be associated with the Delta station for many years. During intermittent visits I have seen the marsh in its varying moods. I can only say that our author-artist has caught the spirit of the birds and their environment as successfully in his drawings as in his writing.

WILLIAM ROWAN

Department of Zoology
University of Alberta

Author's Preface

THIS is a story of the travels of waterfowl. Many discussions of bird passage begin with migration, but I choose to speak first of the flights of ducks and geese on their home range. The wider journeys are not to be understood, I believe, without an examination first of the patterns of local behavior. Part I of this book is therefore an analysis of the movements of waterfowl on their home range on the Delta Marsh in southern Manitoba.

Migration is discussed in Part II as I have studied it directly in the field, mostly in Manitoba, and as I have followed it in the literature for other regions. During the preparation of the manuscript, some helpful friends inquired, in effect: "What you say about waterfowl is understood, but how does one explain the migrations of Arctic Tern and Golden Plover?" I can but reply that this book concerns the birds I have watched. I hope others will make more extensive studies of tern and plover, but I have tried to heed Farner's warning against "the rather frequent tendency to transfer conclusions concerning one species into explanations concerning another." Moreover, this is merely a discussion; I have not aimed at over-all conclusions. I feel, with Herbert Spencer, that "the truth generally lies in the co-ordination of antagonistic opinions," and I simply report observations and ideas that will, I hope, stimulate further study.

A pigeon fancier I know acknowledges no mystery in the homing behavior of his flock. "How do they find their way? By instinct, of course!" So, too, some have explained migration; many unknowns have been catalogued under the convenient tab of instinct. Such an approach does not always take into account our present understanding of bird behavior. However dominant the inborn heritage of action, each bird lives freely in an elastic environment where its responses to its companions and surroundings are constantly being modified through experience. I believe that the migrant may be instinctively related to the patterns of its ecological environment and selects those most closely fitting its innate breeding requirements, but that it must learn its geographical place in its world. The act of migration may be inherent, but the world in which this takes place is learned. If this is so, then for some species the route of migration is handed down through tradition — and this is the theme of Part III.

Throughout the book *waterfowl* refers to North American ducks, geese, and swans of the Family *Anatidae*.

H. A. H.

Delta Waterfowl Research Station
Delta, Manitoba
November 1955

Table of Contents

PART I

Travels of Waterfowl

"When a bird hath flown through the air, there is no token of her way to be found, but the light air being beaten with the stroke of her wings, and parted with the violent noise and motion of them, is passed through, and therein afterwards no sign where she went is to be found."

Wisdom of Solomon

1

Patterns of Local Movement

LISTEN! . . . No, it's only the wind.

"*But listen!* Quiet, Tim, you fool hound-dog." No, it is only the children at their game.

"*Listen!* . . . No, it is nothing at all." A heavy black cloud hangs in the west; through a rift the sun bathes the marsh in gold. The evening flight has begun; small parties of ducks lift from the bay, flying into the northwest. The tall poplar by the channel is dark with a thousand blackbirds creaking and tinkling.

"Listen, listen! . . . Yes, it *is* the swan! *The Whistling Swans are back!*"

Our eyes scan the purple east. There they are: fourteen great white birds halfway across the bay, coming straight toward us, their high-pitched voices yodeling loud and clear. They swerve, moving north to the lake. They turn again, swinging wide; now they are coming back, the south wind on their breasts. Now they are overhead. What a sight to behold! They are dropping, dropping. A dozen yards above the water their necks arch, they set their wings, spreading feet wide like Canvasback. Then softly they alight near Archie's Point. Another leg of their northward journey is completed.

A band of Whistling Swan seen in the evening light of the first day of spring stirs the heart and soul of a man so that, for a moment, his communion with the wilderness is complete. Yet tonight I feel more than the beauty of the scene itself. Here, mind you, in the fading day when you or I might lose ourselves in the maze of marshland, this band of swan has come from far beyond the horizon to a place they have not visited since last spring. There was no faltering; they came unerringly to this small corner of marsh that has been the April rendezvous of Whistling Swans for at least forty years. Tomorrow there will be more, and more again on following days, until the chorus of their multitudes will not let us sleep. Then, sometime in mid-May, they will be on with their journey and Archie's Point will be swanless until next April. . . .

TRAVELS OF WATERFOWL

Saturday night! For those who live in the country, this is the big event of the week: early supper, hurry with the dishes, change to best clothes, and off to town for three hours of shopping and small talk. Last evening Joan and I crossed the marsh at sunset on our way to Portage la Prairie. We had just slipped past Slack's Bluff when Joan touched my arm and I brought the car to a stop. *"There, over toward Portage Creek.* What are they, ducks or geese?" Far to the southeast there hung a thin line above the horizon, a frail wisp of thread, barely visible. We watched in silence as it grew until finally we could make out its components. *"Geese!"* Then, of a sudden, their voices drifted to us on the south wind. *"Wavies!"* We stepped from the car to stand in the gathering dusk as the birds passed. Most were Blue Geese, but their lines were punctuated here and there by Lesser Snow Geese. They flew in a wide line from which sprouted small branches, the whole forming a great blunt "V." As the mass moved it rose and fell as if riding a rolling swell, the individuals within the flock ever shifting position so that the pattern changed constantly. The geese were in full and constant voice, a guttural gabbling accented by high, nasal shouts, by no means as rousing as the whoop of swans or the bark of Canada Geese, but sweet music, nevertheless, over the April prairie.

The flock held steady course; then at a point near Slack's Bluff it turned sharply toward the annual lakeshore stopping place at the mouth of the Whitemud River. As their voices faded, there came a louder clangor from the southeast. As far as we could see came the geese, one broad "V" after another. It was a great moment in my life, and I removed my hat in unconscious response to some inner urge of respect as they passed.

Each flock followed the same route as the first, and as the second group approached Slack's Bluff it turned sharply to the west. Every successive band held a steady course until it reached the turning place where the bend west was made. Not only were these birds moving toward a destination, but their trailway was marked by some special pattern which they followed. Maybe it was Slack's Bluff. Maybe it was the arrangement of the fields or the plan of the marsh and lake beyond or some other features of the landscape near or far. Whatever it was, these geese moving in the boundless prairie skies followed some cue that held them to their route.

The sun has dropped into the lake. It is an April evening, not of one day or of one year, but of at least three hundred April days of sixteen years. I am standing at the bayside. Before me is the vast expanse of marshland still frozen except at the edges, where a black moat of water separates ice from tules. Behind, to the north, is the narrow ridge of woodland that marks the south shore of Lake Manitoba. Beyond that, far past the northern horizon, are the marshes of Winnipegosis, of the Saskatchewan, of the MacKenzie.

The setting sun is the signal for Mallards and Pintails to leave these dark waters and move to other marshlands. Paired drakes and hens in company with their kind rise from the bays and go directly into the northwest. I am impressed by their precision, for, although their numbers are scattered far and wide over the marsh, the departure is not along a solidly broad front. Instead, as the bands leave the bays, the flight resolves into well-defined lanes of travel. The movement over the lakeshore is not in a wide sweep. The crossings are at passes. From where I stand I can see a flight over the village

of Delta; there is another over Dr. Cadham's garden, and still another not far to the east. It has been so for countless springs — the trails to the northwest cross the lake ridge at the same places year after year. Are these passes cues to orientation, each a step in the long journey from the wintering grounds to the breeding marshes far beyond?

The annual return of the Whistling Swan [*] to their April rendezvous, the turning of the wavies at Slack's Bluff, the lakeshore crossings of the Mallard and Pintail are examples of the avian reaction to the pattern of landscape. These movements are not indiscriminate, nor are they directed primarily toward the final destination somewhere beyond. Here is an awareness of special plots of terrain along the way, responses to mere pinpoints on the map of total migratory movements. Here are the resting places and local crossings that are just as incidental, yet just as important, to the over-all journey as a Chicago transfer is to a transcontinental railway passenger. Clearly the Delta Marsh is a key point in the northward travels of a great number of waterfowl. Yet in Manitoba this is but one of many such stopping places. The Libau and Netley marshes at the south end of Lake Winnipeg are hosts to wildfowl each spring. Whitewater Lake, the marshes of Lake Dauphin and Lake Winnipegosis, and the delta of the Saskatchewan are all focal points where ducks, geese, and swans cross or stop for a while on their travels to the breeding grounds. These lakes and marshes are steps along the highway of migration.

There is a temptation to think of the journeys of waterfowl in terms of such steps. For instance, the Canvasback from Chesapeake Bay has a route marked by important stopping places at Lake Erie, Lake Winnebago in Wisconsin, Lake Christina in Minnesota, and Delta in Manitoba, to name but a few. The pattern is so broad, however, that any discussion would soon become lost in complexities should it begin with this wide aspect of migration. The following chapters of Part I, therefore, consider only the local movements of waterfowl on their home range on the Delta Marsh.

The Delta Marsh lies at the south end of Lake Manitoba, separated from the lake by a low, narrow, heavily-wooded sand ridge that skirts the shoreline. Behind the ridge, and protected by it from the lake, the marsh spreads south to reach the rich agricultural land of the Portage Plains. East and west the marshland stretches more than twenty miles, and at its deepest point there are five miles between the agricultural prairie and the lake ridge. From

[*] See Appendix I for scientific names.

6

the air it is seen as a complex pattern of shallow bays, connecting channels, sloughs, and small potholes, all fringed with bulrush or cattail and set in a matrix of *Phragmites*, the tall "yellow cane."

Throughout the season, from spring break-up in April until freeze-up in November, the Delta Marsh has its own population of waterfowl. Early, this is made up mostly of breeding pairs, but soon bands of drakes that have abandoned their nesting hens come to the big marsh for their molting period. Here they don the drab eclipse plumage and become flightless, for ducks, like geese and swans, lose the flight feathers of the wing all at once and are unable to fly until new pinions are grown. Birds-of-the-year add to local numbers; and before summer is old, many youngsters raised elsewhere come to Delta. From early August until heavy frost there are constant arrivals and departures, comings and goings, some birds staying only a few days, others remaining weeks or months.

Not one of these wildfowl finds that a given part of the marsh serves all its needs. There may be a mile or more between the hen's nest and her territory. Most birds find their feeding, loafing, and graveling places at separate locations, often far apart; and each may have more than one locality for these activities. Some Mallards in late summer and autumn regularly travel ten to fifteen miles from their loafing bars to the stubble fields, such trips being made twice daily. Except during the flightless period, each duck takes daily and often lengthy journeys within the realm of the marshland.

In the travel from marsh to lake, the local ducks cross the wooded ridge at the same passes the transients used when they departed northward in migration. When a flock is flushed from the marsh, the birds seldom fly directly

to the lake by the shortest route. Instead they bend their flight east or west toward one of the passes where they cross over the trees to the lake. In August and through autumn Mallards and Pintails that loaf on the lakeshore move over these same passes in their journeys to the stubble fields. Many times I have watched a flock of Lesser Scaup, Redhead, or Canvasback cruise along the lakeshore for a mile or more, then suddenly swing south to cross over a pass to the marsh. One July a band of pre-eclipse Redhead drakes fed daily in a bay east of the village. A quarter-mile flight due north would have given them a direct route; but instead of taking the short cut, they usually moved west a mile to cross at a favored pass.

In general, the width of the lakeshore passes at Delta is 100 to 400 yards, although the core of a pass, through which goes the major flight line, often is narrower than this. The main passage of birds through the pass may vary from day to day, the travel within the boundaries apparently being dictated by the wind's direction. It is not true that all trading is confined to passes; now and then a flock makes a crossing well to one side or the other. On days of heavy traffic, however, hundreds of ducks fly over the pass for every dozen going elsewhere. So closely does the great majority hold to the crossings that these lanes of travel are well-known to guides and hunters.

I have watched the flights over the lakeshore through sixteen years. The pathways have been the same as long as the oldest guides can remember. Dr. Fred Cadham, who has hunted the Delta Marsh since boyhood, tells me that the pass over his cottage has been the same since 1898. For at least fifty-six years — many generations in the life of waterfowl — ducks have moved between marsh and lake on this same path. I suspect the history of Cadham's Pass is much older than this.

The gunner's eye detects little reason for this regularity as he watches from marsh level. But a bird's-eye view from an aircraft reveals a sharp relation between the flight lines and the pattern of the terrain (Figure 1). Most passes are at narrows where marsh water comes close to the lake ridge. Others are at channels flowing near the ridge or cutting through to enter the lake. Some are at old creek beds, long dry and overgrown, yet clearly defined from the air. In short, the pass is where there is the shortest distance between marsh and lake.

Such trailways are not confined to the lakeshore. These are doorways to the north, but the marsh itself is a pattern of aerial lanes as well marked by the flights of waterfowl as the roads on a highway map. In the marsh the travel follows the path of least resistance; that is to say, the trails take the

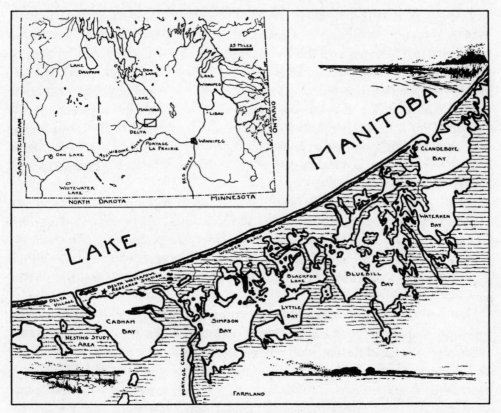

Figure 1. The pattern of the Delta Marsh

easiest low-altitude routes over land, usually following the shortest path between two water areas. Where two water areas are connected by gap, channel, or creek, this is the passageway for waterfowl. In the absence of a waterway, the pass is at the narrowest neck of land separating two areas; or a flight may follow a dry channel bed that once linked two bodies of water. Where a creek meanders aimlessly, the more direct overland route may be favored.

The lakeshore passes are used regardless of wind and weather, but many marsh crossings serve only in certain winds. A given pass may be used regularly when the wind blows from the northwest or southeast, but may seldom or never be followed when the wind is from another direction, at which time travel is made by some more favorable course. Thus, in moving over the marsh, the duck has several trailways, from which one is selected according to the wind. Many a gunner has been disappointed when a shifting wind robbed him of a flight of ducks he had located the previous day. One afternoon Peter Ward and I stood at a narrow neck of land between two

9

large bays. About 3 P.M. there began a flight of Canvasback that moved over us in an apparently endless stream until we departed at dusk. The wind was just south of west, and the birds came out of the northeast, alighting in the bay west of us to feed on the abundant beds of sago pondweed. It happened that we had but half a dozen shells apiece; hence it was with keen anticipation that Ward returned to the spot the following afternoon, well equipped for a fine shoot. But the wind had changed and, although he remained until dusk, no birds crossed the narrows. As he paddled home, Pete found the west bay again littered with Canvasback which apparently had arrived by some other route.

Some passes are very narrow. The crossing of ducks just mentioned was confined to a span hardly more than 30 yards wide. At one narrow gap the lane of flight is not more than 25 yards across, the width of the waterway. I know of several other passes that are similarly restricted. On the other hand, where a long thin strip of land separates two large lakes, the passes may be very wide.

Many of the passes are used by all species of ducks. Some, however, are followed frequently by one species and seldom used by others. I believe this is simply because different kinds move to different places to loaf and feed. Canvasbacks that rest daily on the open water of Cadham Bay fly east to their feeding waters over a route that is seldom followed by Mallards. Mallards crossing the marsh to stubble fields take flight lines rarely used by Canvasbacks. Several passes at Delta are used heavily only in late autumn, when Lesser Scaup crowd the marsh.

Since the marsh is a maze of scattered potholes, channels, bays, and sloughs, a flight of any distance must take a duck over a number of passes. The pass itself is merely a step in the flight trail. In general, traffic from one pass to another follows well-defined routes. Where ducks cross large bodies

of open water, the travel usually is straight and direct. But where the landscape has outstanding landmarks, the flight may be influenced by these. Where, for example, an open body of water is broken by an island, flight lines generally cut close to the isle. Where a bay has an undulating shoreline or clumps of islands, the trails digress according to these land patterns. Travel frequently follows the shoreline, usually swinging around rather than across points of land jutting into the bay. Where the shoreline is much broken, the trail moves from point to point. The main course of travel seldom swings over islands, more frequently following the waterways between them.

The height at which the bird moves greatly influences the course of travel. When flying low, a duck tends to obey land patterns in almost every detail; a shoreline or a creek is followed through all its meanderings. When moving high, the flight is more direct. The general course of a creek is followed, for instance, but the line of flight "cuts corners" and does not wind as the creek does.

On several recent occasions the establishment of new trails has come in response to changes in the pattern of the marsh. In the late autumn of 1945 a pond was dug at Station headquarters, located in a dry field where ducks seldom crossed. Next spring, waterfowl began using it, and in their approach arrived along regular flight paths never used before. In a south wind the line most frequently taken by Blue-winged Teal cuts over my yard, and we now see ducks flying past the kitchen window, where they seldom came before.

The tight adherence to trailways is well known to the hunter who sets out his rig of decoys where the ducks will cross. Gunners often refer to the pathways as "leads," and the most successful native guides are those who are familiar with these in any wind. Some locations are "handed down" from father to son among the guides. Old Dan Ducharme once took me to a lead where the Duke of York had shot when he visited the marsh in 1901. This place is still a choice location for gunning Canvasback in a south wind.

No doubt every marsh and lake across the land has its leads and passes, its "Narrows" or its "Hole-in-the-wall" where generations of gunners have shot. Wildfowlers, as a matter of fact, distinguish "pass shooting" from other types of gunning, and some of the most famous duck-hunting places are at passes. When a gunner travels to a new ground, he spends the first day of his visit studying the pattern of the flights to detect the flight lines. One old-time gunner visiting Delta for the first time spent a few minutes with a map of the marsh and then went directly to a narrows connecting two bays, where he found himself located on one of the best passes in the region.

At Buckeye Lake, Ohio, Trautman (1940:88) observed that in the diving ducks "the outstanding feature of arriving flocks was their pronounced tendency to approach the lake at or within a fourth of a mile of Sellers Point. During twelve years of observations at least 65 per cent of all arriving flocks came to the lake within a fourth of a mile of that point." In southern Oregon, Robert H. Smith (letter) noted that in local feeding flights out of Klamath Valley "both ducks and geese follow passes across the ridges to other parts of the basin and these passes are favorite shooting spots, particularly if it is windy. It is an odd sensation to hide among the sagebrush and junipers on a mountain pass and watch the birds beat their way up to you."

Geese and swans, like ducks, cross the lakeshore at the same places year after year. Some of these passes are the same as those used by ducks; others are at independent crossings which ducks seldom follow. Given the same wind, geese fly day after day along a line of flight from lake to stubble fields, often maintaining this regularity despite a daily barrage of gunfire met along the way. The geese seem more sensitive than ducks to changes in wind direction, however, and the slightest shift in the breeze will often prompt them to select a different flight-line. In a location I have watched for many years, the geese, I am confident, will come over in a southwest wind. In all other winds they cross elsewhere and, after many fruitless dawn experiences, I have learned that one may as well stay home as to go there when the wind is wrong.

Waterfowl are not the only birds that use regular lanes of travel. Reynaud (1899) noticed that other kinds follow "air roads invisible to our eyes, but which can be revealed by observation. The bird, like the quadruped, contracts the habit of always returning to the same point by the same route." In autumn the Black-bellied Plovers loaf on the lakeshore sandbars and, like Mallards (but not with them), they make twice-daily trips across the marsh to the prairie, where they feed on fallow fields rather than on stubble. In these feeding travels, plover move along the same flight lines day after day. When the Franklin's Gulls trade back and forth between lake and prairie, their travel shows a regularity similar to that of waterfowl. In the Herring Gull, Tinbergen (1952:5) found that the route of local travel in dune country "changes with changing wind." Black-crowned Night Herons follow established routes to the feeding shallows. A pair of crows I watched one year used the same route daily when traveling between lake ridge and the

meadowland a mile south of the marsh. A robin almost always flies to the same fencepost in my yard before dropping to the lawn. When children frighten the Yellow Warbler from her nest by the hatchery door, she departs the same way every time. The Yellow-headed Blackbirds that steal grain from the duck pen generally use a routine approach. Day after day the Marsh Hawk that nests near the channel may be seen on its regular course down the north side of Cadham Bay.

Here is an orderly pattern of movement. The waterfowl of the Delta Marsh respond to the physical design of their environment in much the same way as elk or mice follow their earth-worn trails. But unlike the mammals, whose feet mark the paths for all to see, the bird leaves no record of its passing. These waterfowl must obey the natural shape of the land and water when moving from one area to another, responding to visual cues as these are presented by points and bays, channels and islands, reeds and willows.

Here is a rule of order, a design of habit. Free as the winds to fly when, where, and how they might choose, wildfowl hold almost as closely to lanes of passage as do earthbound mammals. Such habit, such conservation of energy, is probably a universal trait of animals. The game trails of larger mammals are well known to hunters; and who is there who has not seen the Meadow Mouse path in an old field? Our own lives we know to be influenced by habit. This permits us to accomplish complicated acts with the least expenditure of energy; it simplifies our world. Daily we take the same route to school or office, although many variations of the trail might be followed. We walk along the same streets, over regular short cuts to shop at the usual stores, and pick up the morning paper at the same corner because it is easier to follow an established pattern than to pioneer a new trail every day.

"There are few aspects of animal behavior that have been more neglected by present-day zoologists than learning, which we may provisionally define as that internal process which manifests itself as *adaptive change in individual behavior as a result of experience.*" W. H. Thorpe (1950:387)

2

Learned Response to the Environment

THE system of aerial trails about a duck marsh is evidence that waterfowl react positively to their environment. What is behind this response to their surroundings? Is this rigid, set, innate behavior? A downy Canvasback less than a day old benefits from neither past experience nor parental guidance when it first takes to water; it swims without an intervening period of learning. Thenceforward throughout its life as a duckling and as an adult, its activities are directed primarily toward its aquatic world. In flight the duck's movements are physically unbounded; it is free to go where its wings might take it. Yet its aerial journeys are restricted largely by the pattern of water on the earth below. Hence, in its selection of trailways about a marsh, a duck may be following, in large measure, an inborn attachment to water.

We must believe, however, that adherence to regular flight trails and passes is far above the level of purely inborn behavior. This we know to be true because the trail has its beginning and end; a duck departs from a special place and arrives at a particular destination. The starting point, the trail, and the destination vary with individuals and with groups; different birds or flocks select different starting points, trails, and destinations, and these are always small parts of a complex landscape. Such travel cannot rely on innate behavior alone. The loafing spots, the feeding places, and the trails must be found, either by exploratory movements or by following the actions of experienced companions. In other words, the feeding and loafing places are learned, and the trails between these are learned routes. A duck, then, is innately attracted to its special environment, but it *learns* its position within that sphere.

14

Let us now consider a duckling, a downy Canvasback that has just emerged from its shell. Shortly after its down is dry it ventures forth into the world equipped with a remarkable set of actions with which it successfully meets its environment. It can walk. The moment it touches water it swims. It can dive under water. The complicated process of picking up an object with its bill is readily accomplished. The initial actions are not learned movements; these are the duckling's endowment, its inborn heritage. The fact that a bird hatched alone in an incubator accomplishes these same acts before it ever sees another of its kind, or before it has lived to experience its environment is evidence that they are not learned. This we know as *inborn, innate,* or *instinctive* behavior.*

As the duck grows older there is a *maturation* of further instinctive acts These begin to function as the time for their use arrives, just as the feathers of the specific color pattern develop on a growth schedule. The act of flight, for instance, is not learned. This is merely the development of an instinct that will gain maturity when the primary feathers of the wing are fully grown and the bird is physically ready to fly. Ducks raised in small pens where flight was impossible were able to fly when first cast into the air. The act of flight is as much a heritage as walking, but does not mature until the

* Thorpe (1951a:3) explains that before about 1935 the term *instinct* "had tended to fall out of use among biologists, while the psychological schools of behavior study tended to use it for behavior which is: 1. Relatively complex; 2. Markedly constant and therefore presumed to be inherited; and 3. Related to a situation rather than to locally-defined stimulus. In the last 15 years, however, comparative ethologists have been using the term in a much more precise sense and have been finding it almost essential for their discussions. The attempt has been made to formulate this more recent usage in the following definition: Instinct: *An inherited and adapted system of co-ordination within the nervous system as a whole, which when activated finds expression in behavior culminating in a fixed action pattern. It is organized on a hierarchical basis, both on the afferent and efferent sides. When charged, it shows evidence of action-specific-potential and a readiness for release by an environmental releaser.*" Tinbergen, in his book *The Study of Instinct* (1951:112), says that "it may seem a little early to attempt a definition of 'an instinct'; yet in my opinion, such an attempt could be of value for future research. I will tentatively define an instinct as a hierarchically organized nervous mechanism which is susceptible to certain priming, releasing and directing impulses of internal as well as of external origin, and which responds to these impulses by coordinated movements that contribute to the maintenance of the individual and the species."

15

Mating displays of Canvasback

wings have reached the necessary stage of development. Until the duck has completed its life cycle, which in most species covers a period of about fifteen months (from birth to rearing of young and post-breeding molt), new innate actions become ready for use as the need for their function arises. The hen does not build her nest until she is nearly a year old; but when nesting time arrives, the structure is completed without any previous experience and is essentially the same as nests of her ancestors. Mating behavior, the displays and voicings characteristic of pair formation and nuptial life, while they may see rudimentary expression during the natal or juvenile period, are not fully developed until the bird enters its reproductive cycle.

We see, now, that the basic actions by which a duck meets its world are inborn rather than learned. Notwithstanding the strength of this inborn guidance, each bird's behavior is modified by learning; each individual must learn to meet its environment. Lorenz (1935) clearly shows how the object toward which an innate activity is directed may be learned. Examine, for instance, the feeding actions. Eating movements are innate, but the object toward which those actions are directed — food — is learned. A duck learns what to eat and what not to eat. Furthermore it learns what foods it prefers and those that are of secondary palatability. The development of feeding behavior in captive-reared Canvasback ducklings at Delta is as follows: First the feeding actions are indiscriminately directed toward almost any object the duckling encounters. This behavior begins in the incubator when the birds, but a few hours old, explore the wire with their bills. Then, when the ducklings are placed in brooder pens, the exploratory billings continue, nibbling at the wires, at the cloth screen, at straw and sticks. Objects which are not food may be eaten. When, on their second day, chopped egg is placed before them, it is billed only casually at first in this random sampling. But the egg, of all objects in the pen, is edible; soon the

16

feeding actions are directed almost entirely toward the food trays. Hard-boiled egg, let us note, is a new food to Canvasback, unknown to its species in the wild.

In a few days the diet of the downy Canvasback is changed, egg being replaced by a mash of mixed cereals, dried greens, and powdered animal products — again, a new food in the natural history of Canvasback. This is accepted readily. Here, with mash, the youngsters soon demonstrate learned discrimination. They show a dislike of ground corn, expertly separating this from other ingredients of their meal. I suspect that this same approach to food takes place in the wild; through the experience of trial and error the duckling finds the food most useful to it. True, the youngling follows its mother, being led by her to choice feeding localities. Some foods may be learned by the example of her feeding behavior, but it is clear that much of the nourishment is found independently. Many times I have seen the mother diving, while the young fed at the surface, no doubt on some other food.

It is the same with flight. The bird flies instinctively, but it must learn to relate this act to its environment. For instance, a duck must learn the fine art of alighting. Young on their first flights are often hesitant and apparently bewildered when approaching a landing, often coming down with a hard splash. They must learn to direct the course of their aerial travels. The movements of the tail-rudder are often so awkward in new-flying juveniles that these actions clearly distinguish them from adults. In the making of a turn, for example, the tail may be tipped too far to one side; then the bird over-compensates with "reverse rudder" and the tail tips too far in the opposite direction. The use and dangers of the wind must be learned. Down-wind landings are such frequent mishaps in young waterfowl that one must believe that it is only through experience that they learn to alight facing the wind. They learn to relate their speed of flight to terrestial objects so that they do not overshoot their mark. During these early days of flight there develops the unity of instinct and learning by which the bird masters its aerial environment.

It is much the same with other basic movements. A duck swims instinctively, but *it must learn where to swim*. On land, when it travels there (as when a hen walks through the grass to her nest), it walks instinctively, but it learns where to walk. Its courtship and reproductive activities are instinctive, but it learns the companions toward which these activities are directed. Thus, while a duck's behavior is ruled by instinct, its place in the

17

environment and in its society is learned. "A very large part of learning in birds is to be considered as the process of adjusting fixed automatisms or patterns of behavior to the changes and chances of the world" (Thorpe, 1951b:8).

The duck does not learn what it *wants* to learn; there is no evidence of any conscious direction of experiences and activities toward learning. It learns those companions and parts of its environment toward which it is directed by its instincts. Since the pattern of inborn behavior shows no measurable variation from one generation to the next, the species behavior shows little change. The wild Canvasback of today learns the same things its ancestors learned: the foods that are edible, the feeding places, the routes to and from food, the mate, the nest site, the nest and the young. When confronted with new situations related to basic rules of life, however, the Canvasback and other ducks are remarkably plastic in their ability to learn their relation to new (for the species) objects and places. I have already noted the young Canvasback's ability to learn foods not naturally available. Captive ducks at Delta learn to recognize the human "companions" who supply their needs, and they recognize objects related to food, such as the grain pail. They learn the functional parts of their highly artificial environment: metal swimming tank, food trays, brooders. In the wild, too, ducks have learned to adjust themselves to changes. None of the cultivated cereal grains are natural foods, for example, but Mallard and Pintail now seek these for food.

Some species accommodate themselves to changes more readily than others. In our banding traps we find all kinds, young and old alike, feeding readily on wheat or barley. Indeed, these grains soon become preferred foods, young ducks returning again and again to the traps for meals. But only two species, Mallard and Pintail, regularly forage in the stubble fields for these exotics. In some regions, these two species now feed almost exclusively on cultivated grains in late summer and autumn, despite an abundance of natural food. Arthur S. Hawkins tells me that in Illinois there is evidence that the Wood Duck is learning to feed on upland corn fields. Often we see individual variations in the pattern of learning — that is to say, in a large flock of captives, certain birds learn places and objects not learned by others. A captive female European Widgeon, for example, has learned to jump to the top of a wire frame in the winter pen at Delta, and for three years she has spent much of her time perched there, although no other ducks have followed her action.

18

LEARNED RESPONSE TO THE ENVIRONMENT

Several farmers on the Portage Plains have told me of their experience in moving duck nests during spring cultivation. When the hen is flushed in front of the tractor, the farmer lifts the nest carefully and moves it to a new location, where straw is often thrown over it for cover. Many times, according to these accounts, the hen returns to accept the nest in its new location and continue her incubation. Sowls (1951:56) gives an account of one Pintail hen which tolerated the moving of her nest four times. It was moved about seven feet (the width of the cultivator) each of the first three times and twenty feet on the fourth shift, so that when the farmer, Murray Werbiski, showed Sowls the incubating hen, her nest was at least forty-one feet from its original location.

Ducklings reared by foster mothers learn to adapt themselves to parents of entirely different species (Lorenz, 1935, 1937). A brood of Gadwall hatched and reared at Delta by a White Leghorn hen accepted her as their mother and learned some of her gallinaceous calls, to which they responded.

It is easier to cite examples of the duck's ability to learn than it is to establish the point beyond which learning ceases to function. For example, the female is aware of the location of her nest in the intricate grassy pattern of the meadow, but she does not learn the identity of her eggs. Some nesting females have been known to sit for long periods on stones. A brood mother learns the identity of her youngsters, but she cannot count them. When a brood is disturbed, the hen may return to retrieve only a part of her family. If others are beyond sight and sound, one or two young will satisfy her maternal instincts and she does not seek out the remainder of her family. A duck or goose with one wing permanently pinioned by amputation does not learn that it is unable to fly; when pursued it makes futile attempts to take wing.

It is not the purpose here to make a thorough analysis of learned behavior.* I simply wish to show how the bird learns its position in its environment and among its companions and that such behavior is directed by the ruling instinct. We must observe, however, that a duck learns not only by its own experiences, but also from the experienced actions of social companions. A captive duck living in isolation learns the objects to be eaten and those to be avoided quite independently. It learns its position within its environment so that it moves to its feeding tray, water tank, or brooder when hungry, thirsty, or cold. It may reach adulthood, learning which ob-

* For a discussion of learning in birds and a recent bibliography on the subject, the reader is urged to read Thorpe, 1951b.

jects enable it to satisfy its innate requirements, thus demonstrating the ability of the single bird to learn through its own experiences. An isolated duck, however, is found only in the laboratory, for in the wild, waterfowl are gregarious and highly social. From the beginning, in the society of the brood, the duck lives in the companionship of other members of its kind, and the actions of the individual are ever influenced by the behavior of the society. Hence we must discuss learned behavior as it relates to the individual in its social group.

In their society the waterfowl do many things together. They feed together; and this is a more efficient way of life than isolated search by each individual for its own separate food supply. They loaf together; and alertness to danger is more efficient in a resting group than with the lone bird. The society is functional. Companion-hunger is not merely the desire for associates; it is the urge to do things in companionship. We note, too, that every waterfowl society is made up of lesser social groups, each bound together by common behavior characteristics. On the May marsh, for instance, we find the following social units: *pairs in migration, resident pairs on territory, prenuptial courting parties, hens with broods, stag parties of molting males.* Each bird, then, desires not only companionship; it seeks special kinds of companions (Lorenz, 1935, 1937). Some of the social groups so formed are exclusive societies, membership depending upon the individual's position in the reproductive cycle. Members of these different assemblages are most discriminating in their choice of companions. In May a molting drake never joins a cluster of courting birds, nor do the sexually active males team up with the molters. Nor do pairs join courting birds. Each belongs to the clan of its own kind, not simply because it is the same species, but because it behaves as its chosen companions behave. On a sunny April afternoon one may distinguish at least three of these societies and witness their complete isolation, although circumstances bring them close together. Among the Canvasback on the bay there is an isolated pair, no doubt local breeders. Feeding busily nearby are five pairs. Each hen holds close to her drake, but it is obvious that all together make up a unit band, probably pairs that are migrating together. Finally there are five drakes and a hen together, the males alternately displaying and pursuing the female, a prenuptial courting party. No group intrudes on the others, nor is there intermingling of the societies.

There must be some means of communication by which the social bond is established and maintained. So with waterfowl there is a rudimentary

"language." In part, this language is expressed vocally; a duck is aware of its companions through auditory as well as visual perception. The peeping of ducklings holds the brood together in dense vegetation, and their voicings identify their position to their mother. In turn, the ducklings follow the low voice of the parent when she moves ahead of them in dense growth. When Mallards and Pintails fly northward on April evenings, I hear their soft chuckles, which undoubtedly are a factor in holding bands together when overtaken by darkness. On evenings when Coots move in spring passage I can mark the pattern of their unseen numbers by voices drifting down. April nights are alive with the cheeps of migrant songbirds. Such simple notes are termed "contact-calls." The contact-call has no seasonal periodicity. Often it is as clear a mark of identification as the feathers themselves. It identifies the *individual* of the species and its *position*. Such notes are generally short, simple, and, for many species, easily imitated by man. While I was writing this page, a Black-crowned Night Heron passed over the marsh close by, and from my door I uttered a loud "quock." The bird turned immediately to bend its flight my way. Contact-calls function to hold a group of birds together, and probably tell very little of what the individual is doing.

21

Ducks and geese have a rather broad vocabulary above the level of the contact-call, special voicings that identify the *situation* as well as position. In situations related primarily to survival there is a vocabulary which, like the identification call, is not seasonal. It functions to identify the situation at any time of the year: the presence of food, the contentment of safe loafing, alarm. The Mallard hen gives a rapid "tuckata-tuckata-tuckata" series of notes in the presence of feed. A series of loud, descending quacks, which Lorenz (1953) terms the "decrescendo call" and which hunters refer to as the "hail call," is given only in undisturbed groups of Mallard. A low, single "whank" is uttered in alarm. The feeding and hail calls are imitated the world over by hunters to lure Mallards to the gun. The Canada Goose has a distinct note for alarm and the presence of food. One of the most beautiful utterances of waterfowl is the departure "song" of the Whistling Swan, a melodious, soft, muted series of notes which in my experience always precedes the take-off run when the birds are about to fly. This pre-flight melody is probably the "swan song" of legend, for when a swan is shot and falls crippled to the water, it utters this call as it tries in vain to join its fellows in the sky.

For each social group of the reproductive season there are notes that identify the *condition* of the bird as well as the situation. These are presented only during the times of the year coinciding with the periods of the reproductive cycle to which they are hinged. Such voicings are uttered by and draw responses from only those individuals which, by reason of their physiological condition, fit the special group of sexually active birds. In prenuptial courtship, all drakes have notes that advertise their sexual status, such as the catlike "mee-owh" of the Redhead drake or the sharp whistle of the male Pintail. Only sexually active birds respond to this breeding-season vocabulary. By following a group from prenuptial courtship to the mated pair, we find some notes of the drake to be directed only toward males, these no doubt constituting sexual challenge. Other calls and displays are aimed primarily at the female. In the family group, both young and mother have voicings delivered only in certain situations — that is, when traveling, when escaping danger, when captured by enemy.

All the *notes* of a duck are innate. The *response* of a fellow duck to those notes may be inborn, as probably applies in courtship; or the voice of a companion may be learned, as the young learn the call-note of the mother (Fabricius, 1951). There is some interspecific response to calls identifying situation. I have seen Pintails turn sharply toward the feeding call of a

22

female Mallard. Such individuals no doubt have lived with Mallards, thus having learned to associate this series of notes with a favorable situation.

It is essential that we understand the limits of this "language." This is not communication as we know it in our highly articulate human intercourse. The call of a bird is an innate vocal response to certain stimuli. These may be inner stimuli, such as are induced by hormonal changes in the sexually active bird. Or the responses may be to outer stimuli, such as the presence of food or enemy. The voice is merely the inborn response to a condition or situation. The reaction on the part of the companion, whether innate or learned, is an answer to an outer stimulus, the note heard. Full response, however, depends upon inner forces. A passing Mallard may not come to the feed call unless the stimulus of an empty gizzard directs it to respond. The Canvasback hen does not respond to the courting note of a Canvasback drake unless her position in the sexual cycle so directs her.

An insight into the operation of the avian vocabulary may be had, I believe, by drawing an analogy from human behavior. Baby tumbles down the steps and immediately begins to cry. The crying of the infant is not consciously directed toward the parent; the situation demands that the baby cry and it cannot avoid the act. The child's mother responds by running to the scene of the accident, directed there by the child's voice and her parental drive. The voice in ducks is similar to the cry of the injured human infant in that it identifies the *individual* and it may also identify the *situation* and the *condition*; but the voice does not consciously convey a message.

Certain sounds, not vocal, which are related to functional movements, may serve as signals. I have lured Mallard, Gadwall, and Blue-winged Teal into a dense stand of bulrush by swishing my hand in the water to simulate feeding sounds. Martin Bovey told me that on the Currituck Sound he saw a guide bring Lesser Scaup to his stool on a calm day by sloshing his feet in the water. There are reactions to certain sounds that are not to be explained. This morning three White-winged Scoters slipped by me at a distance of five hundred feet, heading pell-mell for the open lake. I gave a loud yell and immediately the band turned to fly back over me. Forbush (1925: 276) tells how hunters along the New England coast bring these Scoters within gunshot by firing a charge or by shouting from a dory. I have seen Lesser Scaup and Green-winged Teal swing back over my blind when I beat the paddle sharply on the side of the canoe. A quick wave of the hat or a kick of the boot sometimes serves to turn a flock into the decoys. This might be explained on the basis of curiosity. I suspect, however, that a band of ducks seeking congenial company might turn at almost any noise strange or poorly heard, making the full response when the source was identified. The hunter's rule when calling ducks or geese is to keep quiet after the birds have turned, lest the ruse be detected.

Before leaving the subject of voice, note must be made of the duck's ability to localize sound. Waterfowl readily locate a noise even though they may be moving rapidly through the air and the source of the sound is hidden from their sight. Once a band of passing Redhead drakes wheeled to fly directly over my hiding place when I imitated a Redhead female. In autumn twilight Peter Ward and I have called Mallards directly to our voices, although we were hidden and without decoys.

Movement is another means of communication. All or most functional actions serve as signals. For instance, in ducks the quickly lifted head is a signal of alarm. A hunter attempts to sneak up on a flock of loafing Mallards, but one bird sees him, lifts its head, and in a flash every head in the flock is raised, all alert, although only one bird saw the hunter's movement. The lifted head of the first bird was simply an adjustment; he raised his eye-level to see better. His movement released similar actions in his companions which, either innately or through conditioning, associate the sudden lifting of the head with the presence of danger. When the hunter makes another false move, the entire flock is away in a flash, although only several may have seen his second blunder. The action of an individual is repeated by the flock. Obviously this rapid reaction is of great survival value; escape movements would be far less efficient if each duck examined the cause of an alarm before departing.

The native guide's explanation of the first Mallard's behavior would be that this bird *told* the others of the hunter's presence. We know that his action, as a signal, is merely a response to a situation. The drake does not intentionally communicate with his fellows, and his behavior is the same when he is alone. Let us note that the lifted head is not a stereotyped response to danger, but depends entirely on the Mallard's condition. During the summer wing-molt, when the male is flightless, he quickly *lowers* his head when aware of danger, and the lowered head is the signal for other flightless males to lower theirs. The flightless drake does not wish to see better but to avoid being seen, and with lowered head he is much less conspicuous. The same behavior is to be noted in a wounded duck.

When the mother Blue-winged Teal feigns injury in the presence of a

In Canada Geese there is a nervous shaking and uptilting of
the head when a bird is disturbed.

man, she does not communicate a message of danger to her young. When
they hear her distress notes, they seek to escape perils of which they are
not aware; the response is to the mother's voice, not to the danger. Thus
one summer day a village-bred family of Blue-winged Teal walked into my
yard, the babies still wearing the egg-tooth, evidence that they were less
than forty-eight hours out of the shell. The mother was very tame, not at
all bothered by us as we followed close behind, nor were the babies disturbed. We herded the family into the corner of the fence, and there I
gently lifted the hen from the ground. The moment I touched her she uttered an alarm note, and the ducklings quickly hid in the grass.

In Canada Geese, as in several other geese, there is a nervous uptilting
and shaking of the head when a bird is disturbed. As one individual begins
this action, its companions become alert, and the movement is repeated by
all members of the flock. When shaking reaches a certain degree of intensity,
the birds invariably take to the air. "Such formalized preparatory movements often have communicative function, each individual of the species
being brought into the flying mood by its companions' movements" (Tinbergen, 1942:90).

Again, if we consider the social releasers as a part of the bird's vocabulary, we may draw an analogy from human behavior. We, too, have a vocabulary of signals. A neighbor drops in to sit for a chat. Half an hour later he
places his hands on the sides of the chair. He has not yet said, "Well, I must
be running along." But the signal of his hands cannot be mistaken, and the

25

moment he makes the next move — pressing down on his hands — I am rising too, ready to bid him goodbye. Children quickly learn to interpret the actions of parents or teacher, anticipating pending behavior on the basis of signals.

As with voice signals, there may be interspecific responses to action signals. When I approach a flock of mixed species of ducks loafing on a sand bar, they all raise their heads, regardless of the species of the individual that first responded to my presence. Many species of ducks react to the alarm signal of Canada Goose, and these geese to the actions of ducks. Feeding actions draw interspecific responses; ducks of many kinds react to the feeding movements of Whistling Swans. When the swan dips its head to dig for sago tubers, ducks swim over to rob the gleanings. Canvasbacks and Redheads often join feeding Lesser Scaup; Pintails join Mallards.

The reply to a signal, whether vocal or active, is often immediate — as sharp, almost, as the response of the electric light to the turn of a switch. This is especially true of situations related to reproduction or to survival, where instant reaction is the key to life. All social communication, however, is not limited to the sharp response. Every action of an individual or group identifies its behavior to other members of the society. Since it is easier for members of a social group to do things at the same time, every action is a cue or signal, and the behavior of the individual is repeated by the crowd. If a duck had a creed it would be: Do as others do; go where others go. When one bird happens on a choice bed of food, it is easier for the group to feed there than for each member to seek out its own special plot. When one of a band of Lesser Scaups begins to dive busily over a sago bed it has just located, its lead is the signal for companions to come hither and feed in the same place. When one small party finds a safe loafing bar, the locality soon is the resting place of many. In any social gathering of waterfowl the members do the same things at the same places at the same times. In old birds this may be merely a matter of convenience; in ducklings, the very survival of the individual hinges on co-ordinating its behavior with that of its companions. A bird thus learns by following the actions of others more experienced.

A striking example of group behavior is seen when a gathering is confronted by an entirely new situation. In late April, when Lesser Scaups litter the bay in their many hundreds, they depart quickly from the edge in escape movements when I walk boldly to the shore. But when I sneak through the tules unseen, then remove my plaid shirt to wave it above my

head, the nearest birds stop their feeding to watch, first in alarm, then to swim closer to gain a better view of this strange thing. Soon most of the ducks within a radius of a hundred yards have stopped feeding and are swimming toward the shirt. Many of these, because of the undulating shore-line, cannot see the shirt; they are following others that do see it. Such "tolling," often accomplished with a dog, was once a common ruse of hunters to bring birds to the gun. By the same methods, antelope and sometimes deer may be brought within gun range. How like our own human behavior! Surely each of us at some time has interrupted the business of the moment to follow with quickened step a gathering crowd of people without knowing what draws them together.

The same sympathetic behavior is to be seen in the selection of flight routes. When I flush a band of Mallards on the lakeshore in August, they do not depart individually to all points of the compass. After the initial surprise, there is a regrouping, and most of the birds go away together in one direction to some other part of the lake or marsh. Since these August aggregations often take on new members daily, it may be assumed that some of these are newcomers which are merely following the actions of experienced birds. One duck goes where its companions go and in doing so it learns the way. The same holds for young birds, such as the color-banded individuals which first meet the world from the Station ponds. At first their outward journeys take them no farther than the nearby slough or bay edge, and in such flights they are in their own small company. It is not long, however, before they return with unbanded, wild birds and then depart to distant regions of the marsh with these, no doubt sharing experiences as well as learning new places together.

TRAVELS OF WATERFOWL

So it must be in its travels about the marsh, the duck learns its place in the environment, learns the location of the various areas it uses for life's requirements, and learns the routes, the leads, and passes that link one place with the other. Some of these places and routes may be learned independently, but often the bird is first directed to these by the actions of experienced companions. In companionship with others, each bird gradually expands the range of its activities as it learns to accommodate itself to an ever enlarging world.

3

The Visual World

THESE ducks of the Delta Marsh use their environment in an orderly fashion; there is a pattern to their travels. They learn to follow the arrangements of land and water, reeds and willows, that make every corner of this marshland different from any other part of the world. The duck accommodates itself to the environment that meets the eye; it learns the places in its world by seeing them; its local orientation depends upon eyesight. A clue to the importance of sight is to be found in the size of the avian eye. One is misled by outward appearances, for the cornea is enclosed in a relatively small lid-opening. When the skin is removed, the eye structure is found to occupy a very large part of the head, and the two eyes of a Mallard weigh nearly as much as its brain (Figure 2).

In examining the world of waterfowl, it must not be assumed that earth, sky, and all things between appear the same to man and bird. Indeed, the true nature of the world has been the study of philosophers since the beginning of civilization; earlier than the year 400 B.C., Protagoras exclaimed that "what seems to me is to me, what seems to you is to you" (Jeans, 1943:32). Leibnitz believed that he was "able to prove that not only light, color, heat and the like, but motion, shape, and extension too were mere apparent qualities," and Berkeley claimed that "all the choir of heaven and furniture of earth, in a word all those bodies which compose the mighty frame of the world, have not any substance without the mind" (Barnett, 1948:306). We become aware of the poorly defined boundaries between science and philosophy when speaking to a color-blind friend about the things we perceive. There is no science to aid in the hopeless attempt to define the color red to such a companion. He simply does not perceive red as we do, nor do we see it as he does. Thus the visible world for him is not

29

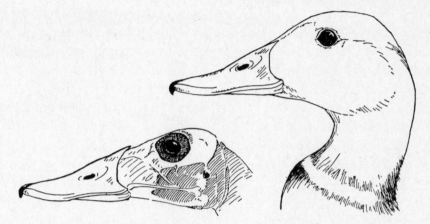

Figure 2. Eye of Mallard drake. The combined weight of the two eyes was 3.2 grams. The brain weighed 5.3 grams.

entirely the same as ours, and science shows no pathway leading to a common understanding.

The naturalist often assumes that bird and man look upon a landscape that appears alike to both. Yet the world of man and bird cannot be the same; the bird's eye is structurally different, and its actions, experiences, and visual perspectives are different. The eyes of the duck, goose, and swan are placed on the sides of the head, and by such an arrangement the waterfowl enjoys the advantage of horizon-wide vision. In a glance a duck may see nearly twice as much of the landscape as a man can take in. Among gregarious birds this wide visual field permits each individual to see its companions on all sides, which is of special importance in flock movements. An enemy does not easily approach unseen from behind. The broad view of the landscape is an aid to orientation during travel; in an instant a duck sees where it was a moment earlier, where it is now, and where it is going. Man understands the value of such wide vision when he ventures into strange country; it is characteristic of human beings to turn the head many times in unfamiliar surroundings to examine the region just traversed.

Though having this advantage of wide vision, the duck lacks the ability possessed by man and the owl to perceive the landscape with stereoscopic solidity; there cannot be the same awareness of depth and distance that is inherent in our own binocular vision. To be sure, the eyes of the waterfowl are set slightly forward so that there is some overlapping of the visual field, hence a narrow binocular span (Figure 3). In feeding, a duck faces its food

30

directly and selects grain precisely with its bill. Often, when food floats on the water, it reaches out with its bill neatly to take a morsel from the surface. In sexual fights and in the frequent bodily encounters of courting birds, it thrusts its bill straightforward in a well-aimed blow. Such direct actions suggest depth perception for a narrow zone directly facing the duck.

But it is obvious, both from the structure and the behavior of the duck, that there is monocular fixation for all parts of the landscape beyond reach of the bill. While writing this paragraph, I visited the winter pens where there are more than a hundred ducks and geese of a dozen species. As I entered the room, each turned its bill to one side or the other to view me with one eye. Not a single bird had its forehead in my direction. So, at other times, the object of interest is examined with one eye. This is especially noticeable when a hawk or an aircraft crosses over the pen and the birds tilt their heads to watch. Often I have seen waterfowl tip their heads when in flight, as when a band of Whistling Swans comes directly over my hiding place, suddenly taking notice of my presence. A most interesting observation of the monocular response of a pet parakeet to its visual world was related to me by Robert L. Lillestrand. The bird, a pet of Roy P. Van Devener, was released in a bedroom which had rose-colored wallpaper patterned in a floral design with thin vines. The little parakeet, then only six weeks old and with no experience of the outdoor world, attempted to alight on the painted vines. The same thing occurred on later releases in the room, and it was not till the bird was nine months old that it learned the impossibility of using the painted stems as its perch.

For a man there is little stereoscopic effect in the landscape beyond fifty or sixty yards from the eyes. As an aerial traveler, the bird has lost little and

Figure 3. Drake Ruddy Duck
showing the eye position
typical of waterfowl

gained much in the lateral position of the eyes. At high altitudes depth perception is little needed. Close to the earth, however, and particularly when alighting, there must be some awareness of the three-dimensional character of the environment. Pumphrey (1948:182) has pointed out that such depth perception hinges on time and motion, that "the appreciation of distance has to be built up by a succession of glances from different points toward the same point of the field." He refers, of course, to parallax. The moment the bird is in flight, the position of the eye in relation to objects in the landscape is ever changing. The most rapid changes are in the nearest objects, hence the relativity of motion is the clue to the depth of the landscape. "Near objects seem to move extensively in the opposite direction as compared with far objects, while the latter seem to move slightly, in the *same* sense as the head movements, in relation to the nearer objects. It is chiefly this cue which enables a one-eyed man to move about in an unfamiliar roomful of furniture without bumping into things any more often than a two-eyed person" (Walls, 1942:314).

We human beings employ parallax daily in measuring our environment, and it must be the most important clue the bird has in the perception of the landscape's three-dimensional character. For birds the motion of travel establishes the parallax; the more rapid the flight, the more keen is the awareness of depth. In some species there are instinctive body actions which apparently function to increase the effect of parallax. Walls (1942:342) reminds us that some "birds when walking (fowls, pigeons, doves) and others when swimming (coots and gallinules) make perpetual forward-and-backward oscillatory movements of the head. It has been claimed that the eyes never actually move backward through space — the forward movement of the body just cancels the backward movements of the head. Thus, although the body moves forward steadily, the head moves forward through space by jerks and pauses. In effect, the eyes obtain a rapid succession of previews of the surroundings from constantly new angles. The forward movements of the head being so quick, each new parallactic observation of the field is made almost simultaneously with the preceding one, and the exaggeration of the apparent relative motions of objects at different distances furnishes a basis for the estimation of distance and relief."

While ducks and geese do not jerk the head as does the Coot, still their heads are often in motion when traveling through dense cover. The head of a swan is seldom idle as it swims. In low-flying ducks there often is an up and down swinging of the head, and on several occasions I have seen a Green-winged Teal skimming along just above the reeds with its head in constant motion. J. C. Lynch, pilot-biologist for the U.S. Fish and Wildlife Service, and a specialist in low flying, told me that it is most helpful to the pilot of an aircraft at low elevations to look at the ground from first one side of the plane, then from the other. This is termed "scanning" and is especially useful in judging distance when bringing a light plane in for a landing.

Other clues to distance possibly are learned. The size of the retinal image depends on the distance of the object from the eye, but as a guide to distance the bird must have a familiarity with the object seen. Perspective is another clue which depends to some extent on a familiarity with the components of the landscape. Aerial perspective, the variation in color due to atmospheric influences, probably is used by birds in the perception of distance. All these clues no doubt serve in establishing the awareness of altitude when in flight.

The structure of the eye has a profound influence on perception (Figure 4). Pumphrey (1948:174, 182) points out that the retina of the bird "is shaped so as to lie almost wholly in the image plane, so that all distant objects within the visual angle are sharply focused on the photo-sensitive cells, whereas in the human eye this is only true of objects lying close to

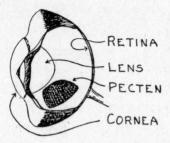

Figure 4. Eye of Mallard (twice natural size), cut away to show position of retina, lens, and pecten

RETINA
LENS
PECTEN
CORNEA

the optic axis. . . . For man, the distance element enters into every glance, but the appreciation of detail of the field has to be built up by a succession of glances from the same point and directed to different parts of the field. For the bird, detail enters immediately into every glance." Let us measure the focal angle of our own human eye by looking up from this page to the landscape beyond the window. To read the entire scene we must shift our eyes back and forth. When the eyes are at rest, only the narrow field directly in the line of vision is in focus. On either side of this narrow focal angle we are aware of form, color, and movement, but these are out of focus and may not be understood completely until the eye is moved. From its eye structure, we must believe that the duck or goose viewing this same landscape perceives much more of it in sharp focus. In a single glance, then, the duck obtains a sharply defined image of much of the landscape meeting the eye. It perceives clearly in an instant what a man can understand only after a series of shifting glances. Of course, we must remember that the scanning movements of the human eye are very rapid, the speed compensating in part for the narrow field of sharp vision.

Man has long acknowledged avian superiority in visual acuity (sharpness of vision), and the example of the falconer's experience is traditional. "It was the habit of the medieval falconer to carry a caged shrike on his saddle, to keep track of the falcon. As long as the shrike acted fearful and excited, the hawker knew that his proud tercel was in sight — though not to him!" (Walls, 1942:169).

All who have lived close to waterfowl have witnessed their awareness of objects we human beings could not perceive. One afternoon I sat watching a band of Mallards loafing on a lakeshore sand bar. In the distant sky there appeared a hawk which, as it approached more closely, I identified as a Pigeon Hawk. From the time this bird was first seen until, after passing within a hundred yards of the ducks, it disappeared in the east, I observed no reaction on the part of the waterfowl. The hawk seemed nothing

34

more nor less in their lives than the drifting leaves of a nearby poplar. Shortly afterward the ducks suddenly stood up on the sand bar, some of them swimming away. Looking westward I saw a bird of rapid wing-beat approaching at low elevation. It was several seconds before I was sure that this was a hawk and some moments more before I could be certain it was a Duck Hawk and not another Pigeon Hawk. When the predator was within two hundred yards, all the ducks were in the water. None flew and, as the falcon passed over, most of them dived, some frantically in water too shallow to cover them. After the hawk had gone on, a few of the Mallards flew away, but most returned to their island to pick up the lazy thread of their afternoon siesta. At this point I will not raise the argument whether the enemy-fear was instinctive or learned. The matter of importance is that these birds recognized their enemy long before I did.

The photoreceptive cells of the eye lie within the outer layer of cells of the retina and are of two types, the *rods* and the *cones,* so named because of their shapes. The rod cells are more sensitive to light intensity, responding to much lower degrees of illumination than the cones. Within their restricted range, however, "the cones are responsive to much smaller changes in intensity; and it is the cones which are responsible for color vision. The cone system is consequently suited for the registration of detail in a brightly illuminated visual field. The rod system, because of its extensive summation, is comparatively incapable of resolving detail but can register an achromatic picture of the gross features of the field at illuminations so low that the cone system is quite blind. We might expect, therefore, to find, as in fact we do, that cones are predominant in the retinae of eyes which are exclusively diurnal, and rods in eyes used only at night. Acuity (the power of resolving detail) and sensitivity are inverse requirements which cannot be fully satisfied in the same eye" (Pumphrey, 1948:177). By and large, the waterfowl come as close as any bird toward meeting the mixed requirements of day and night vision. Their acuity is sharp and they are active by day; and yet in many respects they are crepuscular birds, moving swiftly and surely in the dusk of morning and evening. Ducks are active under a full moon through the night, especially during the breeding season. But on dark and moonless nights, with the added curtain of cloud, their travel about the marsh comes to a halt.

In birds, especially those swift of wing that feed in the open, it is most important that there be a clear image of near and far objects at every instant. In man the adjustment of focus is accomplished by an involuntary muscular adjustment of the lens. In birds both the lens and the cornea are altered in accommodation; hence two parts of the eye function to maintain instant sharpness of both near and far parts of the visual field, and objects rapidly approaching the eye are held in focus.

The best experimental work, Pumphrey says (1948:185), seems to establish that "there is very little difference between the color vision of birds and man," but he goes on to explain why he believes that even though "the limits of color vision seem to be the same for man and birds, it is likely, nevertheless, that color sense plays a more emphatic part in the visual sensations of diurnal birds than of man." Kalmbach (1943), who studied the feeding responses of wild Mallards to colored grains, found that "waterfowl have shown a degree of aversion to unnaturally colored grain, though the discrimination by ducks is less emphatic than with passerine and gallinaceous birds. This, it is felt, is due largely to the 'puddling' method of feeding which operates probably as much by the sense of touch as by sight."

Vanderplank (1934) and Wojtusiak (1949), among others, have presented what they believe to be evidence of avian awareness of infrared. Griffin (1952a:369) has made a careful review of the many studies of visual sensitivity to infrared radiation, concluding that there is "strong evidence that the visible spectrum of birds is approximately the same as that of the human eye" and that "theories of bird navigation based upon sensitivity to thermal radiation from bodies of low temperature scarcely deserve serious consideration." Pumphrey (1948) concurs in this view. Supporters of the view that birds are sensitive to infrared claim that such perception accounts for the bird's ability to fly in heavy darkness or through fog; but I have observed that waterfowl refuse to travel in dense fog or complete darkness.

The pecten, a fanlike structure in the posterior chamber of the eyeball, is universally present in birds (Figure 4). Its function is still speculative, and many theories have been advanced in regard to its role in vision. An important lead was presented by Menner (1938), who observed not only that the foliations of the pecten cast shadows on a functional part of the retina but that these foliations, hence the shadows, varied with different kinds of birds. The pecten proved to be the most highly developed in diurnal birds with good visual acuity, such as hawks, and the least in nocturnal species. Walls (1942) remarked that before Menner, some thirty theories had been advanced regarding the function of the pecten, and Griffin (1953:227) offers a conjecture that might be given, he says, "the serial number '32'." He points out that if, as Kramer's studies (1952) suggest, the sun is useful to a bird in navigation, then the pecten's function might be to this end, just as a sextant serves man in his navigation.

"What would be more useful to a bird than a built-in yardstick laid out upon its retina, a series of fixed points against which the bird might learn to estimate the angular distance of the sun above the horizon? Furthermore, to guide itself by means of the sun a bird obviously must spend some time looking at its intensely bright disk, a process which is uncomfortable, to say the least, for the human eye. Hence perhaps the evolution of the pecten with its plicated outline of densely pigmented tissue and with the rich blood supply which would serve to carry away excess heat from the sun's image if this image should fall on any part of the pecten. Considering the extent to which the avian eye is fixed in its socket, in contrast to the great freedom of rotation of the human eyeball, it is a plausible supposition that the definite outline of the two pectens, plus the fixed points provided by the foveas, might provide the bird with a visual frame of reference against which the position and movements of the sun could be gauged."

In the lives of all waterfowl the perception of movement is a very important function of the eye. Every hunter knows of the Mallard's immediate reaction to the slightest motion. He may tip his face or move his hand ever so slightly; but even though the approaching bird may still be well beyond gunshot, it alters its course or "flares" upward to avoid danger. Indeed, one of the most important things in wildfowling is the art of remaining motionless. The downy Canvasback shows a keen awareness of movement; only a few days after being hatched it is able to strike swiftly to snap a fly from the air. Waterfowl live in a world that is important to them in terms of movement. At rest they must be ever aware of the motion of enemies, companions, and living food. On the water, subject to the pressure of wind and waves, they must perceive movement to maintain their local orientation. In the air it is the apparent flow of the world beneath that gives them their awareness of movement through space.

The eye of the bird is specially adapted to the perception of movement. The panoramic vision of these waterfowl serves to introduce movement to the eye over a wide span of the landscape. Their high visual acuity and the breadth of the sharp retinal image likewise serve to give them a keen awareness of motion. Movement is perceived in the changing illumination of the visual field. If the background is moving (cattails in a breeze), if the color of the shifting object is quite the same as the background (a brown-coated hunter crawling in front of autumn cattails), and if the object moves slowly, awareness of motion is difficult. But where the background is stationary, the color contrast sharp between background and object, and the movement rapid, awareness is keen. We must judge that ducks are more successful than men in detecting motion under adverse conditions of speed and background. Their field of movement perception is probably greater than that of men not only because of the position and structure of the eye, but because of their different response to the environment. Men are highly sensitive to movement on a horizontal plane, since they meet their world largely between their feet and the horizon. Ducks, on the other hand, meet the world from above when flying; and they must be ever aware of their aerial environment when on the ground.

The visual world of the waterfowl, then, while probably having the same colors as that of man, is much wider. It is viewed monocularly, and more of its detail is perceived sharply at a glance. Perception of movement is keener than in man, the power to resolve detail is greater, and the avian eye accommodates itself to changes in the position of objects more quickly. It is impossible, with our binocular vision and narrow visual field, to imagine how the world appears to a duck, but it is easy to understand how perception is highly efficient for spatial orientation.

At this point we must acknowledge that visual perception concerns more than the eye, both in birds and men. The eye is simply the window of the brain. The eyes of a man (and of a bird) receive stimuli, such as rays of light, from the outer world, "and these produce electric changes which are propagated over his nerves to his brain. Here they produce further changes, as the result of which—after a series of processes we do not in the least understand—his mind acquires perceptions, to use Hume's terminology, of the outer world" (Jeans, 1943:6). Bird and man respond not directly to their environment, but only to the image that reaches the brain. Seeing is merely the physical reception of an image; the delicate organ of sight, in effect, is the camera. Perception follows only when the brain has "examined" the image. Thus the visual world depends not only on the nature of the eye, but on that of the brain as well, and each animal lives in its own perceptual world which in some way is distinct from that of any other individual.

We who live outside the worlds of birds study avian perception through their response to their environment. We know they are aware of something only when they show behavior. As we watch the flight of Mallards out to stubble every evening along the same creek bed, we judge that they are aware of the terrain, just as they are of the narrows between two lakes which they cross regularly. When the drake holds close to his mate through all the days of migration, we conclude that he perceives in her some character that distinguishes this particular hen from all others. When the Canvasback hen finds the way through the tules to her nest, she must be aware of environmental patterns.

"The important thing to realize," says Russell (1934:181), "is that the animal's perceptual world is essentially a practical or functional one. The animal attends to, perceives, and shows behavior in respect of, only those events, objects and characters of objects that are at the moment functionally important to it, those about which it is impelled *to do something*; only these have valence for it." Such valence ° hinges on the condition of the bird: on its age, its sexual status, the time of the day and the time of the year. The mother is valent for the ducklings only during the period of growth, the nesting cover has valence for only the nesting hen, and she has valence for her drake only a part of the year.

Some components of the environment must have valence because of the innate make-up of the bird. In our captive ponds are Canvasbacks and Pintails that have been hatched together and raised as companions in the same pens. Until nearly a year old they share this captive environment. When May arrives, however, the Canvasback hens select emergent vegetation for nesting cover, while the Pintails walk up on the dry ground to seek out nesting places in grass some distance from water. Such selection follows the visual inspection of the entire landscape, of which a part is perceived as the place for nesting, the choice between emergent and upland cover being inborn. When young hand-reared Mallards are released to the wild, they soon seek out the part of the landscape that is their never-before-seen birthright. Set free in the grassy thickets behind the lakeshore, they soon move to the emergent beds of bulrush at the shoreline shallows.

This seems a simple shift, and yet it does represent a choice between favorable and unfavorable environment that is not based on experience. Our Pintails and Mallards seek out the rushy borders when given freedom, but the young Redheads and Canvasbacks go to the open water that is the natural haunt of their wild brethren. In his studies of ducklings (1951:167) Fabricius found that "the newly hatched birds showed some apparently

---

° Russell (1934:179) considers as "*valent*, or possessing valence, those objects, or characters of objects, and those events, in the perceptual world of an animal, in respect of which it shows behavior."

innate reactions to the features of the country. The young birds went into the water spontaneously and swam out even if they were not conducted into the water. Young tufted ducks and shovellers which are left to themselves were — even when newly hatched — strongly attracted to reeds, whereas young eiders avoided reeds and instead were especially fond of swimming along open rocky shores." Mayr remarks (1942:246) that "naturalists have always marvelled at the unfailing accuracy with which animals can find the right ecological niche to which their species is adapted." And Thorpe suggests (1949:86) that "one can safely assume that, quite apart from the recognition of a particular locality, birds can recognize the right *type* of environment for themselves. If this were not so, every year would find birds trying unsuccessfully to breed in all sorts of unsuitable places. This recognition of an environmental type may be very largely the result of experience, but it is in line with the modern concepts of instinctive behavior to assume that there may be an innate hereditary, primarily visual recognition of the right type of environment."

The valence of certain components of the bird's visual world hinges on time and condition. Thus the Mallard drake on his breeding territory distinguishes between migrant Mallard pairs passing overhead and resident pairs that threaten to alight on his domain. The former draw no response from him, but the intruders are driven away. He is aware of behavior differences by which sexual intruders are distinguished from passing migrants of the same species. Perception of these differences depends upon the drake's position in the sexual cycle. A few days earlier he was a gregarious being and perceived all Mallards as companions; a few weeks later this will be true of him again.

As we watch a gathering of spring transients at the edge of the ice on Cadham Bay, we notice two Canvasback drakes that go about their business without paying the slightest attention to the females of close-by pairs of Canvasback. But suddenly a hen of their kind, followed by three drakes, alights. Immediately the unattached males join this courting group. Here is selection and rejection hinging on physiological condition. The unmated drakes ignore the paired hens but pursue the single female. The mated drakes disregard the single hen to remain at the sides of their own mates. Every sexually active duck accepts or rejects those of its companions which its sexual status directs it to acknowledge or ignore. This calls for sharp awareness of behavior. The lone drake must perceive the difference in behavior between a mated and an unmated hen. The Mallard must distinguish

Mallard drake rising to defend his pond

behavior differences between the sexual intruder and the uninterested migrant. Surely such physiological influence governs our own human awareness of companions. The youth of twenty years perceives certain characteristics in a girl of his own age of which the lad of ten is not aware.

Against this sharp awareness in the spring, let us compare the behavior of autumn. When hunting far afield I seldom carry bulky decoys. I use the first birds bagged, arranging them in the shallows or on the stubble with their necks held up with willow wands. Even at a distance of one hundred yards or more a man can detect the counterfeit. I wait with confidence, however, and if it is a day for gunning, it is not long before some duck has come to this stool. I (and many other hunters) have resorted to methods even cruder than this. On the lakeshore I have formed duck-sized mounds of sand in the shallow water. The sand is too soft to be arranged in true duck form: these are merely small oval mounds placed in loose formation with most of them pointing into the wind. This fools no duck in daylight; but in the same evening light in which the spring drake distinguishes an intruder from a migrant, I have seen autumn Mallards swing in close to my sand decoys and even alight amongst them. Where the Lesser Snow and Blue Geese fly in autumn, hunters often bring them into gun range with newspapers or white rags tied to little sticks arranged in flock formation.

Lorenz (1937:247) found that his tame but free-living Jackdaws would attack him furiously when he carried a black bathing suit in his hand and that "anything glistening black and dangling, carried by any living creature would release the very same reaction in the Jackdaws. . . . In a bird that readily recognizes and discriminates fellow-members of the flock, it is rather surprising that the process of releasing the social defending reaction so closely resembles that which elicits the responses of lower organisms. . . . An instinctive reaction of survival value, when directed exclusively to a particular object, may be released as if through a surprisingly small choice among the large number of stimuli normally emanating from the object." The white of small rags arranged in flock formation is sufficient to release the gathering behavior in traveling Blue and Lesser Snow Geese, bringing them within range of hunters' guns. The white of the rags is a "key-stimulus"; and all such colors or plumage patterns, structures or actions, that draw responses from social companions, Lorenz (1937) has termed *releasers* (*Auslöser*). (See also Baerends, 1950; Tinbergen, 1951.)

It is very interesting that the female Pintail, which distinguishes her drake from all other males, does not perceive differences between her own eggs and stones or wooden eggs placed in her nest (Farley , 1939:57; Sowls, 1955:103). Even though the stones are seen several times a day, the hen continues to incubate, satisfied with the "feel" of the small rocks under her breast.

Perception of the visual world may be conditioned by learning and experience. The Mallard drake has an innate awareness of certain sexual actions of the Mallard female, but he must learn the identity of his own sexual partner. The duckling must learn its parent. The female may be innately attracted to a certain type of nesting cover but she learns to find the place of her nest. I believe that each duck learns to perceive characteristics in the landscape as guides to orientation. The large meadow meets the innate nesting requirements of many Pintail hens, yet each must perceive variations in the monotonous pattern that direct her to her own nest site. Laven (1949) carried out an interesting experiment in nest-perception in the Ringed Plover. This little shore bird nests on open beaches. When one encounters a pair, it may be an hour or more before the nest can be located, even though it is "in plain sight" close by. If we let our eyes stray from the nest after it is found, it may be several minutes before the eggs are relocated, so closely do they resemble their background. Laven removed eggs from a nest, then obliterated the cavity and tracks nearby. Even so, the birds found the site without difficulty. But when he changed the nature of the environment to a distance of three meters around the nest by leveling it off, the plovers were disoriented. They must have followed visual cues presented by the whole of the local landscape. I presume this applies to nesting ducks, for even when the nesting cover has been removed by fire or mowing, I have seen hens return to their nests, guided there, probably, by cues presented by the landscape patterns beyond the immediate vicinity of the nest.

Canada Geese are interesting subjects to study because they are so responsive in voice as well as in action. The flock of Canada Geese at Delta is, so to speak, a part of the little community. The birds live but a few yards from our homes and offices; we watch them, as they watch us, many hours a day. Our normal human activities are accepted without "comment" by the geese. When I walk past the pen they do not seem to notice me; but when I pick up a large box from the truck and carry it on my shoulders to the hatchery, the geese lift their heads high, and give voice as evidence of their awareness of something new. One brisk September afternoon I noticed the birds suddenly alert, all looking toward my house, many of them uttering the gutteral notes of disturbance. In the first autumn chill my son Albert had donned his new red, white, and blue hockey sweater which he had never worn before. Here, suddenly, was a bright, strange thing against the landscape. The geese noticed it immediately. They watched for several minutes, then resumed their feeding, never again to react to the sweater.

Where, as with geese lifting their heads to a man carrying a box, there is a sharp response to the object seen, the valence of the object is established by the birds' behavior. Indeed, it is only by the birds' action that we can measure and study their awareness of the components of their environment But action surely is not the only criterion of awareness. For example, I step from the hatchery to the pond side where the geese are resting and not one moves. A moment later a stranger steps out and the geese lift their heads to acknowledge his entry. If I walk toward them they hold their ground; if the stranger approaches, they retreat. They respond directly to the stranger, but they are aware of me and their very lack of action is evidence of this. On the pasture I have often stood among the cattle during the evening stubble flight. The ducks come low over the grazing beasts, but flare upward when they pass over me. In their action they acknowledge me as an enemy even though I have not moved; but their lack of response to the cattle surely cannot be evidence that they do not perceive these animals as harmless components of the scene.

Watching the daily travels of waterfowl, we see them moving in a familiar environment. It is clear that each bird recognizes the various aspects of its range—the nesting meadow, the slough, the Station pond, the edge of Cadham Bay. We see them approach these from different directions, traveling by different routes as the wind varies. They must perceive the parts of their range as familiar from many visual aspects. Yet the home range of a duck, I suspect, is not made up of so many discrete objects or landmarks; the bird probably reacts to the whole of its familiar visual world.

Various portions of the range may have valence according to time and condition, the nesting meadow, the sand bar, the slough each being perceived according to the individual's physical requirements for these places. In local travel only proximate patterns have valency. In the flight to stubble much more of the landscape may be important to orientation. In long travels and in migration, the sun or sky-brightness, cloud formations, or (at night) the moon and other heavenly bodies may be perceived, not as discrete guides, but as parts of the whole. When a duck has become lost, however, as in a storm or in a flight over unfamiliar terrain, one isolated part of the visual world may then have valence. Thus a duck flying over strange, dry prairie responds abruptly to the shimmer of sun on water; a goose flying over unbroken forest reacts directly to the silver streak of a river interrupting the solid green of spruce. Then, perhaps, the relation between the bird and one single part of the environment is of much the same order as the mechanism of the social releaser. And just as the response to the social releaser may lead to error (as Snow Geese joining white rags), the bird often errs in its response to single parts of the environment. Each year many water birds alight on wet roads. Ducks and geese are able to take wing after discovery of their mistake, but annually large numbers of loons and grebes are stranded where they have alighted on highways far from water.

In our study of avian perception we are in much the same position as the blind men examining the elephant. The whole of the truth cannot be understood by study, however careful and complete, of the parts. To the laboratory student studying the releaser mechanisms, the breadth of perception of birds seems very limited indeed, whereas to the field observer the birds' familiar response to the whole of the wide visual field may be overwhelmingly impressive. What we must do is to continue the controlled studies of isolated parts of the visual world. Controlled studies of social relations have developed rather widely during the past twenty years; but it has not been until recently, as in the pioneering studies of Kramer (1951, 1952) and Matthews (1951a, b; 1952), that responses to individual components of the physical environment have been examined. And then, along with these controlled experiments, we must surely carry on with more field studies, like those of Griffin (1952a, b), who watched the behavior of free-flying experimental birds from an aircraft, and with more field work like that of L. Tinbergen (1941), Deelder (1949), the Lacks (1949), Svärdson (1953), and others who study the behavior of wild birds in the very act of traveling cross-country from one place to another.

4

The Function of Memory

THE ducks of the Delta Marsh move familiarly within an environment they have learned. Some have been hatched there, learning their place in ever increasing spans. Others have been reared elsewhere, arriving at Delta in summer or fall. When flying from one place to another for feed, rest, or grit, these residents travel over country that is familiar through the experience of use; but no matter how broad or narrow the local experience, there must always come a time for departure from the northland. Some juveniles disperse from their natal range soon after taking wing. After the midsummer molt, many males leave for other places. By late August the southward migration is in full swing, with the Blue-winged Teal leading the parade. Successive flights bring a constant turnover of arrivals and departures until finally, when November ice covers the bays, all waterfowl migrate southward. They are gone from Delta for five months. Some, such as the Blue-winged Teal, are away even longer. Most bluewings have left by the first week of October and they do not return until late April, an absence of nearly seven months.

When spring brings these wildfowl back from the wintering grounds, we know that many return to their old haunts. Sowls's study (1949) of marked females leaves little doubt of the close tie between the breeding hen and her nesting locality. Not only does she come back to her marsh, but frequently to the same meadow where she had nested previously. Sowls (1955) also showed how young females return home after their first migration. Regional fidelity is further suggested in banding records such as those of Sullivan (1953), who captured a Canvasback hen and brood at his lodge on the Libau Marsh. Four years later a hunter shot the mother less than a mile from the place of original capture. While many drakes do not make a direct spring return to their native marsh, banding studies suggest that, after the breeding period is ended, they often revisit familiar places.

Here is a continuity in learned behavior from one season to the next. These waterfowl "pick up" the routine of their lives in a familiar environment despite an absence long in both time and space. Such continuity is explained in terms of *memory*. Rowan (1931:81) remarks that "of the many interesting facts brought out by bird banding, none is more striking than the return of given individuals to the same nesting box year after year, in some cases with thousands of miles of travel to their credit during the intervening nine or ten months. That topographical memory is involved in a feat of this nature seems more than likely." Lincoln (1950a:29) speaks of "retentive memories" in migrants; and many others working with bird movements have explained the recognition of old haunts in terms of memory. Seldom, however, is the word defined; each reader is free to make his own individual judgment of a function he does not thoroughly understand in himself, much less in birds. Gerard (1953:118) points out that "even to identify memory, let alone explain it, is no simple matter. . . . Is a film a memory of light in chemicals and a tape recording a memory of sound in magnetism? Is a library a memory of thought in books and a brain a memory of thoughts in protoplasm?"

In developing this discussion, I feel obliged to digress briefly to consider the function of memory in our own lives. To most of us the word implies conscious recollection, the mental process whereby past experiences are recalled to present awareness. When searching the past to give memory a play, we readily call to mind many segments of personal history, such as the plan of our first schoolroom, the old barn, the corner store. It is possible to recollect hundreds of places, incidents, and companions, retrieving these from the near or distant past. In our doing so, the memory function is accompanied by imagery; our mind's eye "sees" the shape of experiences we recall. In careful examination of our past, however, we realize that the recollective memory has its limitations. The total of our experience is not remembered; we know that much of the past cannot be brought to present awareness at will.

This part of the personal life story not to be remembered at command is, nevertheless, brought to awareness by certain related cues. When cleaning the attic I come across toys of childhood and suddenly remember something that could never have been recalled without my first discovering the playthings. Seven years ago I ate a meal in a neighboring city where I was in a restaurant not longer than thirty minutes. Afterward the place had no importance in my life, never so much as entering my mind until I returned to the city and went there for another meal. As I approached the building I could but vaguely recall its gross details; then, as I stepped within the door, I was suddenly in a familiar place. This was not a new or strange room; I had been there before. As my eyes wandered, many details I could not have remembered a moment before were now familiar. The position of the kitchen door, the rack of glasses, the mirror behind the pies were hardly different in arrangement and pattern from those in many other restaurants I have visited or in thousands I had never seen. Yet this room I experienced briefly seven years ago was a familiar place.

As a lad of eight I spent a day at Estes Park where I caught my first trout. My next trip there was thirty-two years later; and, while I could recall only a few details of the place, I was able to find at once the very bend in the stream where I had taken my first fish. On the road to Amaranth, Manitoba, there is a whitewashed log cabin which is important to me only once a year. On the first day of Prairie Chicken hunting, it is suddenly remembered because when it comes to view the next turn is to the favorite hunting grounds. How vastly important is this continuity of personal history! Although memory cannot serve to bring all our life story to awareness, there is a retentiveness by which continuity is maintained, with the present always built on the past, each new instant modified by earlier experiences.

Many trips might be taken over the same route until it is known "by heart," the impressions deepened till more and more of the landscape is subject to conscious recollection. The point is, however, that one trip over a trail is sufficient to render it familiar, even though memory does not function to recall the details to mind after the trip is completed. Nor, despite the depth of impression resulting from many trips, will memory of the whole route ever be at the call of the will. Few can remember all the details of the route between the dining room table and the refrigerator in their own

homes, much less the wayside configurations in a trip of a hundred miles. Yet we see the former daily, and the latter may be accomplished a second time without the aid of a map. "Mental states of every kind — sensations, feelings, ideas — which were at one time present in consciousness and then have disappeared from it, have not with their disappearance absolutely ceased to exist. Although the inwardly-turned look may no longer be able to find them, nevertheless they have not been utterly destroyed and an nulled, but in a certain manner they continue to exist, stored up, so to speak, in the memory" (Ebbinghaus, 1913).

I believe that these analogies with human experiences make for a better understanding of memory in waterfowl. We speak here not of the recollective memory, but of the subconscious retentiveness which "is the basal fact of life. All growth and development in an organism depends upon continuity. . . . The events of a life story would form no story, could have no continuity, one with another, unless at every moment the past lived into the present. But such continuity does not necessarily involve knowledge of the past. . . . In retentivenes, the past is continued into the present and loses itself in making the present what it is" (Gulliksen, 1950). By some process we do not understand, visual experiences become part of an organism, so that the sum total of its being is not only flesh and blood, bone and nerve, but includes the memory traces of parts of the world that have been seen and experienced and that always exist within.

The duckling has memory of its mother and distinguishes her from all other females. You and I standing beside the pond cannot distinguish each female of a kind with constant surety, yet the duckling still wearing the egg-tooth directs its activities toward the one hen that is its parent. This holds even when the mother returns after separation from her family. Heinroth (1911) showed that this recognition of the mother was not inborn; the young are not innately attracted to their genetic parent. Young geese, Heinroth observed, may become attached to the human caretaker who first handled them, accepting this man as their parent. Ducklings hatched under a domestic chicken recognize her as their mother. Thenceforward this chicken to which they directed their first actions remains their mother, even though they may be brought into association with females of their own species; and they recognize their gallinaceous parent from all other chickens. Lorenz (1935, 1937) called this mother-recognition "imprinting," pointing out that the young do not recognize their mother instinctively, but must be conditioned to her. "Parents and young thus appear to inherit a generalized ability to form a family association, the specific features of which are not inherited" (Cushing and Ramsay, 1949:82).

Fabricius (1951), who studied imprinting in wild ducks, concluded that "it is not possible to draw a sharp line between imprinting and ordinary conditioning." Thorpe (1944:80) has proposed extending "the original definition of imprinting to cover the possibility of attachment not to a living object but to the immediate locality first perceived by the newly emerged organism." I agree in principle with this suggestion, but the term itself, "imprinting," is, I think, now so widely applied to the parent-child relationship that the word can hardly be given a wider connotation without misunderstanding.

Visual images of the surroundings as well as of the parent must be impressed upon the young bird from the very beginning of its life story. In the captive pens, ducklings become familiar with the arrangement of the brooder enclosures within a few hours. Ducklings only a day or two old move in an oriented manner about the complex pattern of the Station pond. In the wild, ducklings may range widely with their parents (Evans, 1951; Dzubin, 1954), but there is evidence of an oriented use of the ponds and sloughs in which they live. I have found parentless ducklings ranging on the same part of the marsh throughout their growing period.

A remarkable evidence of retentiveness was shown in the behavior of several captive-reared Pintails at Delta. In the days before the establishment of captive ponds at Delta, juvenile hand-reared ducks were removed eight or ten miles away, where they were given their freedom at the edge of the lake or marsh. On three different occasions a young Pintail flew home, where, on our return, we found it walking around the pen, trying to enter the place where it had been reared. On one of these occasions there were no birds in the pen; hence the youngster could not have been guided there by the voice of companions. Chance, I believe, directed these juveniles to fly west along the lakeshore, and they recognized their familiar home as they passed by.

Manitoba's premier, the Honorable D. L. Campbell, told me of the experience of a friend, Wes Owens, who raised a brood of young Mallards in the family farmyard. After taking wing, they gradually expanded their range away from the farm, going out of sight to the wild country beyond. But each night at dusk they returned to the domestic confines of their first home. Peter Ward raised a Mallard female at Delta, giving it full-winged freedom in midsummer. It soon disappeared from the local scene, but one

The decoy pipe at Delta. Recaptures of ducks banded here show how some individuals
return each year to the decoy pond, a familiar stopping place on their
path of migration, a place that must be held in memory
from one season to the next.

bitter day in late autumn it returned to the dooryard of its early days. For
these birds, the artificial environments of their first homes had been impressed on their beings; their memories kept the traces of their natal ranges.
Despite the call of wilder places, they were faithful to the special locality
of earliest experience.

Many pages could be given to a recitation of the tie between the baby
bird and its natal environment. The home, whether in the wild marsh or
within the domestic realm of a farmyard or research station, is learned during the early hours of life. This tie to the home must be nearly as strong as
the bond to the parent. I suspect that the imprinting which Lorenz saw so
clearly in the relationship between the baby bird and its parent must be a
process similar to that of the retention we have been discussing. Visual
experiences with parent and environment are impressed upon the being of
the young bird; thus begins a retentiveness upon which the continuity of
life depends. Since responses between companions (as between mother and

51

child) are much more sharply defined than responses to the environment, it is quite reasonable that Lorenz should first have described this process in the parent-child tie. But surely, as Thorpe declares, this process of rapid learning relates the infant to its environment in the same manner that it conditions it to its mother.

I suggest further that this recording of visual perceptions is not limited to early life but is a constant and life-lasting process relating the bird to its world. The retention of visual experiences is the key to life's continuity, by which the past is ever related to the present. Each hour and day of life the visual experiences of the present create the past upon which the future depends. Through the traces it has left on the memory, a landscape seen only briefly is familiar after an absence, whether it be the natal slough or a stopping place on the wayside of migration. The function of memory might be likened to a reel of movie film. The memory, like the film, records images in individual segments to make up the continuous whole. New records are made as the bird pioneers into new regions. Then, as a duck flies over a countryside it has visited before, the pattern of the landscape, as seen each instant, is familiar. Once out of sight, the scene is stored away to be recalled only by the next trip over the same place. As in the movie, the landscape meeting the eye at the present instant has meaning only in the context of the familiar scenes that have just been viewed. The present becomes the past the moment it is seen.

Here in my hand is a Baldpate hen, trapped on our Decoy where she was banded last fall. She is a spring migrant lingering briefly at a familiar stopping place on the way to her home. And what of her mate? She distinguishes him from all males of the kind, and the two join on the pond after she is free from my hand. This process of retention must go on through all the days of life, ending only when life itself comes to a close. We measure its strength when we watch the response of the duckling to its mother or when we record the return of a bird to the nesting place; but it must hold that in all periods of the life history, each individual lives efficiently in the present because of its link with the past.

So far I have spoken of the visual world, but we must not forget physical experiences that are perceived not only by the eye, but by other senses as well. For example, the catching of a duck is felt as well as seen. The two objects related to catching are man and hand-net. When I walk about the pen, my simple presence evokes no response from the ducks and geese. Nor do they react to the net which hangs on the wall. Even when I stand close to the net, there is no response. But when I grasp the net in my hands, the birds scurry away and shortly are safe in the center of the pond. Nearby is a bucket I have forgotten while I work at the Decoy. Neither I nor the bucket draws any response from the ducks; but the instant I step over to pick it up, the birds walk toward me or to the corner of the pond where they usually are fed. Here are sharp associations. Man plus net equals catching experience; man plus bucket equals food. The two objects must be acting together to draw responses, being neutral features of the landscape when isolated from each other.

I have considered only the relation between the past and the present in the continuity of a waterfowl's life. There is evidence of deliberate actions which, although hinged to the past, are aimed at the future. An example is the behavior of our Whistling Swans, old "pensioners" that live at Delta because shot wounds will not permit them to take wing. Their hearts are wild, and when spring or autumn winds blow, they become restless. Again and again, sometimes for more than an hour, they race across the pond in frantic, futile attempts to reach the freedom that calls. In this action, a swan walks deliberately to the downwind end of the pond, faces into the wind, utters the pre-flight call of all Whistling Swans, then starts his race across the water. The destination is the far shore. This attained, he flaps his wings, preens for a moment, then walks back to the south end of the pond. It seems to me that when he goes toward the downwind edge of the pond, all his past experiences press him to the place where he will start his flight run. Moreover, he not only selects the downwind position, but many times I have watched these great birds choose the exact point on the shore that will give them the longest run across the water, just as the pilot of an aircraft measures Cadham Bay for his take-off. A difference of a few feet at the start means several more yards for the run, and the birds invariably stand where they face the widest stretch of water. Thus, so it seems, past take-off experiences direct the swan to the point opposite the longest span of water where the flight run will take place.

To carry this point further, let us examine the behavior of a nesting duck. She sits on her loafing spot, from which one of several inner stimuli may bend her to move to a special destination. She may fly to her source of grit on the lakeshore, to a choice feeding place in a neighboring slough, or to her nest in the meadow. The impending movement will be in response to the stimuli from a gritless gizzard, an empty crop, or a full-formed egg in the oviduct. She has no control over these stimuli; she can only respond to their respective urges. She must direct this response to the proper destination: lakeshore, slough, or meadow. Since (as holds for some hens on their loafing places) she cannot see any of these destinations, it must be assumed that when she directs her movement toward the proper goal, she does so on the basis of past experience. Her destination is not in sight, but her flight goes in the proper way. Past experience guides present action to carry her to the unseen future. Without such preselection she could not move precisely, as we see she does, to the goal the inner stimuli direct her to attain. All three destinations are familiar places, but none can exist to her in the present because each place is beyond eyesight. Thus there must be a flow of continuity not only from the past to the present but projected into the immediate future.

The same continuity of action from the past into the future may be seen in Mallards flighting to stubble. When they depart from the lakeshore at dawn, the path of their travel from the very beginning leads them to a particular destination which must have been selected when the journey began. The field is a prospective factor for these birds; physically it can exist only in their future because it is several miles beyond their eyesight, hence the field cannot be a part of their present. Yet somehow the place lives in these Mallards' present at the time of departure, or how else could they make the direct and orderly journey? Retentiveness gives duration to life, "the continuous progress of the past which gnaws into the future" (Bergson, 1911a).

Once more we come to that indefinite boundary between science and philosophy. Lashley (1950) points out that in the three hundred years since Descartes's attempt to explain memory in terms of the action of the brain "much has been learned concerning the nature of the impulses transmitted by nerves. Innumerable studies have defined conditions under which learning is facilitated or retarded, but, in spite of such progress, we seem little nearer to an understanding of the memory trace than was Descartes." Somehow, quite beyond our understanding, there are within and as a part of each bird all the phases of its life story: the places and the companions near and distant both in time and in space, its mother, its first home, its mate, its nest, its home range and territory, its molting place, its wintering area. However alike two ducks may be in their physical structure, however similar may be the innate behavior of one duck to that of its specific companions, each individual bird is different from all others of its kind by virtue of its unique experiences.

"In the marsh, long windy waves surge across the grassy sloughs, beat against the far willows. A tree tries to argue, bare limbs waving, but there is no detaining the wind." Aldo Leopold, *A Sand County Almanac.*

5

The Aerial Environment

THE aerial environment is the medium of transportation to ranges far and near, a haven in the face of enemies, the source of companions. The sky is the realm of weather, the place of sun and moon, a shroud of darkness, the home of the wind.

On land or water the duck is ever aware of air as a force. It obeys the pressure of the moving air mass by facing the wind. Ducks napping on the Station pond are sensitive to the wind's strength and must paddle with the feet, even as they repose, to keep from being blown ashore. Geese sleeping on the beach all have their breasts aimed at the wind. They are "weathercocking," to borrow an airman's term; the natural streamlining of their bodies offers the least resistance when they face into the wind like weathervanes. All wildfowlers know the relation between ducks and the lee on windy days. Here the decoy hunter sets his rig, the jump shooter plies his canoe; this is where one finds waterfowl in a storm. No wildfowler commits himself to a plan by the evening fireside; he awaits the dawn, when his first act is to test the wind, his guide to location for hide and rig. The finest of all shooting places in a south blow is worthless for gunning when the wind comes from the west.

The duck is always sensitive to the wind when taking off and alighting; it must face the air stream at start and finish of flight. Several times in narrow channels I have forced ducks to take off downwind; each time the bird stalled, its initial thrust being insufficient to make it airborne. Edgar M. Queeny's superb photographs (1947) of waterfowl in flight tell us much of the bird's relation to its aerial environment, his high-speed camera revealing secrets never detected by the unaided eye. His photographs of a Mallard

drake crash-landing with back to wind give eloquent testimony to the importance of obeying the fundamental rules of aerial maneuver.

Once airborne, all physical contact with the earth is lost and the bird no longer has any bodily sensation of the speed or direction of the wind. An awareness of the air flow depends on a visual reference to the earth. In short, the bird, like the human pilot, must appraise the speed and direction of the air mass in which it travels by perceiving the relation between its own movement and the earth below. The duck turning upwind to a gunner's rig sets its course, not by feeling the wind, but by obeying visual cues it perceives in the marsh below.

This problem of wind-perception by flying birds has been a matter of considerable confusion for many groundling ornithologists who believe that the bird is sensitive to the wind pressure as this may be felt or the feathers ruffled on the windward side of the body. Lewis (1939b:22) explains that once the bird is on the wing it is "supported by the stream of air surrounding it and has no solid attachment to anything. It cannot then apprehend the direction of the wind by any pressure of the latter against its body, for, aside from the possible effect of turbulence, the air pressure against its body would be the same on all sides if the bird allowed itself to be swept along as an inert object in the air current. By its own efforts in flying ahead through the surrounding air, the bird causes increased pressure against its forward side, but this result is obtained indifferently and to the same extent whether the bird directs its flight with, or against, or across a uniform stream of air. Except under unusual circumstances, the flying bird therefore presumably has no awareness of the direction or the velocity of the wind or of the direction or velocity of its own movement in relation to the surface of the earth or in relation to the direction or velocity of the wind unless it can perceive some fixed points on the earth or, for knowledge of direction but not of velocity, some recognizable heavenly body or bodies. It may also be presumed that it usually has such awareness as a result of seeing the surface of the earth." Acworth (1946:28) says that to a bird in flight "there is no such thing as 'wind,' the bird being, in fact, in a dead calm so far as pressure is concerned."

This is the stand of airmen, based not on theory, but on the personal experience of flight. "The space in which the pilot flies is not the abstract space of theories, nor the lines and figures of the stereoscope, nor the space of the usual laboratory apparatus for studying depth perception. It does not consist of objects at varying empty distances. It consists chiefly of one basic object, a continuous surface of fundamental importance — the ground. A pilot who cannot see the ground or sea is apt to lose touch with reality in his flying" (Gibson, 1950:59). Without the aid of instruments and without visual reference to the earth, a pilot is unable to judge the direction or the force of the wind and quickly loses geographical orientation. A complaint might be placed against this analogy on the ground that the airman is enclosed within his craft, protected from the air. The objection, however, does not hold on a physical basis; the inability of the pilot to judge the wind aloft may be tested in an open cockpit or by having him thrust his arm into the air stream. With a constant air speed, variations in the direction or the velocity of the wind cannot be perceived, regardless of the craft's relation to the wind.

The speed of the bird's movement over the ground, the *ground speed,* depends upon the force and direction of the wind relative to the velocity and direction of flight. When a Mallard (or an aircraft) flies 45 miles per hour in still air, its ground speed and its air speed are exactly the same. Its ground speed is reduced when it moves against the wind, so that with a 45 m.p.h. air speed, the ground speed is 30 m.p.h. when the bird flies directly into a 15 m.p.h. wind. Against a 30 m.p.h. wind its ground speed is reduced to 15 m.p.h. With a 15 m.p.h. wind directly on its tail, this Mallard's ground speed is increased to 60 m.p.h. Air speeds of 65 to 70 m.p.h. have been recorded for ducks (Cooke, 1937); and with tail winds of 30 to 40 m.p.h., which sometimes occur during periods of late-autumn migration, waterfowl are able to progress over the ground at speeds better than 100 m.p.h. as indeed we have observed them at Delta in October and November passages.

Very often the goal of travel is not precisely with or against the wind, the duck meeting a quartering or beam flow of air. The bird must then com-

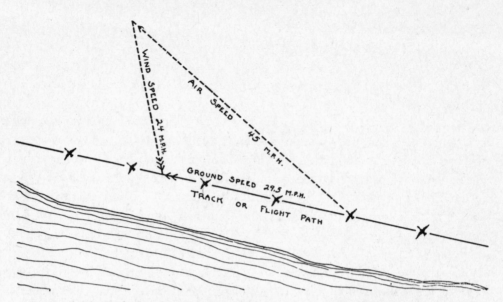

Figure 5. The "calculated course." The bird travels along the shore line, but to hold
this course it must face away from the line of flight into the wind. The slower
its air speed, the more nearly the bird must face into the wind.

pensate for the angular force of the wind to obtain its objective. When
ducks fly westward along the lakeshore, for example, and the wind is blowing from the northwest, the birds do not point like arrows in the direction
of their movement over the ground; their bodies aim into the northwest,
away from the shore and into the wind. Airmen call this "crabbing," a common and essential technique in human flight. The course of the bird is set
by its eyes, thus demanding the bodily adjustment to the force of the wind.
The degree to which the bird must face into the wind depends on the air
speed of the bird and the velocity of the wind according to the "triangle
of velocities" (Allen, 1939; Smith, 1945; Jack, 1953) (Figure 5). This pattern of flight is seen most frequently where waterfowl follow a shoreline or
a river or stream, but I have seen high-flying stubble Mallards "crabbing"
on an overland route to the fields.

Another technique for adjusting to the wind is the "duffer's" course
(Smith, 1945:155), where the bird aims its body continually at its destination without regard to the overland path required to reach its objective
(Figure 6). This technique is most frequently observed where birds are
moving short distances and where the terrain is very broken. Smith (1945)
speaks of starlings flying in a series of duffer's curves from one landmark

Figure 6. The "duffer's course." Here the bird aims its body always toward the objective. Flight path "A" shows the duffer's course when a bird with a 40 m.p.h. air speed flies against a quartering wind of 28 m.p.h. In flight path "B" the bird crosses a 28 m.p.h. wind, while in flight path "C" the bird is favored by a 28 m.p.h. wind quartering from behind. The birds shown on each of the flight paths have flown an equal time interval, the bird of flight path "C" having nearly reached its objective, the bird of flight path "A" having gone only a third of the way. With no wind at all, the flight path would be a straight line from start to finish.

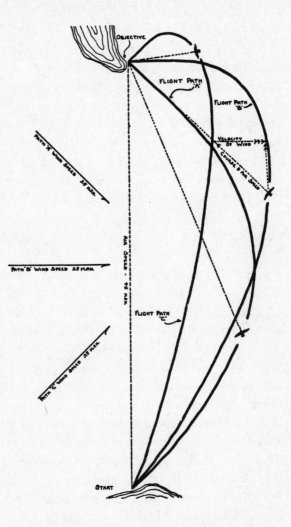

to the next in cross-country travel. At Delta I have seen this not only in blackbirds, but in Blue-winged Teal flying along the edge of Cadham Bay in a series of curves from one point of reeds to the next. One sees ducks following the duffer's course when they come in to the decoys, and this technique is often used in making landings either on water or ashore. When a bird has been flying with the wind from behind, it frequently adopts the duffer's course as it turns to make its landing into the wind.

When the speed of the wind is greater than a bird's air speed, forward motion over the ground is impossible. More than once I have seen Mallards hanging for several seconds in mid-air when meeting the strong lake breeze pouring into the mouth of the Delta channel. I have watched Canada Geese moving to stubble against heavy wind at a ground speed of only 4 m.p.h. In the face of winds that approach their air speed, ducks and geese may remain grounded in sheltered situations, and several times in periods of strong south winds I have known Mallards to forego their afternoon feeding flight. Often, however, these stubble birds ride the north wind for a quick trip to the fields, then are required to "inch" their way back to the marsh after their meal. It is common knowledge amongst gunners that waterfowl moving against a strong wind fly much closer to the ground than usual. I once met Mallards flying against a 40 m.p.h. wind only ten or fifteen feet above the ground, some birds dropping almost to the field. It is known that ground friction reduces the speed of the wind near the earth's surface, and it is reasonable to assume that the low-flying birds seek the slower currents of low altitude.

The flow of the air over the earth is not without variation; hence there are frequent changes in the relation of the bird to the air mass in which it travels. Because of hills and valleys, buildings, trees and other obstacles, and also because of differential warming of the land, as between lake and shore or plowed field and cropland, the constant flow of the wind is often interrupted by eddies and gusts. "Such gusts of wind are often sudden and violent and it is sometimes true that birds near the earth's surface do, for a fraction of a second, get struck by a gust with a consequent lifting of feathers. But the inertia of a bird is so low that it almost instantly assumes the velocity of the gust and is once more in a dead calm" (Smith, 1945:154). This feather-lifting, of course, may occur on the top of the wing and the back when a bird slows its flight close to the point of stalling. Then "the air flow no longer follows the contour of the wing's upper surface, and a condition known as 'flow separation' has taken place. When this occurs, a partial vacuum on the upper wing surface results and the coverts are pushed out of place by a reversed air flow rushing over the area" (Queeny, 1947:108). We may have visual evidence of gusts, as where ducks cross the lake ridge to rise abruptly in the face of the updraft over the shore. Woodcock (1940) tells how gulls at sea search for convection eddies and when found "one sees them change abruptly from a wing-flapping horizontal flight to a steep climb." Human beings experience this effect of turbulence when traveling in an aircraft. The passenger perceives the plane's entrance into a rising column of air as a "bump," but this awareness of the new air mass is fleeting, lasting only for that instant when the shift is made from one air mass to the other.

A descending Canvasback

Waterfowl sometimes encounter difficult navigational problems when flying with a strong tail wind. I have seen Lesser Scaup arrive with a north wind on Cadham Bay, then swing around to join a flock of birds on the water. In making the swing they were carried so far south of the flock that they alighted many yards short of their objective. Several times our young Canada Geese have crashed into trees on the lakeshore when coming off the lake in a strong northwest wind. They apparently were unable to judge their speed accurately enough to maneuver over the trees in time to prevent an accident. Sometimes in late autumn when the last open hole is closed to the reeds and the wind blows strongly shoreward, ducks are obliged to land with the wind to their backs, and after circling the pond several times, they come down to crash with heavy splashes or to slide across the ice on their tails.

When a duck makes a landing under unstable air conditions, the body may be shifted rapidly into many positions and the feet thrown wide for balance as the bird maneuvers downward; but the head holds its position steady with the horizon, as if the neck were the pivot upon which the body swung. This steadiness of the head must be of tremendous importance to a bird's safe arrival from flight, especially in landings made under turbulent conditions or in wooded places. While this stability of the head, regardless of body posture, no doubt serves the visual process during flight, it does not result from the function of the eyes — that is to say, visual orientation alone is not responsible for this balance. Thus, when a duck or goose, or any other bird, is blindfolded with a hood or mask, the body may be turned left or right, up or down, but the head remains constantly oriented to gravity, hold-

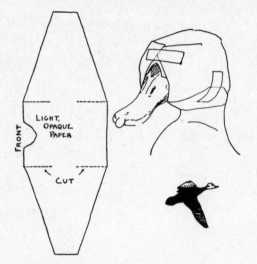

Figure 7. The Carrick blindfold. Made of light, opaque paper. The size and shape vary according to the species.

ing steady posture. In short, the duck does not need to see its surroundings in order to keep the balanced position of its head.

Not only is the blindfolded bird able to balance its head when held in the hand, but when it is cast into the air, body and head quickly assume the posture of flight. Like a cat falling with its feet to the ground, the blind-folded bird quickly adjusts to its belly-down flight attitude when cast aloft. A blindfolded Blue-winged Teal, or any other duck, when thrown into the air with tail or belly upward, twists in a flash to flight posture and flies away. In experiments designed by William H. Carrick (1949) we flew 249 blind-folded birds of eighteen species at Delta between 1946 and 1952 (Figure 7).* Regardless of how these blindfolded birds were cast into the air, suc-cessful flight was the rule rather than the exception and only 5 per cent refused to fly.

The ability of birds to right themselves and fly when they cannot see their surroundings or the sun depends heavily upon the balancing function of the vestibule of the ear with its semicircular canals and otolith organs (Lowenstein, 1950; Wendt, 1951). Wendt points out, however, that muscle receptors also play an important role in establishing body posture and "it is not always easy to separate vestibular effects from other factors." Paton (1928), who studied the equilibrium of the domestic Mallard, concluded that "some visceral change is produced as a result of the disturbance of

* The species flown with blindfold were: Mallard, Pintail, Green-winged Teal, Blue-winged Teal, Redhead, Marsh Hawk, Cooper's Hawk, Wilson's Snipe, Great Horned Owl, Barn Swallow, Catbird, English Sparrow, Bronzed Grackle, Yellow-headed Blackbird, Red-winged Blackbird, Cowbird, Song Sparrow, Crow.

balance, and that this initiates the various compensatory movements." The whole evolution of the bird, of course, has been toward aerial activity. In this he has certain important advantages over the human pilot, whose heritage is that of man as a terrestrial being.

Once the eyes of the human pilot lose sight of the earth, the horizon, and the sun, he can no longer hold his aircraft on a straight and level course. In a cloud the pilot without instruments quickly becomes disoriented with respect to the earth. Believing he is holding a level course, it is typical of him unwittingly to let his craft move into a spiral turn.

Flight actions are inherent in the bird; man must learn to fly. Moreover, the bird is the flight structure. A man airborne operates by remote control the complex machine in which he sits but of which he is not a part. In bird and aircraft, pressures produce the same forces and stresses upon the flight structure. In the bird, however, every feather springs from a nerve ending, and each flight feather is subjected to varying pressures. Hence the most minute changes in balance create stresses that the bird must perceive much more intimately than the human pilot who is in touch with his plane only through the stick in his hands, the rudder pedals at his feet and the "seat of his pants."

The human pilot is committed to operate his airplane as it was conceived by its designer, while a bird may alter its flight structure in a flash as occasion demands. For instance, in both plane and bird stability is closely related to the dihedral angle* of the wing; as this angle is raised, stability is increased. The dihedral is an unalterable feature of the aircraft's design over which the pilot has no control; but the Mallard descending to a wooded pond, or a blindfolded sparrow, may alter wing angle at will. Moreover, modern aircraft, although they may be stable in the vertical, longitudinal, and lateral axes, are normally designed to be spirally unstable. Such spiral instability is planned for the comfort of pilot and passenger;† but left to itself, such a plane will eventually fly in an ever tightening spiral with a resultant loss in altitude. Thus a human pilot, when confronted with the problem of flying without reference to the horizon (and lacking instruments), must overcome severe handicaps that do not obtain with birds, and it is not entirely fair to make direct comparisons between a blindfolded bird

* The angle at which each side of a wing inclines upward or downward from the horizontal.

† The reason that airplanes are not designed to be spirally stable is that such aircraft are very uncomfortable for the passenger, developing lateral oscillations in rough air which the human stomach is incapable of tolerating (G. S. Trimble, Jr.; letter).

63

and a blind-flying pilot in a standard aircraft. Aerodynamically it is possible to design an airplane spirally stable with high wing dihedral which, like the blindfolded bird, will stay right side up relative to the earth for an indefinite period of flight. By such design, free-flying model aircraft carry successful flight, quite obviously without sensory control.

Just as birds, unlike aircraft, can alter their structural design to increase stability, so, too, their flight structure may instantly achieve a reduction in stability — an advantage, J. M. Smith says (1953:69), "provided there is a parallel increase in the efficiency of control. This can be seen by analogy with aeroplanes. Transport aeroplanes are normally designed with a fairly high degree of stability since safety in steady flight is of greater importance than manoeuvrability. In fighter aircraft, however, manoeuvrability is of first importance, and the stability margin is usually reduced to a minimum." Such control, Smith points out, is greatest in the higher orders of birds where sensory awareness of balance may be more important than structural stability. This variation in inherent structural stability and sensory control may be seen when we compare a loon or a grebe with a Mallard or a Duck Hawk. The loon and grebe, like an arrow sped from its bow, are stable only at a certain velocity; but the Mallard and Duck Hawk are able to shift in a flash from transport-like stability to fighter-plane maneuverability. That a bird is able to compensate for changes in flight structure was shown by a blindfolded Yellow-headed Blackbird which flew 400 yards, then made a successfully gentle landing even though it had lost all its tail feathers.

The "thumb," or winglet, of the bird and the leading edge wing slot in some aircraft are structures that increase stability at low speeds, and thus inhibit stalling. "A bird's winglets lie closely against the leading edges of its wings in cruising flight when the wings have a low angle of attack. In fact, they form a part of this neatly rounded edge. But they are usually raised when turning, pitching, and landing, and they are often raised when climbing. To describe this action of the winglet, one might almost use Ludington's words describing the action of an airplane's wing slot — 'it opens automatically as the angle of attack passes a certain point'" (Queeny, 1947:106).

In the observations made at Delta, hooded birds were given their freedom by being tossed upward into the air. If there was a wind, the bird usually faced into the air stream the moment it began flight, and this initial adjustment was accomplished regardless of the bird's position relative to the wind when it was cast aloft. This orientation was but momentary, how-

ever; the bird faced into the air flow for only an instant, then turned to fly in another direction, usually downwind. It appeared that the impetus of the upthrust into the air was a reference by which the bird made its orientation into the wind, for it was only at this starting instant that the hooded birds seemed truly sensible of a steady flow of air.

It was typical of the hooded bird to carry its flight downwind from the starting place, and exceptions were few (Table 1).* In slow-flying birds, like English Sparrows and Yellow-headed Blackbirds, this downwind drift was usually in patterns of circles. After facing the wind for a moment, the bird turned to swing around in a circle, and each complete turn was a leg in the downwind shift, as indicated in Figure 8, A, C. The direction of this circling was not constant; on any given day some flew clockwise, others counterclockwise. Several times when we flew the same bird twice, it circled to the right on the first flight and to the left on the second.

In a breeze of less than 5 m.p.h. the circles were well formed and the downwind progress was slow. With an increased wind velocity the flight pattern showed a series of loops (Figure 8, D, E, F) rather than full circles, and the downwind progress was more rapid. In flying these loops, the hooded sparrow or blackbird seemed to hang in the air a moment on the upwind turn, its ground speed reduced or, if the speed of the wind was the same as the air speed of the bird, stopped completely. After a moment of hovering into the wind, the bird continued with its circle. When the wind velocity was greater than the air speed of the bird, it traveled backward over the ground during the moment it faced the wind. In heavy winds the pattern of the

* Tables 1 and 2 include only the hooded flights which were made in 1950, '51, and '52. From this point the discussion is based entirely on the results of these flights, for which complete data were recorded. Although notes on behavior were made in all 249 flights, imperfect recording techniques made it impossible to include the earlier experiments in Tables 1 and 2.

circle was reduced to a series of loops, the bird turning at intervals into the air stream, then swinging around to fly swiftly downwind.

To the casual observer, this hesitation when the bird flew into the air current appeared to be an awareness of the wind; but when the pattern of a hooded flight was timed and plotted on paper, it became apparent that the into-wind reduction of ground speed was merely the variation in relative motion due to the bird's position in the moving air mass. Its air speed was constant around the flight circle, as was obvious in a calm. In each into-wind

Figure 8. Flight patterns of blindfolded birds

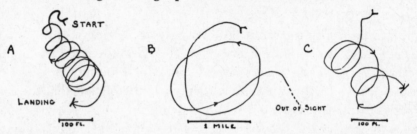

A. Juvenile Yellow-headed Blackbird; wind 2 m.p.h.; flight lasted 55 seconds; bird climbed to 100 feet.

B. Adult male Redhead; wind 5 m.p.h.; bird flew out of sight at elevation of about 300 feet.

C. Juvenile Yellow-headed Blackbird; wind 2 m.p.h.; flight lasted 50 seconds; bird climbed to 100 feet.

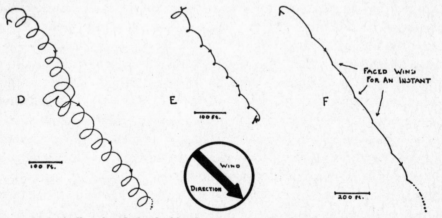

D. Juvenile Yellow-headed Blackbird; wind 4–5 m.p.h.; bird climbed to about 200 feet and flew out of sight.

E. Juvenile English Sparrow; wind 20–25 m.p.h.; bird climbed to about 40 feet.

F. Juvenile male Green-winged Teal; wind 30–35 m.p.h.; elevation 50 feet; bird flew out of sight.

Figure 8 continued

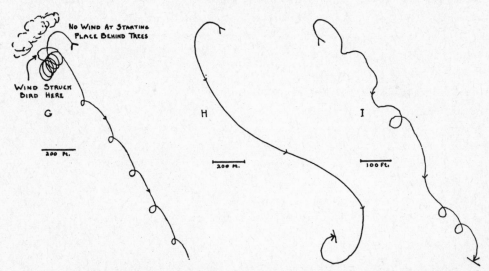

G. Juvenile Yellow-headed Blackbird; wind nil on ground behind trees, 15–20 m.p.h. above tree level; bird climbed to about 150 feet and flew out of sight.

H. Adult male Pintail; wind 25 m.p.h.; bird flew at about 100 feet.

I. Juvenile Yellow-headed Blackbird; wind 15 m.p.h.; bird climbed to 150 feet.

leg of a circle, however, the ground speed was reduced by the force of the wind, just as forward motion over the ground was increased by the air flow in every downwind turn. The circles remained constant to the air mass, but were distorted relative to the ground and to the observer, this distortion being proportionate to the strength of the wind. This was shown in the hooded flight of a juvenile Yellow-headed Blackbird set free behind the shelter of trees where there was no wind at ground level. When released, it flew in well-defined circles until it climbed above the trees, where it met a 15 m.p.h. wind. Thenceforward its circling continued at the same rate, but the flight pattern described a series of widely separated loops (Figure 8, G).

The circle was not invariably the pattern in all hooded tests. Some birds adopted flights that varied widely from the true circle (Figure 8, H, I); but these variations, though individually distinct, always followed a pattern of curves that carried the bird downwind from the starting place. In the swift-flying birds, like the ducks, the flight did not fit into the circling pattern as frequently as in the smaller species. This may have been because they so often and so quickly flew out of sight that the true shape of the flight could not be judged. One Redhead made a clean circle a mile in diameter before flying out of sight (Figure 8, B), and three hooded Green-

67

Table 1. Flights of Hooded Birds at Delta, Manitoba, 1950–1952, according to Species

	English Sparrow (No.=22)	Yellow-headed Blackbird (No.=30)	Red-winged Blackbird (No.=10)	Cowbird (No.=6)	Barn Swallow (No.=4)	Domestic Pigeon (No.=2)	Jacksnipe (No.=1)	Redhead (No.=2)	Pintail (No.=1)	Green-winged Teal (No.=3)	Total of all Birds (No.=81)
Refused to fly or crashed immediately after being cast aloft	0	2	1	0	0	0	0	1	0	0	4
Remained in air less than 1 minute											
Crashed or hit ground hard on alighting	0	4	2	0	0	0	0	0	0	0	6
Made gentle landing	18	13	2	3	3	1	1	0	0	0	41
Remained in air more than 1 minute											
Crashed or hit ground hard on alighting	0	3	3	0	0	0	0	0	0	0	6
Made gentle landing	1	4	2	2	0	1	0	0	1	0	11
Flew out of sight	3	4	0	1	1	0	0	1	0	3	13
Maintained orientation into wind	0	1*	0	0	0	0	0	0	0	0	1
Did not maintain orientation into wind	22	29	10	6	4	2	1	1	1	3	79
Flew downwind from starting place	22	29	10	4	4	2	1	1	1	3	77
Flew across the wind	0	1	0	2	0	0	0	0	0	0	3
Flew into the wind	0	0	0	0	0	0	0	0	0	0	0
Flew in clear-cut circles or loops	22	23	7	3	4	2	1	1	1	3	67
Flew in unclassifiable patterns	0	7	3	3	0	0	0	0	0	0	13

* This bird flew into a series of gusts.

winged Teal set free in a 25–30 m.p.h. wind made distinct into-wind loops such as those characteristic of the sparrows (Figure 8, F).

This downwind drift of the blindfolded birds finds an interesting analogy in the behavior of the fry of Chum Salmon, *Oncorhynchus keta*, as described by Hoar (1953). "Chum Salmon fry emerging from gravel of the lower reaches of coastal streams swim vigorously into currents and maintain their position during the day—even in quite rapid water. They are lively little fish and do not behave in any way like floating plankton. . . . As the light intensity falls, rheotactic responses, which are to a large degree dependent on vision, fail, and these fish pass downstream in shoals. The fact that such mass movements occur during a rather precise period of the night is probably due to the dark adaptation of the eye and a period of night blindness. It is not necessary to assume that fish transported in this way will move at the same rate as floating objects. They are active fish and as they dart to and fro will move most easily and farthest with the current, and will, at night, go downstream rapidly until they can again see to maintain position with respect to fixed objects." For the salmon fry in darkness or the bird flying blindly, the total of any movement, regardless of whether the pattern is circling or otherwise, must add up to a down-current drift when the eyes cannot see some stable part of the environment.

Wing-stroke and other flight actions of the hooded birds varied according to the species. In those, such as ducks, with a heavy wing load the beat was rapid, strong, and deliberate.* Once a hooded duck was in flight, there often was no characteristic of action distinguishing it from another flying naturally with full sight. Such rapid travel was a necessity for these birds if they were to remain aloft, just as the jet aircraft with its heavy wing load must fly faster than the broad-winged "cub" type. In sparrows and others with light wing loadings, there was a wide variation in flight action. Some hooded blackbirds and sparrows flew in a natural manner; but many, especially among the English Sparrows, adopted a hovering flight like that used by free-flying birds when alighting.

Most of the birds in these tests were young-of-the-year taken in banding traps and flown shortly after their capture. Many of the English Sparrows and Yellow-headed Blackbirds still showed the yellow gape as evidence of their recent departure from the nest. I was able to detect no difference be-

---

* "Wing load" is the ratio between wing area and body weight. Poole (1938) has computed wing loadings of many wild birds, showing, for example, that the English Sparrow has a wing load of 3.78 centimeters per gram of body weight while the Blue-winged Teal has a wing load of 1.10.

TABLE 2. FLIGHTS OF HOODED BIRDS AT DELTA, MANITOBA, 1950–1952, ACCORDING TO AGE OF BIRDS

	English Sparrow		Yellow-headed Blackbird		Cowbird		All Other Species		Total of All Species		
	Adult (No.=3)	Juvenile (No.=19)	Adult (No.=3)	Juvenile (No.=27)	Adult (No.=3)	Juvenile (No.=3)	Adult (No.=10)	Juvenile (No.=13)	Adult (No.=19)	Juvenile (No.=62)	All Ages (No.=81)
Refused to fly or crashed immediately after being cast aloft	0	0	0	2	0	0	1	1	1	3	4
Remained in air less than 1 minute											
Crashed or hit ground hard on alighting	0	0	0	4	0	0	0	2	0	6	6
Made gentle landing	1	17	2	11	1	2	5	2	9	32	41
Remained in air more than 1 minute											
Crashed or hit ground hard on alighting	0	0	0	3	0	0	0	3	0	6	6
Made gentle landing	1	0	0	4	1	1	2	2	4	7	11
Flew out of sight	1	2	1	3	1	0	2	3	5	8	13
Maintained orientation into wind	0	0	0	1*	0	0	0	0	0	1	1
Did not maintain orientation into wind	3	19	3	26	3	3	19	13	18	61	79
Flew downwind from starting place	3	19	3	26	2	2	19	13	18	61	79
Flew across the wind	0	0	0	1	1	1	0	0	2	1	3
Flew into the wind	0	0	0	0	0	0	0	0	0	0	0
Flew in clear-cut circles or loops	3	19	3	20	2	1	19	10	17	50	67
Flew in unclassifiable patterns	0	0	0	7	1	2	0	3	1	12	13

* This bird flew into a series of gusts.

tween juveniles and adults in the hooded flights. Of twenty juvenile English Sparrows flown in 1951 and 1952, none crashed and three remained on the wing until they had circled out of sight (Table 2).

The hooded birds generally spiraled upward to a certain elevation, then leveled off to continue the downwind movement at that height. The optimum flying level was approximately the same for all birds of a species on a given day, but there were specific differences; for example, Yellow-headed Blackbirds always flew higher than English Sparrows. The flight level was lowest for the English Sparrow, which mounted from twenty to fifty feet, depending on the strength of the wind. In stiff winds there seldom was a stable flight level; the subjects often spiraled upward until lost to sight. William Carrick has suggested that this flight level depends on ground turbulence, the depth of such disturbance being shallower in light winds.

While these hooded birds were not able to orient their flight to the wind when it blew without variation, they did show awareness of sudden, sharp shifts in the air flow, as on a gusty day when they were met by a quick change of wind from a new direction. The bird showed its awareness by facing the gust. But, as after its initial thrust into the air, this moment of orientation was fleeting and the circling flight was quickly resumed.

Although unable to orient to the wind, hooded birds, especially the passerines, often responded skillfully to auditory cues. When hooded English Sparrows were released near a clump of willows in which wild companions chirped, they flew directly toward these voices without circling. A Red-winged Blackbird released near trees where wind whistled in the branches flew directly toward this grove, crashing therein. If we talked loudly during a hooded flight or whistled or made other noises, the hooded birds often faced abruptly in our direction.

Of birds which accomplished successful flight, only 20 per cent of those we saw come to earth descended with a hard crash. Most of the birds either spiraled down gently at a shallow angle, or "parachuted" with hovering wings. If parachuting, the bird showed its awareness of descent by thrusting its legs forward in landing atti-

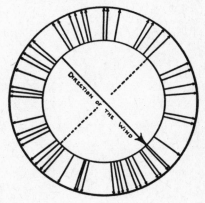

Figure 9. Direction of landings relative to the wind as observed in 51 hooded flights, 1950

tude. When these hooded birds came to earth they gave further evidence of their inability to perceive the wind's direction, for there was no into-wind pattern of alighting. Their landings aimed at all points of the compass, regardless of wind direction (Figure 9).

Here, then, is the successful accomplishment of blind flight. The waterfowl and these other birds are inherently attuned to movement within their medium. They are innately balanced in their aerial environment as fish are in water. The wild bird, even as a juvenile, is able to remain aloft in flight even though it cannot see the ground. But if the bird does not have visual contact with the earth, it must lose its orientation with the wind when traveling in a moving air mass and thus be displaced geographically without awareness of this displacement.

6

Awareness of Time and Space

As waterfowl come and go from one part of the marsh to another, there is a regularity in their daily travels. We men have formed the habit of dividing the day into hours of the clock, but birds have no such artificial regulator. The break of dawn is the beginning of the waterfowl day. How well the hunter knows this! Dawn is the wildfowler's joy. No matter how quiet the night or how calm the day that follows, morning twilight brings a flurry of activity to the marsh. Most precise are the Mallards, which leave their shorelines for the stubble fields at the first hint of day; throughout the autumn one may rise to greet this flight, to hear overhead the wings that cannot be seen because the dome of sky is still in darkness. This dawn flight comes out in one full sweep, and most of the birds pass over within a few minutes after one hears the first whicker of wings, each flock following the next so rapidly that they are seldom out of one's earshot. As day unfolds, the movement dwindles. Now flocks are several minutes apart; and finally there are none at all except the odd duck or small band moving aimlessly, birds that were disturbed when they met guns or tractors at the field of their choice. This lull lasts only twenty or thirty minutes. Then, before the sun tops the horizon, some are returning to lake or marsh, the silhouettes of their swollen necks giving evidence that they have fed well. These returning wedges usually fly at a greater elevation than on the outflight, and hunters who leave home at daybreak often believe them to be of birds that have spent the night on the fields.

When skies are clear, stubble flights begin at nearly the same time every dawn, about fifty minutes before sunrise in early October. Bossenmaier (1953a) found that when the sky is overcast, the journey is not so early as on bright mornings, the blanket of cloud delaying the threshold light which is the cue sending the birds off to the fields. As the arrival of dawn is slightly

The Mallards finish their breakfast on the fields and return to the
marsh before the sun tops the horizon.

delayed each morning, so in the course of an autumn the morning flight is
deferred accordingly, and in October the passage to the fields starts more
than an hour later than in August.

Mallards must respond to the light of the sun. This is not remarkable,
but it is an important point in our understanding of waterfowl. Clearly they
are aware of the sun and act upon that awareness in a positive manner.
When Mallards shot in the dawn flight are examined, we find their gizzards
empty. These stubble birds are ready for food well ahead of dawn, but they
hold to their sand bars until the stain in the east is their signal to make away
to the fields.

After returning from stubble, Mallards loaf, preen, and find their grit,
then take their morning nap on lakeshore or mud bar. In the afternoon they
fly once more across the marsh to their second meal of the day. The beginning of this afternoon passage is never so precise as that of dawn and is
more frequently modified by other influences. For example, I have never

known the wind to start the morning birds before the break of light, but a noon wind usually sends the fowl to the fields earlier than they choose to go on calm days. The afternoon flight continues longer, always lasting more than an hour and frequently consuming several hours. After the first ducks appear, there is a steady passage, so that on a heavily used flight line the supply of birds sometimes seems inexhaustible from early afternoon until sunset.

I suspect that the timing of the afternoon flight is related to metabolism. Assuming that a Mallard takes its meal at the same time each morning, it is reasonable to believe that hunger must be felt at about the same time each afternoon. The ducks do not return to the fields while breakfast is still heavy in their gizzards; but once digestion has progressed to the point of hunger, this stimulus urges them to the prairies for a second meal. The wide spread of the afternoon movement is further evidence, I believe, of the role of hunger. In the dawn flight, all are pressed at about the same time by this common urge. Once on their way, however, they are not equally successful in taking their meal. Some find a close, safe, and abundant food supply, then return quickly to the lake. Others are disturbed by hunters or by farming activity, and they must fly to a second or a third farm. All do not travel the same distance to feed. It is plain that each band does not breakfast at the same time; hence, although the first are returning to their loafing bars before sunup, others, not so fortunate, drift back to the lake all through the forenoon. So it seems that these morning variations must cause the differences in the timing of the afternoon flights. Birds that come back from the fields early are probably the first to go out in the afternoon.

The second passage moves in the full light of day. When the shooting season arrives, however, ducks feeding in areas heavily hunted sometimes delay their meal until dusk. South of the village of Delta, where there is much gunning, I have found ducks waiting until sunset before venturing to stubble. Several miles farther west, where the hunting pressure is less severe, the birds feed earlier and return to the lake before sundown. The Delta Mallards apparently shift from "gizzard" time to sun time.

I have spoken only of the Mallard, but of course the Pintail and a small number of Black Ducks, mixed with the Mallards, make regular flights to the stubble, following a schedule like that described for the "greenheads."

It seems clear that the timing of stubble flights follows two types of cues: the *metabolic cue* and the *solar cue*. The former is measured by the interval between the filling of the bird's crop and the first hunger. If food

75

is taken at the same time each morning and the post-feeding period daily spent in the regular manner, the duck must receive stimuli from the digestive tract directing it to its second meal at about the same hour each afternoon. The metabolic cue is modified by the solar cue. In the timing of the dawn flight, hunger is secondary to light. Crop and gizzard may be empty some time before dawn, but the hungry bird awaits the light of day before going to breakfast.

Among our captives there is a sharp awareness of time that seems to obey the metabolic cue. They are fed at a given hour each day, but if for some reason the feeding is delayed, they gather around the edge of the pond awaiting their handout. Some of the geese walk to the granary at the appointed hour.

Unlike the Mallards, Canada Geese often start out for the fields after sunup.

Canada Geese, like Mallards, go to stubble each morning, but unlike these ducks they do not respond to the sharp division between night and dawn. The big honkers usually remain on their night roost until the sky is bright and the details of the landscape are well lighted. Some keep a routine that does not take them to the fields until after sunup. Nevertheless, they are regular in their delayed breakfast travel; if the weather remains constant they are seen on the way to the fields at about the same time each morning. For a week in early October I watched a group of Canada Geese leave the lake every day between 6:45 and 7:00 A.M. Another flock crossed Slack's field daily within a few minutes of 8:00 A.M. Geese must be hungry at dawn, and several morning birds I have shot on the out-flight had empty gizzards. It is neither dawn-light nor hunger by which the time of their departure is regulated. Somehow they must be aware of intervals of time. That such awareness of time must exist seems evident in the pioneering studies of Gustav Kramer (1951, 1952). His work suggests that birds do, indeed, appreciate intervals of daytime on the basis of the sun's position and the angle-speed of its movement—a perception of periods of time between sunrise and sunset. Canada Geese measure the interval between dawn and that point of the morning when they fly out to feed. A similar perception of interval was noted for bees by von Frisch (1950:78), who tells us that "bees have a good memory for time. If one feeds them at a certain spot for a few days between ten and twelve o'clock, they visit this spot for the next few days from ten to twelve even though the food dish is empty."

Many other birds go out to feed on regular schedules. The autumn marsh is the roosting place for Redwings and other blackbirds that launch forth to the farmland at the same time each morning. The blackbirds, however, hold to their roosts while the Mallards are outbound, and it is three-quarters of an hour after the first duck flights that they leave for breakfast. Next come the Herring Gulls, forewarning the goose hunter to keep his eye on the horizon for the first sight of Canada Geese. Seibert (1951), who studied the feeding flights of herons, observed that the "time of sunset and sunrise was found to be the most important factor controlling the arrival and departure of all species." Nice (1935) watched the regular morning movements of Starlings and Bronzed Grackles and found that the "first Starlings left the roost at lower light values than did the Grackles . . ." At Delta the small Richardson's Geese regularly depart for the fields earlier than the Canada Geese; they are often shot during the dawn flight of Mallards, while Canadas are seldom killed on farmland so early as dawn.

Geese, like Mallards, take their second meal in the afternoon, following regular schedules. At Skunk Creek I watched a flock of Canada Geese go over the trees at about four o'clock every afternoon for five days. As with ducks, there is individual variation in the time of the afternoon feeding trip, so that all geese do not leave the lake at the same time. At the mouth of the Whitemud River there is a traditional spring and autumn rendezvous where geese loaf and preen not far from shore. I have watched the afternoon departures as one flock after another breaks away from the main body and starts toward the prairie. Sometimes more than two hours are consumed before the last band goes out to feed. I suspect that this spread, as in ducks, may be due to differences among them in the place and success of the morning meal, those breakfasting first probably getting away earliest in the afternoon.

Fatigue is another cue to the passage of time. Each day there is a period of rest in the rhythm of activity of all waterfowl. On our pond such loafing is a part of the pen routine among both wild and captive birds. They doze at the pond's edge or float with the head turned over the back, the bill tucked under the scapular feathers, the eyes nearly shut in complete repose. All are occupied with their nap at the same time. Minor disturbances do not cause them to interrupt their rest, and even though the wind blows hard, they continue to sleep. Then suddenly, without apparent outer influence, first one, then the next, lifts its head. Shortly a bird will flex its wings, and the entire flock is awake.

The morning bath of waterfowl is a sight to behold, particularly when large geese and swans are so occupied. There is a wild splashing of wings as they douse themselves. Then follows a dipping of the head and neck, with still more wing-splashing. Finally one bird after another rolls over on its back, flapping its wings while upside down in the water. Sometimes a mad excitement overtakes the crowd. One bird races across the surface as if the devil himself were on its tail. Then in full stride it dives. The instant it comes up it goes down again; up it comes, down it goes. All the birds in the flock may be consumed in this devil-chase, helter-skelter, this way and that, over the water and down under. After a few minutes the divings end. The flock regains composure and settles quietly to the job of preening.

I give these details because such antics attracted the attention of Dr. Roper Cadham one Sunday on his way to the store. He stopped his car for a moment to watch the geese in their wild splashings and divings on the Station pond, then drove on to the village. There, on the channel, another band of Canada Geese was occupied in the same way. Here were two groups of birds doing the same thing at the same time. They were in the flightless period of the summer molt so that there could have been no interchange from one group to the other. The flocks were a quarter of a mile apart, with trees and buildings intervening; hence one band could not have seen the other's actions, nor did sound of their activity carry so far. I suspect that the channel geese and those at the pond fed at about the same time in the morning, and thus they began their post-breakfast bath and frolic at about the same moment.

I have never seen adult waterfowl driven to the point of exhaustion in their local movements, but when new arrivals reach the marsh on migration, their behavior is that of tired birds. Trautman observed (1940:90) that "the newly arrived birds seemed very tired, for upon alighting most of them tucked their bills under the feathers of their back or wings and apparently went to sleep." Of migrant Mallards arriving in Arkansas, Queeny says (1947:37), "They are exhausted. Some have lost as much as half a pound during their flight. If they become aware of an interloper, they do not fly away . . ."

In downy young I have watched what amounts to a relation between fatigue and the passage of time. Once I followed a brood of Redheads along a road at the marsh edge. They traveled ahead of me undisturbed as I observed at a distance with field glasses. From their location I judged that they had walked about two miles when I first encountered them. They toddled along behind their mother, then squatted down for a rest of three or four minutes while she waited patiently. Soon they went on again, only to stop once more to rest. Their stops were made every forty or fifty yards and apparently were timed according to their requirement for rest.

Regularity of activity has been noted in other birds. Pettingill (1936) has discussed the relation between the sun and the beginning of the morning and evening "peenting" in the Woodcock. This begins at about the same moment each twilight, but as the sun sets later each day, there is a similar delay in the beginning of the evening "song." Nice (1943:108), working with songbirds, observed that "each species has its own 'Waking-Light' " and that in some kinds the first song, like the feeding flight of the Canada Goose, does not begin until long after the first glow of dawn. Palmgren (1949), who has given an excellent review of the experimental work on the diurnal rhythm in birds, points out that in the European Robin "light is not the only factor. If the natural light is shut off and the cages lighted with constant light intensity day and night, the sleeping time nevertheless remains on the whole unchanged for some time." He concludes that sleep "behaves as an autonomous periodical function, although largely controlled by the light conditions." Armstrong (1954) and Cullen (1954), presenting careful reviews of the literature and reports of their own original observations of birds living under continuous daylight, conclude that little is known regarding the "factors which may modify the length of a bird's working day" (Armstrong), and that "there is still a virtually untouched field of investigation of diurnal rhythm in the Arctic" (Cullen).

There is a similar regularity in the activities of mammals. A doe White-tailed Deer and her fawn passed down a trail within sight of my office each afternoon for a week, the two reaching this spot within a few moments of four o'clock. Those who live on the western prairies know the sunset song of the coyote. Along the edge of the Delta Marsh skunks begin to wander along the road at the same hour of twilight each evening. At Cornell University my Pointer dog Nelly had a routine of classes which she attended more precisely than some students. She always entered a classroom quietly, walked to her usual corner, and flopped down to endure the lecture hour. The Library bell was the usual announcement ending class, but Nelly invariably became restless a moment or two before the bell rang. In one room, where she had a conspicuous position up front, her pre-bell rise and yawn was the students' mark for the end of the hour. I presume that some cue which I could not perceive was her signal of the end of the period. Similar behavior on the part of animals in a zoo is well known; lions and bears follow the actions of their keepers that identify feeding or pen-cleaning time. We know that cattle wend homeward at evening, beckoned by their distended udders as well as by twilight.

We recognize both sun time and metabolic time in our own lives, awakening earlier with the vernal increase in the length of the day. Through the course of the day, many of us find ourselves checking the sun's position. It is a rule with some gunners to walk outward until the sun attains a point halfway between the horizon and its position at the start; then the turn is made toward home, which is reached at sundown. The office worker and the farm hand both recognize the metabolic cues that signal lunch hour. The time of the daily bowel movement obeys metabolic rhythm. Perhaps the most precise response to metabolic time is found in the human infant which is fed on schedule; if this is not met, the baby cries. Woodrow (1951) suggests that "time is always judged indirectly by means of some process that serves as a cue. By a temporal cue is meant any process that changes progressively with the lapse of time. . . . Time is not a thing that, like an apple, may be perceived. Stimuli and patterns of stimuli occupy physical time; and we react to such stimuli by perceptions, judgements, comparisons, estimates, etc."

The discussion so far has considered the natural cause and effect of timed activity. The relation between dawn-light and the rhythm of daily behavior may be measured under artificial conditions. In the brooder house young ducks are quiet all night, and activity does not begin until daybreak. But if we create artificial dawn with electric lights turned on an hour earlier, the birds respond at once. Likewise, the influence of the hunger stimuli may be observed in the pens. The Mallard that has fed well at his morning meal loafs quietly; but the bird that has been held from his breakfast until noon runs to the trays to feed eagerly.

Regarding what he calls a "sense of time," Pumphrey (1948:196) says that it is possible "to adopt either of two radically different theoretical approaches. The sense of time has been regarded as a sense of interval, for which the reference standard is the solar day. And alternatively, the reference standard has been thought to be inherent and associated in some way with the rate of living of the animal organism." I do not think these to be alternative or opposing theories. The rate of living is hinged to the rhythm of the solar day and to the metabolic processes of life; the relation between these constitutes biological time. This relation is not entirely an inborn heritage of the organism, since the timing of its activities may be altered by changing the rhythm of light and dark.

All who have watched the vernal return of waterfowl are aware that activities not only follow a daily schedule, but show a regular response to the time of year. The same species arrive at the same locality at about the same time each spring (see Table 4 in Chapter 9). Nesting has a certain regularity in its beginnings; the first gatherings of molting drakes are seen in about the same week each May; the start of the flightless season has a remarkable regularity; and the first southward movements annually begin at the same time. Just as the daily rhythm of the sun governs the timing of local activity, so the annual solar cycle, with its effects on weather and on the bird itself, influences the schedule of spring arrival (Rowan, 1931). An amazing coincidence of seasonal activity is recorded by Sowls (1955:167), who observed the mass fall migration of November 2, 1946, arriving to pass over the Delta Marsh at 4:15 P.M. His cooperator, Mr. T. H. Schindler, of the

Manitoba Game and Fisheries Branch, that same afternoon watched the first members of the mass migration arrive over the Netley Marsh (68 miles east of Delta) at exactly the same minute.

We can hardly speak of time without considering the bird's orientation in space. Waterfowl are visually oriented to their environment, having learned their place in the world by sight. The channels, passes, leads, and chains of sloughs are followed as they are seen; passes are used again and again because they are learned. No duck, of course, lives on the same home range or even on the same marsh through all of one season. The breeding territory is distinct from the rearing place; there is the molting marsh and there are still other zones of late summer activity. The first move of a bird to a new place is a pioneering venture, albeit this trip may be made with experienced companions. Once settled on a fresh range, the bird learns the new area and is ever linked (so the evidence of banding tells us) to this region of experience. The thread of continuity from range to range strengthens as experiences are repeated; this explains the tendency of waterfowl to revisit the same areas year after year.

The importance of eyesight in spatial orientation is evidenced by the relative heights of travel. Where the distance is short, as when Mallards fly from the Station pond to the bay edge, travel is low. Where the distance is greater, as when they fly to the far shore of the bay, the altitude of flight is increased, and stubble birds on the way to the prairie go still higher. Travelers to nearby fields fly at the edge of gunshot range, around two hundred feet, but Mallards going ten or fifteen miles travel more than twice as high as that. Rowan writes me that he and his hunting partner have "always taken altitude as a direct indication of distance and have regulated our gunning accordingly. The correlation is very marked." In his studies of the Canada Goose in Missouri, Lewis G. Helm (letter) saw a direct relation between length and height of travel, the birds rising higher as the distance of daily feeding flights increased.

The bird on its home range is aware of its position not only through what it immediately sees, however, but through the retention of previous experiences there. In short, the duck is oriented not only to the space of the present, but to this as related to places of past experience. The orientation of the moment is not only to the surroundings seen, but to places over the horizon beyond the edge of visibility. Dr. A. A. Alford and I observed Mallards and Pintails making daily feeding flights to flooded fields south of

Fannestelle, Manitoba, fifty to sixty miles from their night roost on Lake Manitoba. These were as precise and direct to the unseen destination as a flight across a small bay. The birds moved just as surely to a field sixty miles away as to the bay edge plainly seen. It is possible to conduct a simple experiment to demonstrate this relation between the past and the present. In four feet of water in Cadham Bay I dumped a bucket of wheat. Within twenty-four hours some ducks had located this grain. Once found, they fed there regularly. They swam directly to this place — a hidden pinpoint in the vast expanse of water — finding it precisely again and again. The grain could not be seen, and so every trip there depended upon an awareness of something beyond sight.

The bird cannot travel guided by experience alone, of course, and when the landscape is not visible, as in dense fog, local movement comes to a halt. A flock of Canada Geese roosting on Cadham Bay went to their stubble fields when visibility was at about a hundred yards in a light fog; but when this thickened so that we could see no farther than fifty yards, they did not make their trip and loafed all day on the bay. Peter Scott writes me that his flock of free-winged Greater Snow Geese at the Severn Wildfowl Trust "got up in a fog and couldn't get down." Local aerial activity about the marsh is intense on bright, moonlit nights, but there are few or no waterfowl in the air on nights that are overcast and moonless.

Let us remember that the size and complexity of a range are relative to the size and age of the bird. Some ducklings spend their first eight or ten weeks on small sloughs and potholes, their total range of activity covering only a few acres at most. Others may spread their early days over many acres, but the span of activity is restricted by the young bird's requirement to swim or walk wherever it goes. However small in extent, the reedy edges and deep beds of emergent vegetation of the first home are complex grounds for the duckling to learn. To such a downy young, Fannestelle, sixty miles away, is far beyond the edge of eternity. Two months later, however, the home pond is only a small corner of this bird's world as it now flies in an oriented manner about the large marsh and adjacent countryside. For the little duckling the patch of reeds is as large and as complex, relatively speaking, as the whole wide marsh for the same bird after it has grown its wings and taken flight.

When ducks take short, low flights, we infer that the topographic features which their travel obeys — the creeks, channels, and other features of the landscape — are their guides to orientation. In going greater distances

83

overland, as to Fannestelle, they may follow cues presented by blocks of woodland, by stream and river valleys, and, at their destination, by the varying pattern of the fields. Perhaps such man-made features as main roads, grain elevators, and city lights serve in orientation. In 1953 I found a heavy flight of stubble Mallards regularly coursing down a quarter-mile stretch of railway track on flights from grain fields to Longburn Creek, which they then followed to the marsh.

No doubt the sun, as the studies of Kramer (1951, 1952) and Matthews (1951a, b; 1952) suggest, is of importance in the bird's orientation in space, not only when it is directly east or west at dawn and dusk, but through the day. We most readily think of cues to orientation as "landmarks," but certain details of the sky may be important. For example, regularly in fall and spring, and often during summer, thermal currents build a layer of fair-weather cumulus clouds over the Portage Plains, but these are not produced over the colder lake. The result is a sharp line between cloud and blue sky that precisely marks the edge of Lake Manitoba. This effect may last all day, sometimes a regular local feature for many days. I have seen this edge of clouds from the Riding Mountains, seventy miles away; and regularly we see the same cloudline over Lake Winnipeg, sixty miles east of Delta. In summer, thunderheads build up on the west shore of Lake Manitoba and in the interlake country to the east. These often hold their position through much of the afternoon and evening; and their tops may be seen for a hundred miles, lighted clearly long after the countryside is in dusk. Mirage frequently lifts details of the landscape above the true horizon, and I have seen the ice on Lake Manitoba from a distance of eighteen miles.

Edge of cloud bank over south shore of Lake Manitoba. This line of clouds marks the position of the lake for the traveler still many miles away.

To the human wayfarer such sky configurations are always interesting and sometimes helpful as travel guides. It is possible that they may be useful to birds in local orientation. Surely, at least, as we study the bird in its environment, we must acknowledge that there are a great many features of the landscape, not all to be defined simply as "landmarks," that serve as cues to avian orientation.

Because the bird is so free on the wing we often think of its range as boundless. All children, of course, know of the Robin's faithfulness to the city neighborhood, and the work of Howard (1920) and his followers has stressed the confining influence of territorial behavior and the home range in birds. This restriction of activity does not hold for the breeding season alone. The drake may move many miles from the nesting grounds to his molting place, but once there, he settles down to a routine that covers a rather restricted area. The stubble Mallard in August may range as far as Fannestelle to feed, but bandings show that each night it returns with its companions to the same sand bar on the Lake Manitoba shoreline. Juvenile waterfowl may roam far and wide in their late-summer wanderings, but when they stop for a while, banding records show that they usually use the same restricted part of the marsh for feeding and loafing. During migration a banding trap will have many "repeats" of birds that come again and again to the same feeding place during the course of their temporary residence. Seton said (1910) that each animal "has a home-region, even if it is not an actual home. . . . In the idea of a home-region is the germ of territorial rights. At every step it presents close and interesting parallels with the growth of territorial law in man."

Ornithologists have tended to view time and space as a series of discrete, objectively determined units. Time is most often considered as though broken into moments in the flow of life (like the time of morning song) or into periods of life (like the length of incubation). Space is thought of as though segmented into ranges (such as nest and territory) or into lineal distances (such as between nesting place and wintering grounds). Such time and space we measure precisely in hours or miles or in units thereof. By so confining our thought to isolated or limited divisions of time and space, we greatly restrict our understanding of the avian world. Each bird lives in time that is not an instant of the present or a series of present instants; time is the flow of past, present, and future. "Time is as fundamental as space; and it is time, no doubt, that holds the essence of life, and perhaps of all reality. What we have to understand is that time is an accumulation, a growth, a duration" (Durant, 1952:451). Time is relative to motion and to space; hence time is also relative to structure. Time for the flightless duckling, with its short wings and rapid metabolism, is not the same as for the mother with her rapid flight and slower rhythm of body processes. By the clock, to be sure, and by the calendar, time is the same for all — for the duckling, for its mother, and for the observing man. But unquantified, apprehended in life and space and motion, time for the duckling, its mother, and man is very different; each lives in a temporal world of its own.

Space is the medium within which animals live and move. It not only bounds the places and objects of the present, but is the whole of the world in which the bird has lived its past, experiences its present, and will live its future. Space is relative to the perception and the motion of each organism. Time and space are thus inseparable in the life equation. Just as time is relative to structure, so is space. Space for the duckling is far more restricted than for the mother in terms of square feet or miles; yet measured relatively, the world in which the duckling lives is as great and as wide as that of the mature bird.

We must ever remember that just as time and space are not the same for the adult and baby duck, so they are not like entities for man and bird.

PART II

Migrations of Waterfowl

"Dark flying rune against the western glow —
It tells the sweep and loneliness of things,
Symbol of Autumns vanished long ago.
Symbol of coming Springs!"

Pai Ta-shun (Frederick Peterson)

"Home is where one starts from." T. S. Eliot, *Four Quartets*

7

The Cycle of Migration

THERE come unforgettable evenings in late August when a soft calm settles over the marsh. The breeze is spent and the reeds duplicate themselves in perfect reflection. The sky is clear, yet with sundown comes a refreshing chill. The tinkle of water from the canoe paddle and the rustle of a wren in the tules are the only sounds. Here is the world as God made it. Deep in the heart of the wheatland is a pristine wilderness that can differ little from that so loved by the native Cree. This might be the marsh as seen two centuries ago by La Vérendrye. The dark bulrush, the green cattail, and the tall reed have not changed; sky and water are the same; the wren must be a direct descendant of one that chattered here when the explorer's canoe slipped past this very place. Surely all is the same except for the tall grain elevator that rises above the oak bluff six miles to the south.

The peace is broken suddenly by the chuckle of a teal. Who is there so solemn that he listens to the fall note of the Blue-winged Teal without a smile? Here is a challenge offered severely, the youngster's exclamation of its place in this ancient world of bulrush. Hardly before summer becomes routine, autumn is upon us. These Blue-winged Teal, whose voices break the tranquillity of the August evening, are birds-of-the-year. Bred in May, born in June, reared before the wheat is ripe, they are on their way to the wintering grounds before summer is gone. One evening after supper I flush a hundred from the cove; the next morning only a dozen are frightened from the same place. By the equinox the main flight has passed to the south; the end of the first week in October finds only a few stragglers remaining, although there is promise of more fair weather before the shallows close with ice. Whatever the urge, it surely is not the pressure of frost that sends the bluewings to their southland. . . .

What greater place in life can a man attain than a seat by the fire on an October evening? What finer thoughts than of bird, of dog, and of gun? What better companionship than of elder hunters who read aloud from their life stories as they gaze into the hearth? However artificial their environments become, however far from nature they must stray in search of fortune, all wise young men seek a place by the October hearthstone.

I have read many books, have spent many days on the marsh, but there is much I have learned from the words of older hunters. The north wind was their friend before I could hold my father's gun. In calm and storm they lived many years on marshland I am just beginning to know. As the birch logs crackled, I have learned that the Canvasback never wait for the heavy frost. Come mid-October and the cannies are done with Manitoba. In late September their numbers crowd the big marshes so that windrows of pondweed litter the shore downwind of the feeding places. In early October they parade daily, passing from their loafing grounds on open water to the sago beds where they feed. Then, when October is half gone, there comes upon the birds a wild restlessness. In a flock loafing on the water, one bird after another raises its body to flex its wings, so that there is a constant fluttering. Over the marsh, small bands join to form larger flocks. Then the Canvasback are gone, all but a few strays lingering on with the scaup.

This I was told, and all this I have found to be true. Fair weather or foul, the Canvasbacks migrate south before October is finished; they are gone two or three weeks before the bays are frozen.

Casual as the teal flights may be, early as the Canvasback slip away, the freeze-up flight of Mallard and Lesser Scaup is quite another thing. They cling to the northland through October and on into November. Some travel southward, to be sure, like teal and Canvasback, but vast numbers hold to the north as long as open water remains. Then comes the time for passage. The temperature drops and remains below freezing all day; it may touch zero or fall below that mark. The barometer rises, a stiff wind strikes out of the northwest, and before noon the skies are clear. On such a day in November it is the wildfowler's duty to abandon all home ties and go at once to the marsh. It is usual for little flurries of southbound ducks to appear early that afternoon. First one, then another, then more and more, until one glance catches many flocks. They come out of the northwest, often so high that they would not be noticed but for the volume of the flock. They scurry past without stopping. By four o'clock there is not an instant without ducks in every corner of the sky. During the heaviest waves, fifty or sixty flocks a minute may pass over a section of marsh a mile wide; and as far east and west as one can see, waterfowl cross over in steady numbers, small bands and large. The stream of their passage seems endless; then after sundown the rosy twilight changes to cold blue, and the last ducks have passed. Another autumn is gone.

So ends the waterfowl year at Delta. The broad basin of Lake Manitoba is the home of ducks from April until November frost. There they move to and from their feeding and loafing places, between territory and nest, from lakeshore to stubble and return. Day upon day is built the restless activity of living. The daily chain of travel carries them back and forth across familiar terrain. Then suddenly all this is abandoned. The winter is cold and deep. The marsh is without waterfowl until the first hardy birds come back in late March or early April. How do they find their way out of the harsh northland? What guides them back with the soft winds of spring? These are the questions eternal.

Migration is the annually repeated cycle of travel that carries waterfowl away from their birthplace or breeding grounds to temperate wintering waters, returning them to the familiar homeland with the advent of spring. It is important that we think of each migration as beginning and ending in the region of natal experience, with the winter interlude in the south. In the migrational history of a species, to be sure, we might properly consider the impetus as coming from the south, the annual cycle carrying a species to and from its breeding place. For the individual bird, however, the home range on the breeding ground is the start of all migratory movement; and this very same place is the final goal which must be attained to complete the annual cycle. Mayr (1942:240) says that the tendency of birds to return to the same place for reproduction year after year "has been proven by so many studies that it would be unfair to single out a particular one"; and Välikangas (1933), in his classic experiment, showed how the young of wild ducks were tied to the region of birth. He brought eggs of English Mallards to Finland, where they were hatched and where the young were raised and given migratory freedom. Of 62 birds released, 34 came back to their Finland home after their first trip to the wintering grounds.

Sowls (1949, 1950, 1951, 1955) has presented much evidence to show the fidelity of the female to her nesting marsh, his experiments demonstrating that she returns to nest not only in the same meadow, but often in the same part of that field. After studying five species * intensively by following the individual histories of nest-trapped, color-marked hens, he concluded that "they normally return to the original nesting meadow a second and a third and a fourth year, or so long as they survive and the area remains suitable." He also found a remarkable return of young females to the home marsh after their first migration. Of 115 juvenile Pintail hens, for example, 13 per cent came back to Delta to be individually recorded (by leg bands) on the small pond where they were raised. Sowls discovered the nests of 8 of these young females only a short distance from the birthplace. Winter matings in the large aggregations of the southland sometimes join the drake to a female from a region unfamiliar to him and he cannot go to his own home. Thomson (1931, 1945) has given the term "abmigration" to movements, such as those of winter-mated drakes, where a bird native to one region is "found in a subsequent summer in quite a different area." Banding evidence presented by Sowls (1951) and Cartwright (1952) indicates, however, that such males may come back to familiar places, sometimes the natal marsh, after their marital duties are finished.

If we accept the homeland of birth and breeding to be the start and finish of the annual migration cycle, it is clear that a duck travels away from a region of learned experience and returns to a familiar range. However mysterious the act of departure, by whatever guidance it finds its way back, the familiar home is the start and the finish of each individual's migration; *the beginning and ending of the annual migration is a learned place.*

While the tie to home holds for all waterfowl, we must recognize important differences in migrational behavior between geese and swans on the one hand and ducks on the other. In the former there is a strong family bond, parents and children remaining together during southward migration.

* Mallard, Pintail, Gadwall, Blue-winged Teal, Shoveller.

The young are attended by both parents during the period of growth. Mother and father molt their wing feathers and are flightless while attending the young. Children and parents take wing at about the same time in late summer, and they are all together for the trip southward. Mayr (1942:242) sums up the evidence to decide that "geese are among the very few birds in which the family does not break up at the end of the breeding season, but parents and young stay together for nearly a year. They migrate together to the winter quarters, they spend the entire winter together, and they do not separate until after their return to their nesting area." The Elders (1949) show that the "small goose flock is usually a family and that larger flocks are frequently multiples of families rather than mere aggregations of individuals." In our own color-banded, free-winged Canada Geese at Delta we have seen adults and young-of-the-year depart southward together in November and return, still as a united group, the next April. Where such kindred ties apply, the immature accompany the experienced elders and do not pioneer their own first migrations. "There is little doubt that guidance by older, experienced birds plays a decisive part in the directional flying of such species" (Mayr, 1952:394).

In North American ducks there is quite a different arrangement. The father parts company with his mate before the young are hatched,* leaving the nesting area to join other males that, like himself, are molting into the eclipse plumage. In the Mallard and other river ducks the mother usually stays with her ducklings until they are on the wing; then she leaves them to their own devices while she molts the flight feathers. More often in Canvasback and other diving ducks the mother abandons her charges many days (sometimes several weeks) before they are ready to fly. Once free of maternal companionship, the young ducks are completely "on their own"; there is no bond of kinship between parent and juvenile after the break-up.

*An exception is the Ruddy Duck, in which the male frequently, but by no means always, stays for a while with hen and brood. In all other species the drake only rarely is seen with his family.

In ducks, then, the juvenile behaves independently of parent, and its movements outward from natal range are pioneerings. These young wander randomly during late summer, and it is by such explorations that they build their experience; by such roamings they learn their way about. The Egret that wanders to Ontario and the Pintail that strays from Delta to Lake Winnipegosis have much in common. Like the bird of mythology, they may not be aware of where they are going, but they learn where they have been. Just as the downy duckling searches aimlessly for its first food, so must juveniles explore to find their place in the world.

The summer wanderings of young ducks are random only in terms of compass direction; this travel is always aimed toward a favorable habitat.* First, the shift is from water to water; the many hundreds of young raised on the scattered potholes of western Manitoba depart from their narrow ponds and fly to larger places. Small potholes become vacant, larger sloughs have more birds, while big marshes and lakes boast vast aggregations. The heaviest movement is from the small waters to the large, but the innate urge to travel is obeyed by the young of the big marshes too, and every year bandings show that some Delta juveniles depart elsewhere during August and September.

The transfer is also of the few toward the many. Sixes become dozens, dozens become scores, hundreds become thousands until, as old Ernie Cook used to say, "You couldn't get another duck in the bay with a shoehorn." However random the peregrinations of youth, these must eventually carry the youngsters to the mouth of the Saskatchewan, to Lake Winnipegosis, to Whitewater Lake, Libau, Delta, or some other rendezvous, where, from August onward, the open waters and shorelines are strewn with ducks of many kinds. Although forever lost to their parents, many young must eventually meet with experienced adults before autumn is ended. This is evidenced by both banding and bag samples, and although the juveniles often greatly outnumber their elders, it must be the rare young duck that reaches November and the southland without somewhere having joined company with experienced companions.

In spring, all ducks, juveniles as well as adults, have a background of experience, and their return to the breeding grounds cannot be classified as of the unknown, the untried, the inexperienced.

* See Figure 20, p. 145.

"It is not true, as Aristotle asserts, that the same leader heads the migrant column during the whole of their journey." Frederick II, *The Art of Falconry*

8

Flight Trails South

THE sunrise of October 11, 1951, was bright and cloudless. Art Paulson sat in the bow with his gun across his knee while I watched from the stern. There was not a breath of wind. Reflections without a mar. The only birds were a few late bluewings returning now and again to the reeds. Shortly after seven o'clock we saw a band of ducks coming out of the northwest so high that they appeared only as a thread in the sky. More followed, and during the next fifteen minutes we counted twenty flocks. Suddenly the calm broke. Without so much as a breeze for an introduction, a rough wind struck from the northwest, quickly churning the waters of the bay to whitecaps. Now the volume of the flight increased so that any glance found at least a dozen flocks. The travelers were strewn far and wide across the sky, all moving at the same speed, all arriving from the northwest, all crossing to disappear into the southeast. We identified Canvasback and Redhead, Lesser Scaup and Mallard, and there were also Canada Geese. The speed of the wind was measured at twenty-five to thirty miles per hour on the ground, and the ground speed of the migrants appeared to be more than twice that. Any given group flew quickly out of sight, but new birds continued to arrive from the northwest so that the flow was unbroken. Local ducks were put to air by the wind, some flying to protective shores, others rising to join the migration. James F. Bell, who was four miles to the east, told me later that he had watched the flight go over in the same volume, and from other gunners I learned that the movement crossed over the whole marsh. The passage continued until just before noon, and, placing our estimates on the number of birds we saw crossing Delta, I guessed that some 200,000 waterfowl had flown over the marsh in the heaviest morning migration I have ever seen.

More typically, these mass migrations go through in the afternoon, at-

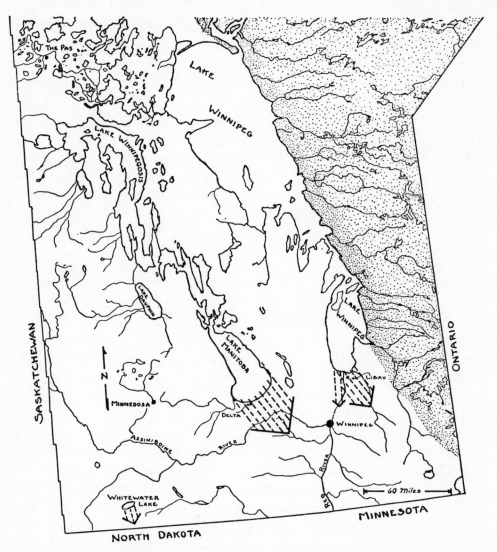

Figure 10. Standard direction of mass fall migration from Whitewater Lake, Lake Manitoba, and Lake Winnipeg marshes. The standard direction from the Delta Marsh is followed by all ducks, holds the same year after year, and is constant regardless of wind direction. Stippled area shows the Pre-Cambrian Shield.

taining their maximum intensity near sundown. The outstanding feature of such avalanches is the uniformity of direction. At Delta, the migrants arrive from the northwest and depart into the southeast. On any given day all flocks and all species go this way, the direction is maintained every day of migration, and the same course is held each year, so that in 1954 the passage went to the same point of the compass as I had marked it for the fall flight in 1938 (Figure 10). While the wind is invariably from the northwest in these main passages, it seldom blows in exactly the same direction as the flight so that the course of the birds is often several degrees east or west of the flow of wind.

With respect to this firmness of direction in the path of autumn migration, Thomson (1953) reminds us of the "modern view that there is a standard direction * for the migration of each species, or community of species . . . This direction leads either straight from the breeding area to the wintering area, or to some intermediate area where the direction is assumed to undergo a change. The capacity to follow such a direction is supposed to be innate in the bird, as part of its migratory instinct, and this hypothesis conforms with the experimental findings of Kramer (e.g., 1952) and Matthews (1952) that birds are able to orient their flight in relation to the position of the sun, making due allowance for the time of day." Note that Thomson refers to the *capacity* to follow a direction as being innate without implying that a bird is innately bound to a certain direction.

The travelers in these mass passages are most often seen in "waves" of flocks, with several or many bands within sight at one time. The movement is always higher than local travel, usually ranging from 500 to about 5,000 feet, with most migrant waterfowl crossing the Delta region between 1,000 and 3,000 feet † (Figure 11). Flock size varies from a dozen or so to strings of a hundred or more, most bands containing from twenty-five to fifty birds. During the course of a passage one may see several or many species, but flocks are seldom mixed, each kind traveling in a group of its own. Individuals of a migrating flock string out in a line forming a blunt arc or, much less frequently, a sharp-pointed V, each bird thus avoiding the slipstream of rough air produced by the movement of its companions.

The mass migration over the Delta Marsh moves in a broad sweep. On a day of a grand passage, hunters scattered over the full width of the marsh report heavy movements; and on such days at Delta, W. A. Murphy has told me of spectacular flights over his East Meadow Ranch on the eastern shore of Lake Manitoba. The width of this passage is probably thirty miles,

* Thomson's phrase here comes from Geyr von Schweppenburg, who at first (1933) used the term *Normalrichtung* and later (1948) *Primärrichtung*, the latter translated by Deelder (1949) as "standard direction" (van Dobben, 1953).

† All statements of elevation given here are based on estimates of two sorts: (1) by comparison with relative-size standards from exact measurements of duck and goose silhouettes (Figure 11); (2) by triangulation. Both field techniques are subject to error, but I feel they are sufficiently in line to evaluate approximate elevations.

Figure 11. Gauge for judging approximate elevation of Mallard-sized duck. When the page is held 20 inches from the eye, the silhouettes (from top to bottom) show the relative size of ducks as seen at heights of 100 feet (good shotgun range), 200 feet (extreme edge of shotgun range), 500 feet, 1,000 feet, 2,000 feet, and 3,000 feet.

conforming to the breadth of Lake Manitoba.

Usually the migrants from the northwest speed over the Delta Marsh without hesitation. On several occasions, however, I have seen them acknowledge their awareness of the marsh by suddenly changing flight formation and direction. After crossing the lake ridge from the northwest I have seen members of a flock suddenly crowd together in a tight group, like a band of blackbirds, appearing suddenly as a dark knot in the sky. These flocks rise and fall, abruptly changing direction, east, west, and north again, with stragglers swinging wide behind as in crack-the-whip. Sometimes one cluster will join another. After some minutes of these gyrations, the groups head south again, soon reforming into their normal strings. Once, on November 14, 1944, when a heavy migration arrived at Delta in weather very cloudy despite a rapidly rising barometer, I saw what amounted to the whole of an afternoon's migration "pile up" over the Delta Marsh, with hundreds of bunched flocks flying in every direction, the sky so heavily loaded with birds that we were sure a collision between bands would certainly occur. At about six thirty the clouds broke — the first clear sky we had seen in two weeks * — and the confusion ended, the migration resolving itself into a di-

* The sun had set, but the patch of open sky, bright in twilight color, illuminated the dark and stormy atmosphere.

rect southeasterly direction, with all flocks disappearing that way before dark (Hochbaum, 1944b). (See Figure 12.)

Trautman (1940:89) observed this bunching of migrant ducks at Buckeye Lake, Ohio; and Chris V. Nelson, who has hunted many years on Lake Christina, Minnesota, writes me that he has seen such behavior in migrating geese as well as in ducks. On October 21, 1950, for example, he watched a migrating flock of sixty Canada Geese crossing the lake from the northwest. "Just as they were leaving Lake Christina, all bedlam seemed to break loose and they flew about wildly, honking vociferously. They went in circles like a dog-fight, seeming very upset — some gaining altitude, some losing altitude. Then, as if responding to a command, they all joined in a perfect V formation and continued their flight in a southeasterly direction."

Figure 12. Normal flock pattern of migrating ducks (left), and "bunching" of gyrating flock

All such gyrations of passage flocks have been seen amongst travelers that reached Delta when the sky was heavily clouded. The birds appeared confused, as if they were pressed by two urges, one to stay, one to travel on despite the unsettled weather. I was thus interested in the observations of Svärdson (1949), who describes similar gyrating behavior in gulls; he concluded that the gyrations developed as a conflict between the "drive-to-go" and the "urge-to-rest." Waterhouse (1949), who has seen gyrations in migrating Rooks and Jackdaws, suggests that they "occasionally become uncertain of direction, sometimes on taking off, sometimes in course of flight. . . . To the resultant state of feeling — assumed to be a compound of desire-to-fly and uncertainty-which-way-to-fly — they react by gyrating."

Other great marshes and lakes are the crossing places for the mass autumn migrations. On the Libau Marsh, at the southeast end of Lake Winnipeg, Colonel Arthur Sullivan and George Longbottom, veteran observers of the fall flight there, tell me the migration is constantly to the southeast in a direction almost exactly the same as we see at Delta. On the Red River, Thomas Schindler and Nolan Perret have told me of flights that go due south. At Whitewater Lake, the departure line which Eugene F. Bossenmaier has plotted for me is slightly more to the south than the direction at Delta (Figure 14).

There is a heavy crossing of migrants at Buckeye Lake, Ohio, and Trautman (1940:90) says that "the ratio between the number of migrating flocks that were observed flying through the area without stopping and those alighting on the lake was about three to one." Ray Sickles, Game Protector for the Pennsylvania State Game Commission, writes me that there is an annual passage of Whistling Swans over Pymatuning Lake, in northwestern Pennsylvania, which is always in a southeasterly direction. He observed a very heavy flight on October 18, 1952, when on night patrol. "Just after midnight the air seemed full of migrating birds . . . At daybreak this was substantiated by what was the most concentrated movement of waterfowl I have ever witnessed. Within an hour several hundred flocks of migrating swans passed over. One person counted 50 flocks averaging 100 to a flock within fifteen minutes. From dawn until about 10:30 A.M. it was impossible to look into the sky without seeing several flocks of swans. By noon the movement had passed on and only a few straggling flocks could be seen. All were very high and traveling in a south-by-east direction. I would guess that 10,000 to 15,000 swans migrated through in that movement and only about 250 stopped at Pymatuning . . . It seems that every time a big migration of swans occurs, the weather is clear and the sky blue."

Delta, Whitewater Lake, and Buckeye Lake are merely pinpoints of water on the migration map, but along river valleys the passage may follow the same watercourse for many miles. Hall (1949:270) recalls a migration he watched on the Mississippi River about thirty miles south of St. Louis. "There'd been a blizzard swept down from the northwest, although no hint of it reached our Missouri countryside. But the waterfowl knew about it and they came pouring down the river that evening and all through the night in countless hundreds of thousands, heading for distant feeding grounds in the warm southland. It seemed to us from our vantage point high above the river that most of the birds which use the Mississippi flyway must have passed that afternoon . . . For as far as we could see, both up and down the river and out across the wide Illinois bottomlands, migrating bands passed swiftly and at every height. There could be no doubt about it: these were travelling ducks. Although the long lines verged and crossed, the movement was steadily southward. Many of the bands flew close enough so we could easily identify them — Mallards and Pintails and Canvasbacks flying steadily; teal passing with swift wingbeat; Widgeon and Gadwall, Shovellers and Redheads; in fact, just about all the ducks which frequent the Mississippi Flyway. And as the sun dropped toward the horizon, painting the cloud banks with long streaks of crimson which were reflected in lighter tones of pink toward the east, we heard the disconsolate crying of Canada Geese, veering in from westward where they had cut across from the Missouri to avoid flying over the city. High above the ducks and still flying in bright sunlight, their breasts glistened as the great birds held swiftly and steadily toward marshlands to the south."

Bellrose (1951:11) says that "most flight routes reach Illinois borders via the rivers of Iowa — Wapsipinicon, Cedar, Des Moines — which afford convenient pathways from the northwestern part of the state to the southeast." Indeed, he has observed river movements from an aircraft, and on November 1, 1951, traced a large migration of Mallards to its source, the valley of the Des Moines, whence the birds came down from the northwest into the Mississippi. In the same breath with which I speak of river passages, I must mention overland travels as well. Bellrose explains that "waterfowl do not hesitate to migrate overland if there is no convenient water course to follow. There are definite routes that ducks follow between the Mississippi and Illinois Rivers. One route leaves the Mississippi at Savanna, passes over Annawan, and branches to enter the Illinois Valley at several points. On November 6, 1948, we saw a pronounced waterfowl movement along this route. The flight was first noticed at 8:45 A.M. along state highway No. 78, three miles north of Annawan. There was a steady procession of Cormorant, Pintail and Mallard flocks, along with a few flocks of Blue and Snow Geese, flying parallel to the highway from this point to Morrison. Early in the afternoon, flocks of Mallards were observed flying down the Mississippi River above Savanna, leaving the river at that point." (See Figure 13.)

Figure 13. Overland pass from the Mississippi River to the Illinois River followed by migrating ducks in the fall

MIGRATIONS OF WATERFOWL

Some overland journeys of these mass migrations carry the birds far, sometimes hundreds of miles, over terrain where we cannot read the pattern of their flight in the scheme of water areas. Several wildfowlers of Saskatchewan and Montana have told me of a late autumn mass movement of ducks that moves due south across central Saskatchewan and eastern Montana. Mr. Harry Jensen, of the U.S. Fish and Wildlife Service, told me of a mass flight he watched pass over eastern North Dakota in the autumn of 1944. The passage, moving south, lasted one and one-half hours and the birds were so high that most of them could not be seen without the aid of binoculars.

Waterfowl favor rivers leading from one part of the range to another, but do not use those crossing this main line of travel. Ducks departing southeast from Delta have an overland flight of about twenty miles to the Assiniboine River, which they might follow to the Red River by turning east. Instead they cross the east-west line of the Assiniboine and continue, to meet the Red River Valley near the Minnesota border.

The volume of the mass passages is tremendous beyond belief. Rowan (1929b) describes a November exodus from Alberta when, as one farmer exclaimed, the migrants were so numerous that "the sky was black with them, flying in formation like geese, in bunches of around thirty to forty. As to numbers, all I can say is that they passed over in thousands." At the peak of a three-day migration Sowls (1947a) estimated that at least 100,000 ducks, mostly Lesser Scaup, flew over the Delta Marsh during one hour on November 6, 1947.

These big "pushes" are seldom confined to one marsh region; there is often a movement of waterfowl over a range that is wide and deep. In 1950 the big freeze-up migration at Delta was on November 8 and 9. Colonel Arthur Sullivan reported major flights over the south end of Lake Winnipeg the same days. At Whitewater Lake, Bossenmaier saw the heaviest flight on the eighth, while at the same time, Merrill Hammond watched the last of the waterfowl leave the Lower Souris Refuge in North Dakota. At Aberdeen, South Dakota, Jerry Stoudt observed a major flight of waterfowl going to the southeast on the eighth, and Warren Nord saw a massive migration of Mallards and diving ducks near Fergus Falls, Minnesota, that same afternoon. D. H. Janzen,[*] traveling in North Dakota, found that the big movement out of that state commenced on November 7 and continued through

* The accounts by Janzen, Hammond, Stoudt, Bossenmaier, and Lynch are from manuscript reports supplied by the U.S. Fish and Wildlife Service.

the next two days; he reported that, "for all practical purposes, the hunting season was over for the State of North Dakota on the evening of the 9th." In Illinois, Frank Bellrose (1951) described the heaviest passage for 1950 between November 9 and 11. Far to the south, on the Louisiana marshes, John Lynch found that "new concentrations of ducks, principally Mallards, showed up on November 8 and for several days thereafter."

The ducks that Nord saw over Fergus Falls on November 8 probably had crossed Delta earlier the same day and comprised the flight that arrived in Illinois on the ninth. We estimated the speed of the birds passing over Delta at from sixty-five to seventy-five miles per hour,[*] with a tail wind. Traveling straight through, their schedule would carry them over Illinois the next day. That such a long journey was taken is suggested by Nord's report, for on

[*] All estimates of ground speed are by timing migrants over a course of known distance or when direction and ground speed permit.

November 9 he found no ducks remaining around Fergus Falls, and the area was frozen over except for a few open holes. All the birds of the Canadian prairies and the northern states apparently cleared out in this big push.

The mass migrations we witness at Delta are related to four phases of the weather: air pressure, wind, temperature, and humidity. Without implying anything as to cause and effect, I have found that a rising barometer, a falling temperature, a drop in relative humidity, and a wind from the northwest establish the weather pattern characteristic of the mass migrations. Indeed, more than once I have predicted the grand passage on the basis of this weather combination.

In a discussion of these weather characteristics, Robert L. Lillestrand, of the General Mills Research Laboratories, pointed out how the relation of winds to the high-pressure (anticyclonic) and low-pressure (cyclonic) air masses might favor southward migration when a "low" passed Delta and a "high" arrived. The clockwise movement of air around the high together with the counterclockwise rush around the low creates a southerly flow of wind. Lillestrand drew a theoretical weather map to illustrate this situation, with the high-pressure area located on the western half of the continent and the low in the east, the trough of winds flowing down the middle between the two air masses. I then examined the weather maps coinciding with the major avalanches of fall passage and found that for Blue-winged Teal in September, Canvasbacks and Redheads in October, and Lesser Scaup and Mallard in November, every major flight took place when there was such a west-east opposition of the high- and low-pressure areas. I have selected the grand passage of November 7, 1947, to illustrate this weather pattern so favorable to the mass movement of autumn migrants (Figure 14).

With respect to this tie between the weather and migration, Landsberg (1948:709) believes that migratory birds "have developed a rather remarkable system of what is called in modern aviation 'pressure-pattern flying.' This is the system that takes advantage of the maximum possible amount of tail wind in long-distance flights." Bagg (1948:147) likewise suggests that there is a strong barometric pressure-pattern in North American weather that stimulates migration. While the southward flow of wind is perhaps the outstanding feature of this favorable weather situation, I cannot believe that it is the only influence starting off these mass movements. I have never known heavy migrations to start out from Delta during the cloudy, unsettled weather immediately preceding the arrival of the high-pressure air mass, even though the wind blew from the northwest, the temperature dropped

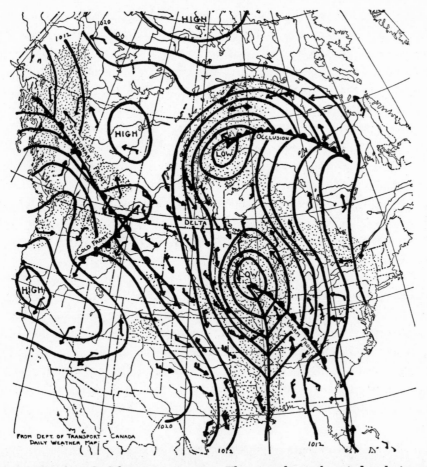

Figure 14. Weather ideal for mass migration. The map shows the wind and air-pressure patterns at 7:30 A.M., November 7, 1947. Mass waterfowl migration reached its peak at Delta just before sundown on November 6, when it was estimated that 100,000 ducks crossed the Delta Marsh in one hour. At the same time heavy migration was noted on other Manitoba marshes, and a mass movement over the Madison, Wisconsin, region was reported by Aldo Leopold (letter). The broad nature of this movement is reflected in reports of waterfowl biologists, presented at the Ninth Midwest Wildlife Conference, showing that 1947's heaviest migration down the Mississippi Flyway occurred at this time: Minnesota, November 6, 7; Wisconsin, November 6, 7, 8; Nebraska, November 6, 8; Michigan, November 8; Illinois, November 7, 8, 9; Indiana, November 9, 10; Ohio, November 6, 10; Missouri, November 6, 7, 8; Kentucky, November 10, 13; Louisiana, November 11.

and the barometer was on the rise. Thus, on the afternoon of October 30, 1954, the heaviest passage of the year crossed Delta during a period favorable in every respect except for repeated snow squalls. But despite the rising barometer, the northwest wind, and the steady stream of migrants passing over during most of the afternoon and early evening, none of the local ducks, concentrated in many thousands, were seen to leave. Next day the weather cleared and by evening the sky was bright. The local ducks started to migrate at about 4:00 P.M., and by sundown we had seen a tremendous movement away from Delta. The waterfowl that passed over in storm on October 30 no doubt had started from their more northern marshes under the clear sky of the high-pressure system that did not bring fair weather to Delta until the next day. I take it from this and from many similar observations that open sky as well as favorable wind is important at the start of mass migrations.

But then, if clear skies are a prerequisite for the beginning of mass migration, the passages carry on, nevertheless, to overtake and fly through bad weather. The speed of migration is the product of the birds' air speed plus the velocity of the wind; hence the migrants travel faster than the weather itself, often, as in the passage of October 30, 1954, catching up with the region of storm ahead. Many times I have observed ducks arriving at Delta in bad weather that was followed shortly by the broad edge of cloud introducing clear skies and fine anticylconic weather. They often passed right on

through, as already described; sometimes they stopped, especially if the storm was severe, leaving hunters to believe that it was the bad weather that forced them south. When travelers choose to continue on in spite of the bad weather they may have overtaken, their flights usually carry them through to some more southern marsh. But the migrants by no means always attain their destination, and sometimes vast numbers of waterfowl perish when forced to ground by bad weather. (See Chapter 12.)

A study of the movements of waterfowl through the autumn reveals that ducks select anticyclonic weather for the start of their mass migrations, but that the weather is not in itself the impetus. In September Mallards do not always migrate with the favorable barometric situation that has a "trigger effect" on Blue-winged Teal. Most Lesser Scaups and Mallards remain at Delta through a mid-October anticyclone during which Redheads and Canvasbacks vacate the country. In the September and October movements there is a falling temperature, but this may not even come close to freezing; and both Blue-winged Teal and Canvasbacks leave a span of fair weather and an abundance of food behind when they go. And while the November migration of Lesser Scaups and Mallards coincides with the freeze-up, hard weather and ice are not in themselves the cause of migration. Some years large numbers of Mallards remain north in mild Novembers and then fail to migrate southward when the inevitable deep cold of December and January arrives, sometimes perishing with open water only a few hundred miles south (Rowan, 1931).

The schedule of the autumn migration is a confusing puzzle, beginning as it does in August and continuing until November. But when the different sex and age groups are studied individually * we find that there is an arrangement of order. At Delta the fall movements have a remarkable regularity from year to year, the exceptions being traceable to extreme weather variations, drastic water-level changes and late breeding seasons. First to go in mid-August are the adult drake Pintails; most of them are on the wing (after the flightless period of the eclipse molt) by early August and have departed from Delta by the end of the second or third week of that month. Following close behind are the adult male Baldpates; so common as flightless molters in midsummer, they move away from Delta in late August or early September and are uncommon for the balance of the autumn. At

* The study of autumn movements has been greatly enhanced by the opportunities of examining large numbers of waterfowl in banding traps and in hunters' bags along the stopping places of migration and by the possibility of making completely objective appraisals of the sex and age composition of these samples (Hochbaum, 1942; Elder, 1946).

about the same time as the Baldpates' departure, adult males of Blue-winged Teal, Shoveller, and Gadwall also go.

The adult Mallard drakes have a coming together in early August, and these, joined by juveniles, make up the stubble aggregations that remain through September and most of October. In late September some of the adult Canvasback and Redhead drakes arrive at Delta from the molting lakes; the bulk of these species then make their departure in mid-October at about the same time as the Lesser Scaups arrive in large numbers.

Some of these early movements are directly traceable to the breeding season. The adult Pintail drakes, for example, depart shortly after they have their new flight feathers; and the end of the flightless season, of course, is related in time to its beginning, which in turn hinges upon the breeding schedule. It is the same in the Baldpate, and the difference in departure dates between Baldpates and Pintails is about the same as the difference between them in breeding schedules. The Baldpate leaves at a later calendar date than the Pintail, but on the same physiological schedule. When Mallards depart in late October or early November they have completed their prenuptial molt and are in full breeding plumage; hence the timing of their migration is one step further removed from the breeding cycle. The same holds for the Lesser Scaup. Weller (1953a) found that nearly one-third of the adult Redhead drakes he examined September 19 and 20, 1952, at Lake Winnipegosis showed some soft primary wing feathers, evidence of their recent flightless period. Perhaps their late-September arrival at Delta is linked with their recovery from the wing molt, which comes later in these diving ducks than in the Pintail. Götz (1929), noting a general relation between molt and autumn migration, proposed the idea of a cycle: breeding, molting, migration. Delayed breeding equals late molt; hence delayed migration.

Although there seems a close tie between molt and migration in some ducks, I am not attempting to give evidence showing any cause-and-effect sequence underlying all fall migration. I simply wish to show how important passages are hinged in time to certain physiological as well as meteorological conditions.

Some of the male aggregations hold together in flocks of their own for some time after the flightless period of the eclipse, and Dawson (1923) tells how adult Pintail drakes reach California during August in bands of their own sex and age class. At Delta I have seen migrating flocks of Canvasbacks and Redheads in late September which seemed to be made up wholly of adult males. A few adult males in all species join with the juveniles in early autumn but, except for the Mallard, the adult drake is an uncommon prize in the hunter's bag on the prairie marshes.

The adult female, which molts later than the adult male and in smaller companies, does not make up aggregations of her own. When she recovers flight after the molt of the wing feathers, she joins the young-of-the-year and, according to the evidence of banding trap and hunter's bag, she migrates with these juveniles, along with a lesser number of adult males.* Sowls (1955:164) has summarized the adult-juvenile ratios of all ducks examined in hunters' bags at Delta between 1938 and 1950 (Table 3). He found a

TABLE 3. AGE RATIOS FOR 10,607 DUCKS EXAMINED IN HUNTERS'
BAGS ON THE DELTA MARSH, 1938–1950*

Species	Adult	Juvenile	Ratio
Mallard	1,279	2,238	1:1.7
Gadwall	174	370	1:2.1
Baldpate	46	185	1:4.0
Pintail	173	255	1:1.5
Green-winged Teal............	41	96	1:2.3
Blue-winged Teal.............	96	323	1:3.4
Shoveller	97	318	1:3.3
Redhead	120	981	1:8.2
Canvasback	306	2,307	1:7.5
Lesser Scaup	305	897	1:2.9

* See Sowls (1955:164) for a complete breakdown of sex ratios.

strong membership of adults in the migratory fall populations, species by species. These samples were taken in late September and through October each year, of birds shot between, just before, or just after migration. If the bags erred from the true population ratios, the bias is probably toward a heavier representation of juveniles, which fly less well and are not so wary as the adults. I believe the strong ratio of juveniles to adults in Redhead and Canvasback reflects their greater vulnerability to the gun in early-season shooting.

Although these hunter samples were taken at random from wild flocks, it might be argued that adults and juveniles were shot from separate flocks. It is true, indeed, that one finds bands made up wholly of young birds, while some adult males keep to groups of their own. But in my hunting experience I have often taken adults and juveniles from the same flock when

* In an exception to this rule, Mallards, especially their stubble aggregations, may show more adult males than females in autumn bags (Hochbaum, 1944).

gunning with a companion; and when an area is vacated by ducks in mass migration, adults and juveniles inevitably are companions.

This ratio of adults to juveniles varies from year to year because of variations in reproductive success (Hickey, 1952), but in an annual breakdown of the Delta bags, and in the more recent bag examinations (Weller, 1953b), there continues a strong element of adult birds.

It is this regular adult component of the population that must be, I believe, the directive element in the mass autumn migrations. These passages are precise, deliberate, orderly, and oriented because of the presence of the experienced birds. This is social orientation in which the actions of the experienced set the direction for all. In these grand avalanches, with thousands of birds and hundreds of flocks, each within sight of another, the individual bird, like a private in a parade, moves with and as his companions. The flock is the individual, "a collective bird, in fact, and however stretched, straggling and complicated . . . the individual element seems wonderfully in abeyance" (Selous, 1931:127).

Without documenting the discussion further, it seems fair to arrive at five conclusions regarding the fall migration of waterfowl:

1. Massive movements of many flocks of ducks traveling at the same time in the same direction are annual events.

2. The standard direction of these mass flights holds the same from year to year.

3. These migrations sweeping vast numbers of ducks down the flyways are regional in character, the shift southward being spread over a range that is wide and deep.

4. Adult and juvenile ducks travel together in these movements.

5. These passages obey topographic features such as lakes, marshes, and rivers when these lead toward the wintering grounds, overland routes being followed when there is no direct watercourse.

Visual observations tell of the regularity of these major movements in both place and direction, but show nothing of the fidelity of individual birds to the trails. Does a duck come each autumn to the same places along the way of migration? The answer is to be found in the records of banding stations, and there is no need to go further than McGinnis Slough for evidence. This is a small lake within twenty-one miles of Chicago's loop. Here, with wise foresight, the Cook County Forest Preserve has created an important, if small, stopping place for waterfowl moving down the Mississippi Flyway; and here were banded some 26,415 ducks and coots during the years 1940–1945 (Mann, Thompson, and Jedlicka, 1947:206). Of these banded birds, there were 3,393 recoveries, 659 of which were recaptures at McGinnis Slough.* Here is the remarkable chronicle of approximately one-fifth of all recoveries being made at the point of first capture, a stopping place on the migratory highway. In the Blue-winged Teal, nearly half of the recoveries were made at McGinnis Slough, and, considering survival rates, these indicate that a large proportion of bluewings followed a migratory lane that brought them south again by way of the same stop-over (for Blue-winged Teal do not winter in northern Illinois.

Many other banding stations between the breeding grounds and wintering quarters show the return of experienced waterfowl. Some stray, some become lost, traveling another route; but the volume of return is sufficient to establish the repeated visit as typical behavior. This return is typical also of many other birds, a characteristic prompting Lincoln (1935b:23) to make the general statement that "many individuals migrate in fall over the same route, year after year, making the same stops and finally arriving at the same precise thicket that served them in previous winters."

I think this evidence of banding allows another conclusion regarding the migration of waterfowl: not only do they start and end the annual cycle of travel at a familiar home range, but the adults visit familiar stopping places along the routes of migration. As the young fly in company with the adults each year, these places and the connecting routes are passed along from one generation to the next in a traditional manner.

The force of these mass migrations, their volume, their local concentrations, their regional width, and the fidelity of adults to a given route all fit into a pattern that has been established by field and banding observations in many places. Let us hasten to admit, however, that this is only part of the story. Matched against this swift, massive precision of the grand fall passages are the random travels of juveniles already discussed (p. 94). The wanderings of young ducks start without the company of adults. As these vagabonds move from one area to another, we see, by their growing numbers, that the dispersals away from home eventually lead to places where waterfowl concentrate in major numbers, places where the young join company with all sex and age classes. Here many young take direct passage with adults in the mass migrations, but we must not conclude that all young gain the southland in this way.

Nor are wanderings confined to young birds. Records of banding sta-

* This refers only to recaptures in years following the year of banding.

Figure 15. Evidence of wandering during migration. Map shows northward dispersal
of fall migrant Blue-winged Teal during the same autumn as they
were banded at McGinnis Slough.

tions south of the breeding range indicate that even after ducks have gained
the southland, many individuals, some of them adults, continue their random travels. Vogt (1934:268) drew attention to this when he found that
some autumn-banded waterfowl were killed the same season in Ontario,
Maine, and at other places far north of his banding station on Long Island.
Mann and his cooperators (1947) observed the same thing to be happening
with many of the ducks that stopped at McGinnis Slough. Of 141 direct
Blue-winged Teal recoveries,[*] 28 bluewings, or 20 per cent, were killed
north of McGinnis Slough (Figure 15). Five of these were adults. Pirnie
(1941:258) found that "in their fall dispersal from southern Michigan, some
Black Ducks and Mallards travel as far as two hundred or more miles west,
north or east." Intensely interesting is the "explosion" of Ring-necked Ducks
shown by Duvall (1949). Banded in southern Louisiana in November and
December, some were recovered west in Texas, north in Tennessee, and east
in Georgia and Florida before the end of the same year. Redheads that
were banded during the summer in Utah were found by Robbins (1949)
to fan out into eight more northern states and one Canadian province. Mann
(1950) gives a picture of a spectacular October shift of waterfowl from the

[*] A "direct recovery" is one in which the band is recovered during the same year the bird
was banded.

112

Lower Souris Refuge, in North Dakota, northward into Manitoba, this amounting to a "reverse migration" involving thousands of birds. During a mild spell after heavy frost in November 1949, the Delta Marsh, empty of Mallards and other waterfowl, was repopulated by great flocks of Mallards which we saw arriving high from the south and southwest. A similar return of Mallards from the south brought an abundance of "green-heads" to a nearly empty Delta Marsh in November 1954.

Probably all ducks at least once each autumn partake in a mass migration sweeping southward over traditional routes, young and old together. At other times, adults as well as juveniles, wander in all directions from stopping places along the way of migration.

9

Homeward Migration

A SMALL platform rises above the north shore of Cadham Bay, and another railed perch overlooks the marsh from the top of Kirchoffer Lodge. Spring evenings we wait at these lookouts to watch the parade of waterfowl leaving Delta in migration. A few ducks, perhaps, will reach their destinations before the last tinge has left the sky, but for many others the evening's flight is but another step in the long journey home. It is eighteen hundred miles from Delta to the mouth of the Mackenzie River, where some must go.

The departure in the heaviest passages of spring occurs just after sundown. On northern prairies twilight and dusk linger more than three hours after the late-April sun has set; at eleven o'clock there still remains a faint sunglow in the northwest on cloudless nights. On evenings of heavy migration there is a steady flow of birds away from Delta until dark. After darkness has settled completely and through the black hours of morning the movement of transients may be heard overhead; but this night schedule never attains the volume of the twilight migration.

In the departure of the travelers there is no circling upward. They take off from the bays and at once set their course, climbing at a shallow angle. Birds leaving the north edge of the marsh cross the ridge just above the trees, while those from the south shore have climbed several hundred feet by the time they gain the lake. The migrants strike out over the open lake without hesitation, most of them making the crossing from the marsh at passes, as described in Chapter 1. From ground level, Lake Manitoba appears as a wide, frozen sea, the far shorelines below the horizon except during mirage. From the height of one hundred feet, however, the west shore and Big Point rise into view, and at two or three hundred feet the Riding Mountains may be seen.

Flocks of spring migrants divide into smaller units on approaching the marsh.

These April flocks leaving Delta are smaller than the migrant bands of October, although, as in autumn, it is usual to see several, often many groups traveling across the sky at the same moment. Sowls (1951:34) found twelve to be the average for migrating Pintail flocks, and I have never seen a departing flock of more than twenty birds. The small clusters usually are made up of birds of one species, although in Mallard and Pintail it is not uncommon to see both kinds together. Most of the river ducks are paired, each hen leading her drake, which follows so closely that the pair rather than the individual makes up the unit of a flock. Some Canvasbacks and other diving ducks are in groups of twos, but many bands boast only one female, probably not yet mated, the several male companions undoubtedly her suitors.

These small companies leaving Delta must join to make larger flocks once the journey is under way, for on the wheat prairie south of the marsh I have seen arriving migrants in flocks of fifty or sixty, sometimes even a hundred or more birds. The individual components of these big companies show themselves when they begin their long, shallow descent to the marsh. Then the body of travelers breaks up into smaller groups, each making its independent arrival at Delta.

Waterfowl reach Delta from two main directions (Figure 16). Some come from the southeast, their source being precisely the same direction into which they departed in the mass migrations of autumn. Others come from due south. I do not know which of these directions produces the greatest flow of spring arrivals, but I believe most of the waterfowl come from the southeast. Surely all the Whistling Swans and most of the diving ducks are from that direction.

In their evening departure, most ducks start out into the northwest to a point of the compass that is the same whence they arrived in autumn. Not all, however, are committed to this standard direction, and flocks sometimes may be seen breaking away to the north. Whistling Swans, like most of the ducks, migrate into the northwest; Canada Geese go northwest, north, or north-northeast; Richardson's Geese head north or north-northeast. In their mass movement away from the prairie country, the Blue Geese and the Lesser Snow Geese invariably fly to the same point of the compass in the east-northeast (Figure 16).

Ducks reaching Delta in spring have their March and April rendezvous in Minnesota and northeastern North Dakota. There, on the lake and marsh country of the prairies, waterfowl from the east coast meet those of the Mississippi Valley. Smith (1946) found that most Canvasbacks migrating through Minnesota make their spring headquarters in the lake region about Ashby, their heaviest numbers occurring on Lake Christina (Figure 16). On April 4, 1942, he counted 2,000 Canvasbacks on Lake Christina; the first Canvasbacks did not reach Delta until ten days later that year. The peak of the Lake Christina population was April 12 and 13, when Smith counted 31,000 and 28,500 Canvasbacks respectively. The next day, April 14, when the first of this species reached Delta, the Lake Christina population dropped to 12,500. Some Canvasbacks arriving at Delta on the fourteenth no doubt came from Lake Christina.

The same holds for other ducks; when the time comes to leave Minnesota waters they fly directly to the Manitoba marshes. Most of the earliest arrivals reach Delta during evening twilight. Ducks are seldom seen through the first mild day of spring; even at sundown none has made its appearance;

Figure 16. Standard directions of spring migration for waterfowl and other migrants arriving in southern Manitoba. Long arrows show direction of approach. Most ducks and most individuals of many other species, such as hawks, blackbirds, Crows, and Flickers, continue on into the northwest. But there are important departures from standard arrival directions at this point, as with the Blue and Lesser Snow Geese, which arrive from the south, but depart into the northeast (short arrow). The map shows the relation of Delta to the main breeding range and wintering range of North American game waterfowl. (Pattern of breeding range compiled from Special Scientific Report: Wildlife No. 25, published jointly by the U.S. Fish and Wildlife Service and the Canadian Wildlife Service, 1953; wintering range from Phillips and Lincoln, 1930, and Day, 1949.)

but before nightfall the first Mallards, and sometimes Pintails with them, have made their return. I gather that these birds started out at sundown not far south, and reached Delta before the light failed. Later on in April, great numbers of migrants are seen arriving during the morning. If the rule of evening departure holds elsewhere as it does at Delta, I presume that these birds have come long distances on an overnight journey.

As in fall, there are "waves" of spring migrants, great numbers moving away at the same time. The timing of these waves closely obeys the weather. South wind and rising temperature mark the onset of the heaviest spring migrations, and a glance at the weather map reveals that this pattern is an exact turnabout of the autumn one precipitating the mass movements of October and November (Figure 17). The high-pressure area is now located on the eastern side of the continent with the low opposing it in the west, the clockwise flow of air around the high and the counterclockwise stream around the low creating the trough of southerly winds moving up the middle of the continent. This, of course, is the situation so clearly described by Bagg and his cooperators (1950:13): "northward movement of migrants in late winter and spring will normally begin under conditions of a barometric gradient falling from east to west and of southerly winds typical of the west-ward portion of a high pressure area (clockwise circulation) moving off to the east or southeast. . . . When a high pressure area is supplemented by a low pressure area (counterclockwise circulation) originating in the south-west and moving northeastward, the influx of warm, moist tropical air is extended and intensified; concurrently, the northward movement of migrants assumes the proportions of a pronounced onrushing wave in the warm sector of the low pressure area." Schenk (1931) has described a similar weather condition in Europe where, with the "low" over England and warm air currents moving up from the Mediterranean, the pattern is ideal for spring migration of Woodcock.

The importance of this meteorological arrangement for mass "pressure pattern" migration was strikingly manifest during the spring of 1954, when the east-west juxtaposition of the "high" and the "low" occurred only once during the whole of April. It was only then that we saw a mass April movement of waterfowl and other birds through the Delta region (Figure 17). During the balance of the month the weather was dominated by a strong, stable high-pressure area in northern Canada and, though migration was not wholly stopped, the travel of waterfowl to and away from Delta was thin for the balance of the month.

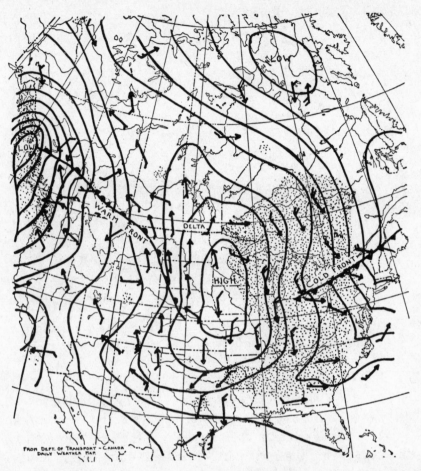

FROM DEPT. OF TRANSPORT - CANADA
DAILY WEATHER MAP

Figure 17. Weather ideal for avalanche of spring migrants. The map shows wind and air-pressure patterns at 7:30 A.M., April 8, 1954. Few migrants had reached southern Manitoba by the first week of April. Canada Geese were the only waterfowl in the province, with most ducks and geese still south of Grand Forks, North Dakota. On April 7 northwest winds of 25–35 m.p.h. rushed from the "high" centered in northern Saskatchewan, creating the worst blizzard of the year, with visibility reduced to 20–30 feet in the drifting snow on the Portage Plains. It was calm and clear by nightfall, however, and the morning of the eighth was bright and sunny, with mild southeast winds of 15–20 m.p.h Red-winged and Rusty Blackbirds appeared in numbers by 9 A.M., and through the middle of the day there was a heavy migration of Rough-legged and Red-tailed Hawks, with lesser numbers of Sparrow Hawks. Canada Geese were seen shortly after sunup and their passage through continued all day, one of Delta's biggest goose migrations on record. The first Whistling Swans and a grand movement of Mallards and Pintails arrived between 3:00 and 4:00 P.M., and a few Great Blue Herons passed through before nightfall. South winds and bright, mild weather continued till about noon on the tenth, with White Pelican, Richardson's Goose, Shoveller, Sandhill Crane, Yellow-headed Blackbird, and Song Sparrow adding their numbers to the grand passage. By 3:00 P.M. on the tenth the wind had shifted to west, then northwest, and the migration ended.

When the nesting grounds are reached, the routes branch again and again to
accommodate each small band until every pair has finally
gained its own home range.

Bagg and his colleagues (1950) point out that favorable arrangement of
the high- and low-pressure areas, "while always of major significance in
spring, may be less absolute in character during the later part of the spring
migration than during the early part." It is thus interesting to observe that
while in late April and early May there was some migration almost every
day, the second biggest waterfowl movement of 1954 left Delta on the evening of May 4, the second time in 1954 when there was the east-west opposition of the high- and low-pressure areas in Canada. The third big rush of
waterfowl, which carried the Swans, Richardson's Geese, and wavies away
from Delta, occurred on May 10 and 11, when the high and low next opposed
each other favorably.

The grand movement of ducks into the northwest observed at Delta, is,
in effect, a major "trunk line" of waterfowl. Great masses of travelers go
together, despite their division into small flocks, in the general direction of
their destination. But it cannot be that these birds are swept along with
this movement; each must bend away from the main stream at the correct
time and place for turning. Some Redheads, for example, reach their Minnesota stopping place together en route from the Atlantic Coast, but those
destined for Delta must now go differently from companions traveling to-

ward the Libau Marsh on Lake Winnipeg. With the breeding range of ducks spread so widely over the northland, the pattern of homeward migration must eventually show as many divisions as there are pairs in flight. In southern regions there are common channels for many thousands of birds. Then come major migratory divides where large groups turn toward one or another breeding region. When the nesting grounds are reached, the routes branch again and again to accommodate each small band until every pair has finally gained its own home range. This requirement for division is the reason for the smaller size of spring flocks.

Some, of course, may take the wrong turn or continue with the main stream when they should have separated from it. The experience of Sowls (1955:15) with his color-banded adults, however, is evidence of the efficiency of spring passage. His marked ducks arrived on their Delta home range with the very first flights of spring, the promptness of this return suggesting a direct passage from the last stopping place.

Awareness of the direction of the destination is suggested by the behavior of the Blue Geese and Lesser Snow Geese when they leave the prairie country in May. They have traveled north up the Mississippi Valley to Canada; but they now turn northeast, and if the line of their flight, as seen in the Delta region, is plotted on a map (Figure 16) it points directly to the region of James Bay, which is their next stopping place (Soper, 1930, 1942). Hickey (1943:28) once "enjoyed a mellow April evening with two friends atop the Palisades along the lower part of the Hudson River near New York City. Hundreds of scaups began flying over our heads at 5:44 P.M. Leaving Long Island Sound, a few miles eastward, the birds were headed in a west-northwest direction over New Jersey's Hills — supposedly for the Finger Lakes." Bent (1925:131) tells how the May departure of White-winged Scoters from the New England coast aims for the Canadian prairie breeding grounds. In 1953 the first Canada Geese seen at Delta flew straight north over the village, and we learned from Ralph Otto that Canadas reached their Dog Lake nesting grounds, sixty miles due north of Delta, later the same day. Probably the birds we watched were headed straight for Dog Lake.

Sometimes we are fortunate enough to witness the actual splitting of a migration. On the morning of April 20, 1952, I saw a steady stream of Canada Geese flying northeast across the Libau Marsh near Colonel Sullivan's lodge, while at the same time, others of the same kind were flying northwest. A very interesting split in the migration of Canada Geese north along the Red River was described to me by J. W. Baldock. Near the town

121

of St. Jean Baptiste, Baldock saw a flock of twenty-seven Canada Geese coming northward along the Red River Valley, and as he watched, nine of these broke away from the main flock to fly in a northwesterly direction. "The remainder of the flock continued north down the Red River. I was watching them with binoculars when two geese left the main flock before they reached St. Jean. They circled to the west and finally flew west-north-west behind the nine which had originally broken away."

The homeward migration is not simply a "north" flight, neither is it constant in direction throughout, nor do all individuals of a species follow the same course all the way. In its entirety and in its individual segments, the direction of the vernal passage depends upon the individual place of home.

The main passage of waterfowl through Delta consumes about three weeks each year, mostly in April; the first week in May brings a close to the heavy travel except in late springs. The migration period for a given species, however, is very long when the entire range is considered, and varies according to the location of the home nesting grounds. Pintails, for example, reach Delta in early April (Table 4) and some years have started nesting before the middle of the month. Others go on to the Arctic, not arriving on

TABLE 4. DISTRIBUTION OF ARRIVAL DATES DURING SIXTEEN YEARS
(1939–1954) AT DELTA, MANITOBA

Species	Number of Years							Total Years Recorded 1939–1954
	March 20–27	March 28–April 4	April 5–12	April 13–20	April 21–28	April 29–May 6	May 7–14	
Canada Goose............	5	7	4					16
Mallard	4	6	5	1				16
Pintail	2	5	7	2				16
American Golden-eye......	2	1	7	5				15
American Merganser.......		2	2	10	1			15
Lesser Snow Goose.......		1	1	4	2	1	1	10
Blue Goose..............		1	1	4	2	1	1	10
Baldpate			5	7	3			15
Canvasback			5	7	3			15
Redhead	1		4	6	3	1		15
Lesser Scaup.............			5	6	4			15
Green-winged Teal........			4	7	3			14
Shoveller			5	5	5			15
Red-breasted Merganser ...			2	2	6		1	11
Ring-necked Duck			2	4	3	1		10
Buffle-head			1	4	4	2		11
White-fronted Goose		1		4	3	1		9
Gadwall			3	5	7		1	16
Blue-winged Teal.........			1	3	10	1		15
Ruddy Duck				1	6	8	1	16
White-winged Scoter......					1	4	10	15

their nesting ranges before the first week in June. Robert H. Smith, who has made extensive studies of breeding waterfowl in the north, tells me that Pintails using the delta of the Mackenzie River do not begin nesting there until early June, fully six weeks after the first Delta Pintails have their eggs and at a time when a few of the earliest Delta hens have half-grown young. Some of these Arctic ducks may winter with or near Manitoba Pintails; perhaps the two start north at about the same time. But some Delta individuals are nearly finished with their reproductive activity before the northernmost birds have started nesting. This same thing, of course, occurs with other kinds of waterfowl: Arctic breeders are still migrating long after southern relatives have produced young.

The force that impels them to move northward must be the same for Delta and Arctic Pintails, but the later stages of the sexual cycle are delayed in the most northern individuals. Wolfson (1942:262), who studied the breeding cycle and migratory behavior of the Oregon Junco, found that resident and migrant birds "differ in their gonadial cycles, although they flock together in the winter and are subjected to the same environmental conditions." These differences were between races or subspecies of the Junco; the migrants may be distinguished taxonomically from the residents. In Pintail, of course, Delta and Mackenzie River birds are not racially different. Because of the hen's fidelity to her home of previous experience, the schedule of the breeding cycle must be linked to the geographic location of home, Delta Pintails nesting in April and those of the Far North in June. The existence of innate differences in breeding time is unlikely, because of the blending of geographical units of population on the wintering grounds, where a Delta drake might take a Mackenzie River hen for his mate. This mixing of blood no doubt accounts for the absence of geographical races in the American Pintail, and is the reason why a variation in time of nesting would not develop as an inborn character in different units of the population. In other words, the progeny of a June-nesting Mackenzie River Pintail would probably nest in April in Manitoba if artificially transported there as downy young. In the Blue and Lesser Snow Geese we find this very thing happening. Captive geese taken from the wild are nesting at Island Park, Portage la Prairie, in May, before their free wild brethren have reached the nesting grounds in the Arctic.

Sowls found the female to be faithful to her breeding place as long as that area remained favorable for nesting. When, as sometimes happens, a duck returns to find her homeland unfit for nesting — as when cover is lost to fire, when agriculture has drained sloughs and potholes, or when the water is gone owing to drought — she must move elsewhere. This happens sometimes on a grand scale. In 1949 a large portion of the mixed prairie country of southern Saskatchewan dried out, and thousands of ducks returned to find their breeding grounds untenantable. They evidently settled elsewhere, and Lynch (1949) says that "it is quite apparent that some ducks moved northward out of the dry grasslands and nested in the wetter Aspen Parklands." Hawkins (1949) detected a late spring influx into Manitoba's pothole country that same year and attributed these delayed arrivals to the Saskatchewan dry-out. Prairie ducks are extremely mobile when compelled to seek new breeding localities, but Hawkins believes that they do not reproduce so successfully after forced moves as when they breed on their home range. It is quite possible that some ducks simply refuse to breed when conditions prove unsuitable, and Kalmbach (letter) suspected this to be the case with the Canvasbacks he studied in the Prince Albert region of Saskatchewan when the nesting grounds were shrunken during the dry year of 1935.

As in the fall, homeward migration moves on a wide front, and when waterfowl pass over Delta we are aware, by word of cooperators, that similar passages are taking place over other marshes. Merrill Hammond and I noted, for example, that in 1949 the first major waterfowl flight of the year reached Delta, Manitoba, and Upham, North Dakota (150 miles to the southwest), on April 8. Weather may cause regional variations, however, and, as there is a tendency for spring to arrive earlier on the western plains, ducks are sometimes well established in southern Alberta before they have reached this same latitude in Manitoba.

Each migrant travels homeward with urgency; whatever the barriers of storm, time, or distance, the bird must bring itself to the homeland for which it hungers. Its whole being has an appetite for the range where reproduction will take place; as the salmon drives relentlessly to the headwaters of the mother stream, so, with its sexual awakening, a duck or goose must satisfy its need for the home marsh. This requirement for a special place or situation falls into the pattern of *appetitive behavior* (Craig, 1918); "internal factors, sometimes together with external stimuli, activate a 'drive' or an 'urge' in an animal" (Tinbergen, 1952:2), this giving rise to behavior directed toward the attainment of a biological goal.[*]

[*] For a further discussion of goals, "consummatory acts," or "consummatory stimuli," see Tinbergen (1951) and Bastock et al. (1953).

The urge to incubate is satisfied when the clutch is completed.

This *drive* Thorpe (1951b:6) identifies as "the complex of internal and external stimuli leading to a given behavior." The goal of appetitive behavior may be a performance of a particular act, e.g., copulation or egg laying, or the attainment of a particular relation with something in the external environment, e.g., incubating a suitable clutch of eggs.

Obviously the whole of the action from the beginning of appetitive behavior to goal cannot be carried out on the level of instincts: the bird must get from the place where a drive is awakened to the special companion, object, or environmental situation where the appetite is sated. There is an interval of time and space where learned behavior serves to guide the individual. Mallard hens the world over have the same appetites when the oviduct is with egg; universally this hunger is satisfied by egg-laying at the nest. But each and every Mallard must learn the way to her own nest. It is in this period between drive and goal "that the adaptive and individual variable responses are found . . . where learning in all its variety enters into the life-story of the animal. . . . Instinct and intelligence are thus interwoven to form the whole pattern of behavior of the individual" (Thorpe, 1951b:7).

Appetites are awakened daily by many drives. There is the everlasting requirement of food, the need for gravel and water, the urge to bathe and preen. Such acts are nonsexual, repeated on a daily basis throughout life, regardless of sexual status. The reproductive drive, on the other hand, is

125

tied to a single period of the annual life cycle. More than this, breeding behavior is divided into certain divisions of the reproductive cycle; as spring advances, there is a sequence of sexual appetites. Some of these may be given in chronological order: *the urge to take a mate*, consummated when the pair is formed; *the appetite for home range and territory*, satisfied when the home marsh is reached; *the need to incubate*, appeased when the clutch is completed. Normally the sexual behavior progresses step by step in an orderly fashion until nesting is finished and the young reared. Sowls (1949) showed, however, that if one link in this chain is broken, the duck may revert to an earlier stage in the cycle. When the nest is destroyed, for instance, the female often returns to egg-laying; if her mate has by then departed, she may go back still another step and seek another drake as her partner.

For migratory waterfowl the appetites of the sexual cycle arise on the wintering waters at a time when the breeding marshes are still in the grip of frost. The first reproductive goal, taking the mate, may be attained in early winter or, sometimes in the Mallard, during autumn. Later, drake and hen migrate together. Her appetites now are for acts that can be consummated only at a special place, the familiar home range. He hungers for behavior which is to be activated only after his mate has settled down on her home range, part of which becomes his defended territory. In some females the appetite for the breeding place may be aroused before she selects her mate, and she migrates unmated, although usually attended by several suitors.

Eagle Clarke (1912), aware of the sexual nature of homing migration, suggested that "the periodic physiological changes in progress at the approach of spring in the shape of the development of the reproductive organs, with their corollary, the reviving instinct of procreation, must prove an overpowering incentive to seek accustomed breeding haunts." The pioneering experiments of Rowan (1926, 1929a, 1931) demonstrated the intimate relation between sexual awakening and homing migration. Inner stimuli of a sexual nature awaken the appetite for the home, which may be attained only by migration.* Fundamentally this drive-to-goal pattern of homing migration differs from other appetitive behavior in the sexual cycle only in terms of time and space. The distance from loafing bar to nest may be only a few minutes and yards; the distance between wintering waters and home marsh

* Since Rowan's original studies there has developed some confusion concerning the exact endocrine seat of these stimuli; but it is not denied that the migrational homing of spring is a sexual act. See Farner (1950) for a careful review and bibliography.

may be many days and hundreds of miles. But only the time and the miles of travel are different; the appetites within the hen on her wintering grounds are in the same category as those sensed by the nesting duck on her loafing bar. In some females, like Mallards that winter and also nest in Missouri or Colorado, there are few barriers between drive and goal. In others there may be two thousand miles or more between the first sexual appetite for the home range and the arrival there. The barriers are in direct ratio to the distance traveled. Temperature, wind, snow, and rain are factors in the schedule of travel to the breeding place, the birds staying back in the face of severe adversities, surging onward in favorable weather. Weather, however, must be a secondary influence on spring migration, incidental rather than fundamental.

There are two possible exceptions to this sexual nature of spring migration of waterfowl to the breeding grounds. In geese and swans, for one example, nesting does not take place the first spring, so that in yearlings the home is not the sexual goal in the same sense as it is in adults. The family bond is strong enough, however, to carry the young along to the summer home of the parents, which do travel on a sexual schedule. Once arrived on their home area, there is intense sexual behavior in these yearlings, even though it does not attain reproduction (Balham, 1953). There are also some ducks, such as Bufflehead and the two Golden-eyes, which do not breed until they are more than one year old. Unlike the geese, the yearlings of these have no family ties. However, there is evidence that some arrive at the breeding grounds independently (Munro, 1942), and we are not entirely sure that, despite the lack of breeding, there is not some sexual awakening. At Delta I have seen yearling American Golden-eyes examining nesting boxes; and for the yearling Barrow's Golden-eye, Munro (1939:272) says that "there is some manifestation of sexual excitement amongst them and they go through various performances which in the adults form part of the reproductive process." Homeward travel for these birds might possibly be classified as a sexual movement even though reproduction does not follow.

I must not let this discussion end without brief mention of some of the other migrants. The sweep of spring migration cannot escape the knowledge of the most casual citizen in Manitoba's April countryside, for the rush of travelers into this nearly birdless world of winter is a daily reminder of spring's arrival on the northern prairies. In the latitude of southern Manitoba in late April and May, there are less than four hours of darkness com-

127

pletely lacking in sunglow, and in the urgency of their homeward migration, a great part of the spring transients go through while there is enough light in the sky for us to see their passage. Most conspicuous of the daytime travelers are the four species of blackbirds,* the Bronzed Grackle, all hawks, swallows, the Crow and Bluejay and the Flicker, which carry on the whole of their migration with sunlight in the sky. Many others among the shorebirds, thrushes, finches, and warblers are conspicuous daytime travelers, although they also migrate heavily after dark.

In all these kinds I have mentioned, the main source of arrival is the southeast; and in some species, such as the Flicker, the total of the season's passage apparently comes from that direction. In the blackbirds, some reach Delta from the straight south, and several times I have followed a flock for miles as I drove along a north-south highway; but most travel across the prairie at the same southeast-northwest angle. They come on a broad front. On the morning of April 27, 1951, Colonel Arthur Sullivan, Premier Douglas L. Campbell, and I encountered twenty-five flocks of blackbirds along the forty-five miles between the outskirts of Winnipeg and Portage la Prairie as we drove westward along highway No. 1. The flocks were rather evenly scattered along the way and most of them were just departing from the wooded river valley, striking northwest across the White Horse Plains. At the same time we saw Flickers everywhere along this course, in trees or starting out to the northwest across the bald prairie. On other days I have seen the movement of blackbirds and Flickers evenly spread all the way east to Libau, Manitoba, a distance of about sixty-five miles, and at other times to Roseneath, seventy miles west of Delta.

When these hawks, blackbirds, Crows, and Flickers cross the marsh and arrive at the edge of Lake Manitoba, they do not continue over the lake, as the ducks do, but turn to follow the shoreline westward. There is thus a concentrated lane of travel along the wooded ridge, with flocks of blackbirds sometimes going over the village of Delta at the rate of two or three flocks a minute. On the morning of April 25, 1951, in a flight lasting from about 6:00 to 9:30 A.M., I estimated that at least 50,000 blackbirds flew over the village.

In their travels the blackbirds have an air speed of about twenty-five miles per hour, and the Flicker and the Crow an air speed of about the same. I have seen blackbirds travel at elevations ranging from a few feet above the ground to approximately 500 feet. Most going past Delta are between 25

* Red-winged, Brewers, Rusty, and Yellow-headed Blackbirds.

Blackbirds migrating west along the lakeshore

and 200 feet, always flying lower when moving against a wind. Crows fly at elevations of less than 300 feet, often well within gun range just above the trees. Flickers go along at treetop level, always as single birds, although one bird is usually in sight of another. All of the swallows, blackbirds, and other diurnal travelers that move with flapping flight carry on their heaviest migrations during the morning, afternoon, and evening hours, resting and feeding during midday. The soaring kinds, such as the broad-winged hawks, travel mostly through the middle of the day when thermal currents give them the greatest lift. I have seen a heavy migration of Rough-legged Hawks end abruptly as the wind died, almost every lone tree far and wide across the prairie suddenly boasting two or three, sometimes a dozen or more, of these big birds.

On a day of southeast wind I found the average ground speed of blackbirds to be thirty miles per hour and the total span of their morning and evening passage eight hours. Thus many birds may have traveled more than two hundred miles. If the migration had been about the same all along the way, those that ended their day at Delta started well south of the international border in Minnesota, while those that set out from Delta went at least a hundred miles across the border into Saskatchewan.

These hawks, blackbirds, Crows, Flickers and others continue westward around the lake until reaching the mouth of the Whitemud River at the southeast corner. Thence they branch into the northwest again (Figure 18). This deflection away from the west shore of Lake Manitoba leaves an area nearly vacant of migrants, much as the hiatus described for the north shore of the Gulf of Mexico (Lowery, 1945; Williams, 1945). For example, between eight and eleven o'clock on the morning of April 16, 1952, Les Garnham, posted at Delta, counted 137 flocks of blackbirds pass westward. The

129

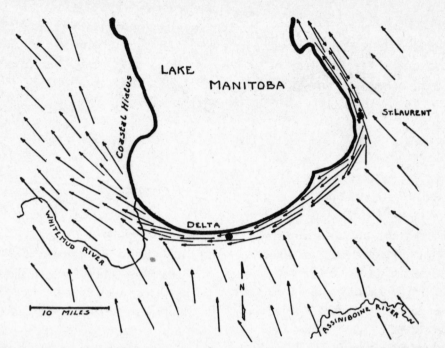

Figure 18. Deflection of blackbirds around Lake Manitoba, showing migratory divide at southeast corner of lake and the coastal hiatus on the west shore. All hawks, Flickers, and all Crows and other passerines follow the same leading lines of the lakeshore, splitting their migration to go up the east shore or around the south end of Lake Manitoba

In reverse migration the direction of travel is directly opposite to that shown here.

same morning Pete Ward and I saw them branching away from the lake at the mouth of the Whitemud River, but when we carefully surveyed about 30 square miles of the farmland along the west shore and on Big Point to the north we saw not a single blackbird. Moreover, Ralph Thompson, a farmer on Big Point, told us that so far that spring he had seen only one flock of blackbirds, although at Delta they had been passing through steadily for ten days.

Just as there is a steady flow of these migrants westward around the south end of Lake Manitoba, so there is another concentrated lane of travel going northwest along the east shore. In short, there is a major migratory divide at Lake Manitoba where the flight, arriving on a broad front, is split, some flocks going one way, some the other. This divide is at the southeast corner of the lake. Peter Ward and I watched this southeast shoreline during a heavy blackbird migration on the morning of April 26, 1951. Flocks arrived steadily from the southeast flying directly to the lakeshore. Here they went one way or the other: some went up the east shore, while others turned to go around the south end of the lake, this choice requiring them to make nearly an about-face swing (Figure 18). This splitting of the flight did not take place sharply at one point of the lakeshore, but occurred over a stretch about twenty miles long. The result was a two-way flow of birds going in opposite directions. This migratory divide is the same for Flickers, Crows, all the hawks, and, indeed, for all the shoreline travelers, and on days when there is a heavy westward flow at Delta I have seen just as steady a passage to the northeast along the eastern shoreline.

This turning place at Lake Manitoba is probably only one of several such decisions the migrants must make during a day of travel. Earlier, there must be a splitting of the flight when some birds branch north to Lake Winnipeg. Mr. A. G. Lawrence, veteran Winnipeg naturalist, has made an energetic search for this turning place of Lake Winnipeg blackbirds and believes there is a major migrational divide at the bend of the Red River near Morris, Manitoba, the same bend where Baldock saw the splitting of the Canada Goose flock (p. 122). Of Flickers I have watched several different flight lines on the same day, all stemming originally from the main current flowing to the northwest. On April 25, 1951, I saw a steady stream of Flickers going northeast across the Libau Marsh toward the east shore of Lake Winnipeg. Another flight went north up the Red River Valley. A steady movement of Flickers went northwest over the prairie between Lake Winnipeg and Lake Manitoba. There was a concentrated flow northwest along the eastern shore of Lake Manitoba and a westward passage over Delta around the south end of the lake. For individuals with far destinations, the wrong turn in Manitoba would be as serious an error as that of a Vancouver-bound railroad passenger boarding the Illinois Central in Chicago.

These diversions of Flickers, blackbirds, and all the other birds from the main currents of migration, the many separate departures from the standard direction, are interesting in view of the relation between weather and migration. The strong southerly flow of winds favors the mass movement of most birds following the standard direction; but it is clear that the migrants are by no means swept along in this current of air. When the turning point is reached, the travelers bend this way or that, even though they must now cross the wind rather than go with it. Blackbirds making the turn around the south end of Lake Manitoba are obliged to face the wind for a while in order to follow their chosen course. Let us note, too, that while the south wind favors the movement of most ducks going to the northwest, the Blue and Lesser Snow Geese travel to the northeast, directly across the main flow of air. Clarke (1912) believed that the clear weather of the high-pressure configuration influenced the start of heavy migrations, but that the wind produced by this barometric arrangement did not control the direction of migration. We must examine other qualities of the anticyclone that influence migrations. In this respect, we have noticed that among the captive birds at Delta, during their winter residence in the indoor pens, there is increased activity — of feeding, fighting, wing-beating and courtship — when the weather changes from "low" to "high," this despite the fact that they are protected from the wind.

Lowery (1951:468) points out that "since the general movement of the air is from the high-pressure area toward a low-pressure area, birds starting their migrations with favorable tail winds are often ultimately carried to a region where conditions are decidedly less favorable. In the vicinity of an area of low pressure the greater turbulence and high wind velocities, combined with the possibly slightly less bouyant property of the air, caused birds to descend. Since low-pressure areas in spring generally precede cold fronts, with an attending shift of wind to the north, an additional barrier to the northward migration of birds is imposed." Very often we see this effect on the travelers at Delta. All morning there may be a steady flow of Juncos, blackbirds, and many others past my office window; then suddenly I am aware that travel has stopped. Great flocks of Juncos are feeding everywhere on the lawn and about the hatchery; the taller trees are loaded with blackbirds and the thickets with Robins, Tree Sparrows, and other small birds, many of which now burst forth in song. A cold, damp wind comes in off the lake, the long cloudline of the front passes overhead, and we know that the heavy passage has stopped for a while.

The westward direction of the movement along the lakeshore at Delta is standard except when (as occurs at least once each year) these migrants turn about to fly steadily in the direction whence they came. I take this to be a reverse migration, such as is described by Natorp (1932), Lewis (1939), and others. Such reverses seem to be associated with sharp changes in the weather pattern. On the morning of April 21, 1951, for example, there was a southeast wind of 5 m.p.h.; the sky was lightly overcast, the temperature, 38° F. From 5:30 to 7:00 A.M. there passed a steady westward flight of blackbirds, mostly Redwings, which at its peak averaged a flock a minute. This traffic slowed down shortly after 7:00, after which single flocks went by at intervals of from fifteen to twenty minutes. There was a small movement of hawks, mostly Red-tailed Hawk, and a massive westward drift of Juncos and Tree Sparrows. About 9:00 o'clock the wind shifted to come from the west, and all westward travel ended an hour later. At noon the wind was blowing about 10 m.p.h. from the northwest, there was a heavy, low overcast, and the temperature dropped below freezing. Shortly after noon I noticed Juncos and Tree Sparrows drifting eastward; all afternoon they moved through the thickets and across the clearings in that direction, the volume of their eastward passage being equal to the morning travel the other way. Flocks of blackbirds and small numbers of Crows also flew eastward. Next morning the wind continued from the northwest, but it was bright and clear. A few Juncos, one flock of blackbirds, and several hawks going west made up the total of the migration for the day, while the Juncos and Tree Sparrows remained about the hatchery in their many hundreds. April 23 was cold and cloudy, with a west wind, and there was no migration. The twenty-fourth broke bright and clear, with a south wind, and there was a short but heavy westward migration of blackbirds and Crows in the morning; but the Juncos and their companions did not travel. The twenty-fifth brought rising temperatures, strong southeast winds, and the heaviest migration of all species for the year.

When these reverses occur at Delta, I have seen evidence of the turnabout on the prairie country to the south, where on such days there is a steady drift of birds to the southeast. Whatever the influence, many birds over a broad region are induced to turn back on their migratory highway, retracing their steps several, sometimes many miles.

Though such reverses occur most frequently in the small species, I have seen similar changes in the flow of waterfowl. On the evening of April 23, 1950, for example, a migration of ducks, mostly Mallards and Pintails, began soon after 7:00 P.M., the birds all going in their usual direction toward the northwest. Shortly after the flight started, ducks began arriving on the marsh from the northwest, and it was apparent that they had turned back soon after they were out over the open lake. The same evening there was a reverse movement of blackbirds and Crows; Juncos and hawks had been going eastward all afternoon. Next morning the prairies were blanketed with three inches of snow. Sowls (1955:19) describes a reverse in which the ducks departed completely from the Delta region.

The homeward passage of birds somehow touches the lives of us all; and yet we have been mainly concerned with these wayfarers when they stop

for a while in the course of their vernal journeys. Arrival dates, species by species, have been faithfully recorded by thousands of observers widely scattered over the land. But we know almost nothing of the timing of the main flow of migration. There is very little information in North America about standard directions, as judged by studies of birds in passage rather than as plotted from banding recoveries. Thomson (1953) says that there has been a tendency to regard visible migration by day as "largely a special opportunity of favored places where spectacular diurnal movements were regularly to be seen; and this in itself may have given impressions that were in some respects misleading. In recent years the possibilities of the method have been more fully appreciated, and this has resulted in a great access of interest in this aspect of the general subject. Dutch and Swedish observers have done outstanding work in showing what can be learnt by systematic study of visible migration, and ornithologists in several other countries are contributing to the total effort." In the light of Griffin's observations on the role of ecological factors in migration, and in view of the exciting discoveries of Kramer and Matthews regarding the influence of the sun, it is important for North American students to give more time to the study of birds in the very act of migration.

> "Spring migration is scarcely completed before there occur certain summer movements which precede the true autumn migration." A. Landsborough Thomson, *Bird Migration*

10

The Classification of Waterfowl Travel

Our word "migrate" comes from the Latin *migratus*, the past participle of *migrare*: "to move from one place to another." It lacks the element of permanent settlement carried in the word "emigrate" and is defined by Webster's Dictionary as "to pass or remove from one region or district to another for temporary residence."

Most of us think of migration as the spring and autumn sweep of birds to and from their nesting ranges. Many authors, however, have used the word with reference to other travel occurring between the two main passages. The literature is thus sometimes confusing; ornithologists seem not to have found in "migration" so precise a meaning as it still holds for laymen. There have been many attempts to correct this situation, like Geyr von Schweppenburg's suggestion (1933) that we adopt the term *Zwischenzug*, or "between-migration," to distinguish all travel taking place between spring and fall. I prefer the more recent idea of Wilkinson (1952). He proposes that we refer to the vernal and autumnal migrations to and from the breeding grounds as *anastrophic* migration — from the Greek ἀναστρέφειν, "to retrace one's steps." All other movement he catalogues as *diasporic* migration — from the Greek διασπορά, "dispersion."

The travels of waterfowl come neatly within these two broad classifications, and placing the various migrations in one or the other category does much to strengthen our understanding.

ANASTROPHIC MIGRATION
Homeward spring migration

Homeward spring migration carries the bird from the place where its sexual drives are awakened to the nesting region where the reproductive

135

appetites are consummated. The distance of homeward migration in ducks varies from a few miles for some individuals which nest near their winter range, to several thousand miles for others of the same species. In ducks which take new mates each year, the destination depends upon the experience of the female returning to her home range. In geese and swans, which mate for life, the pair annually returns to its familial breeding grounds. In ducks, parents and children (which in many species are ready to breed their first spring) are not together as family groups, having separated the previous summer. In geese and swans the homeward-bound adults are accompanied by their yearling children. In the Northern Hemisphere this sexual migration toward the nesting place may begin as early as January for some individuals, while others do not gain their breeding grounds until June. Birds nesting at the southern edge of the breeding range may have young before others of the same species have arrived on nesting places in the extreme north.

The homeward migration of cranes is like that of the geese and swans. Some other birds, like the Crow and the Barn Swallow, reach their nesting place in pairs, as do many ducks; but I do not know whether the female so strongly directs the course of migration as in ducks. The pattern in waterfowl, of course, is very different from that in many passerine birds, such as the Red-winged Blackbird (Allen, 1914), in which the male returns to his breeding territory before the female.

The impetus of homeward migration is sexual, but the exact schedule, by days or weeks, is modified by the weather, with the heaviest spring passages occurring "during the interval between the passage of a warm front through the region and the subsequent arrival of a cold front" (Bagg et al., 1950).

Mass fall migration

Mass fall migration is the act of experienced birds retracing their steps, usually over standard directions in direct passage from the breeding or molting range to the wintering grounds or to traditional stopping places along the way. Mass fall migrations begin in August, after the adult males have completed their flightless period of the eclipse molt, and they continue through the autumn till the final evacuation from the breeding grounds with the arrival of deep frost. Mass movements may be made up entirely of adult males of one species, as in the post-molt flight of adult drake Pintails, or they may be composed of all sex and age classes, with several or many species represented. When a number of species move in mass, each kind, nevertheless, holds to flocks of its own in which juveniles and adults are usually together. Although young-of-the-year may outnumber adults in direct mass migration, these passages are essentially the movements of experienced birds. By this act of travel with the adults, the juveniles, as children (in geese and swans) or as unrelated companions (in ducks), accept the non-genetic heritage of the traditional route, which thus becomes ancient beyond the experience of any living individual and is passed on to succeeding generations by social inheritance.

If inexperienced juveniles arrive at the wintering grounds independently of experienced companions (as some do every August and September), this probably is the result of the undirected wanderings of young-of-the-year, vagabond travel that carries other juveniles of the same kind and at the same time to marshes north or east or west of the natal range.

Mass fall migration accounts for the direct passage of waterfowl by hundreds, thousands, or, in late fall, hundreds of thousands at a time, moving over a region many squares miles in extent. By such passages most individuals of a species or, at the time of deep frost, all waterfowl may evacuate their summer range overnight, leaving only cripples and a few stragglers behind.

The biological impetus for mass fall migration is not understood. In some birds, like adult drake Pintails, the movement is related to the recovery from the flightless period of the eclipse; by links with the molting schedule, its timing may be traced directly to the breeding period. There is considerable variation among species in the time of departure (witness the September passage of Blue-winged Teal and the mid-October departure of Canvasback), but each kind shows a calendar regularity that differs little from year to year. Species migrating in September or early October from the Canadian prairies leave an abundance of food and a span of fair weather behind them.

Though fall departure occurs at about the same time each year, weather has a "trigger effect" which influences the exact day when the mass migration will start. Regardless of the stage of the autumn — mild September or cold November — mass fall migrations begin with the arrival of the clear sky and fair weather of the anticyclone; but once started, migration may overtake and continue through bad weather.

The mass migrations of waterfowl have been poorly documented in the literature, perhaps because the passages so often begin late in the day and move so high that they escape notice. Mass migration is typical of many other groups of birds, but here again, the record is not clear in the literature, and I believe we underrate the importance of this type of traditional passage in the migration of inexperienced young birds.

MIGRATIONS OF WATERFOWL

Solitary fall migration

I have never seen a duck migrating by itself without companions. I have seen lone flocks of ducks, beyond sight of any other traveling groups, following the standard direction to the southeast, as if in migration. No doubt in higher latitudes where numbers are thin, some migration in ducks begins with one flock; but such isolated migration is an extreme rarity in the latitude of southern Manitoba.

Nor in the geese have I ever seen a lone migrant. Strays are occasional in autumn, undoubtedly from flocks which have been broken by hunters. But these quickly join other flocks. Migrating Canada Geese, Richardson's Geese, and White-fronted Geese often move en masse, either by themselves or at the same times as the grand duck migrations. But, much more often than is found with ducks, single flocks are seen following standard directions in migration; such aggregations are probably made up of several families moving as a unit from an isolated range.

In our experience at Delta migration by isolated individuals is nearly as rare in other species as it is in ducks. During late August and September there is a drift of Flickers through Delta and across the prairies. These birds retrace their path of spring migration, going east along the lakeshore past Delta and southeast across the prairie. In passage, each Flicker is usually by itself, flying low just over the treetops. But they go in waves, so that as many as fifty birds have been counted in an hour; and again and again they stop at places of rendezvous, where several, usually a dozen or more, Flickers may be seen together. I once saw a Bittern take wing just at dusk from behind my house (surely he must have been the bird that had been there through the late summer and early fall). He left with a northwest wind of twenty-five miles per hour and started out alone into the southeast. I watched him disappear out over Cadham Bay, and am sure he had committed himself to migration. Black-crowned Night Herons usually migrate southward from Delta in small groups, although I have seen single autumn travelers. The Goshawk, Sharp-skinned Hawk, and Cooper's Hawk are seen as isolated migrants at Delta, in contrast to the grand movements of the Red-tailed Hawk and other Buteos. So, too, the Duck Hawk travels by itself. Among many of the passerines there is no autumnal period of foregathering. The Catbird and the Baltimore Oriole in our yard are there today by themselves, and gone tomorrow. And yet among the night migrants, if individuals of a kind start out by themselves, there is evidence of mass movements of different kinds traveling together at night. During nights when passerines

138

are in passage over Delta we hear the contact calls of birds going over steadily; and Lincoln (1939:77) gives the account of one observer (watching with telescope focused on the moon) who estimated that night migrants passed his point at the rate of 9,000 birds an hour.

DIASPORIC MIGRATION

The molting shift

The molting shift is the mass transfer of mature ducks, mostly drakes, from the nesting ranges to marshes or lakes where they pass the flightless period of the eclipse molt. The journeys begin at the close of the sexual cycle when the male abandons his incubating hen, and end when he arrives at the locality where the wing feathers are shed. The shift may be to another part of the same marsh in which he had his breeding territory or to a place several hundred miles away. The transfer shows no constant geographical direction; some, like the Pintails that go to the Bear River Marshes of Utah or the Baldpates that go to Delta, travel toward the winter range, but others go north or east or west. This is an ecological rearrangement of the population, with a bias toward large marshes on the part of river ducks and toward lakes (sometimes the ocean) on the part of the diving ducks. The shift does not take place in breeding geese or swans, which spend the flightless period with their young near the nesting place; but there may be a molting flight in nonbreeding yearlings and barren adults (Taylor, 1953, and Scott, 1953, for Pinkfooted Geese; Klopman, unpublished, for the Canada Goose).

The timing of this shift shows a remarkable consistency from year to year. At Delta the first bands of postbreeding Mallard and Pintail drakes are always seen by the tenth of May, the earliest large flocks by the end of May, and dropped primary feathers, evidence of the first flightless drakes, by the middle of June. At Whitewater Lake, Manitoba, Bossenmaier (1953a) found only a week's difference between the gathering of the first flocks of Mallard drakes in the very late spring of 1950 and that in the more normal season of 1951. Baldpate and Green-winged Teal drakes regularly arrive at Delta in mid-June, and the first cast primary feathers of Canvasback always drift to the lakeshore in late July. Where nesting has been delayed by adverse spring weather, however, there follows a delay in the peak of the flightless period.

We mark these events by the calendar, but the birds move on biological time: the molt and the molting shifts are hinged to the sexual cycle. Drakes of early-nesting hens are first to molt; males that breed later, molt later. So it is that during the same week in May one may encounter some groups of molting Mallard males, while other Mallard drakes, still paired, are in immaculate breeding dress. In some species, like Mallard and Pintail, the male usually abandons his hen during the early stages of incubation. In others, like Blue-winged Teal and Shoveler, the drake remains on his territory through most or all of incubation, the postnuptial molt into the eclipse beginning before the marital bond is broken. Although the molt into the eclipse starts at about the same time as the hen commences incubation (whether or not the male lingers on the territory nearby), there is yet no complete understanding of the relation between the postnuptial molt and reproductive activity. Seligmann and Shattock (1914) observed that the "seasonal change of plumage in the Mallard is not connected with the spermatogenic function of the testicle," a decision recently confirmed by Höhn (1947).

The postnuptial molt into the drab eclipse plumage progresses gradually, the loss of the pinions and the flightless period of three to four weeks coming as a climax (Figure 19). There is some individual variation in the timing of the wing molt, however, and I found (Hochbaum, 1944a:112) that in old captive Canvasback drakes the flightless period arrived even though there was not yet a complete change into the eclipse plumage. The shift of molting drakes to the place where they pass the flightless stage is likewise gradual. First there is a coming together by twos and threes, such small bands being seen on the nesting range, the males presumably not far

Figure 19. The eclipse molt in the Pintail drake. The male arrives on the breeding grounds wearing the conspicuous white, brown, and gray nuptial plumage (right). When he leaves his incubating female in late April or May, however, he enters the postnuptial molt, donning a drab, inconspicuous, female-like plumage (left). When the molt of the body feathers is nearly complete, the wing feathers are molted all at one time, and the bird is flightless for a period of nearly four weeks.

from their original breeding territories. Then these join to form small flocks of a dozen or so, the progress of the molt now being apparent to the observer's unaided eye. These flocks may go directly to the place where flight is lost; or they may move to yet another intermediate rendezvous, where they join others to make up aggregations of hundreds, and sometimes thousands.

The major molting marshes and lakes are used year after year by flightless adults, and banding returns show that some drakes return to the same place each summer. Yearling males, ending their first breeding season and approaching their first flightless period,* may find their way to molting areas with older drakes, or they may be drawn there by a postbreeding requirement for companionship. Some, no doubt, visited these same places in their juvenile wanderings of the previous summer, for many molting lakes and marshes are also autumn gathering places for all sex and age classes.

There is strong suggestion of appetitive behavior, the birds moving to special ecological situations. During the weeks of foregathering, for instance, many Mallards and other river ducks loaf in large companies on the south shoreline of Lake Manitoba; but there is no evidence that members of these species are flightless on the lake as are Canvasback and other diving ducks. The lakeshore Mallards and their companions always manage to arrive on the marsh when the flight feathers are lost. Since the pinions may be shed all

---

* Although the juvenile passes through a change of body plumage its first autumn, in which it loses the female-like juvenal plumage and takes on the breeding plumage, the flight feathers of the wing are not lost in the autumn molt. The bird wears its first wing feathers through the year.

at once (sometimes in an instant if the bird is startled) these ducks of the lakeshore must have some inner stimuli forewarning them to move from their loafing bars to the special molting environment some time before the wing feathers are lost. Indeed, there is evidence of their awareness of the molt: when a Mallard close to the wing molt is flushed, it does not take off in abrupt rise, as normally, but at a more gentle angle, as if favoring the wing against extreme exertion.

While the molting shift is mostly of males, it is seldom entirely so. The late May and June gatherings often contain a few adult females which, for one reason or another, have abandoned their reproductive attempts for the year. Sometimes, when the hen, thwarted by predators or other adversities, abandons nesting while still attended by a drake, these two maintain their bond as companions and may be seen side by side in the premolting aggregations (Sowls, 1949:270). Unsuccessful females, which accompany the males most abundantly during adverse nesting seasons, move with the drakes to their destinations. For the female population as a whole, however, there is no major shift. The evidence suggests that many hens which have raised their broods travel only short distances or remain on the same marsh for the flightless stage. The wing feather molt of the female does not begin until after she has left her family; hence the flightless schedule is much later than it is in the male, some females being flightless in October (Hochbaum, 1944a).

I have observed no pattern of weather governing the timing of molting shifts, but have noticed that the arrivals and departures of adult drakes in late May and June usually are made in the late afternoon or during twilight. In England Coombes (1950) has made a neat study of the Common Sheld-duck in the act of moving toward its molting place. He found that in July 1949 the molt migration "took place on every evening on which visibility from the point of departure was 'good' or 'perfect,' whereas no migration took place on evenings when visibility was 'poor' or 'bad' . . . Sheld-ducks fly in the worst of weather at sea and along the coast, but are evidently reluctant to face this overland flight except when visibility and weather are favorable." He found that the migration "takes place during about three hours only, and the great bulk of it is concentrated into two hours, one hour before to one hour after sunset."

Ward (1953) gives evidence of a postbreeding movement of adult male Coots from the breeding range to such concentration places as the Delta Marsh, where large numbers pass the flightless season. In the grebes, which,

In the twilight hours of early summer evenings, bands of drakes may be
seen arriving at Delta, usually from the northwest.

like the ducks and the Coot, are flightless during the wing-molt, there is a
shift away from small breeding marshes to larger waters. At Delta the large
Western Grebe, which nests in the marsh, moves to the open waters of Lake
Manitoba, where the wing-molt takes place.

In a great many birds which, unlike the ducks, coots, and grebes, molt
the wing feathers gradually and are not flightless, there is, nevertheless, a
regular postbreeding transfer which involves a large portion of the adult
population. Some of these, like the Tree Swallow and the Bank Swallow,
have a postbreeding shift that carries them annually to the same traditional
stopping places. Thus in the first week in July, Tree Swallows reach Delta
to gather in great numbers on pen wires or on trees which, used year after
year, have long ago been killed by the excrement. So, too, some shore birds
and blackbirds gather at Delta in late June or early July. The first arrivals
are adults, possibly nonbreeders or birds thwarted in their nesting attempts.
But later on the old birds are joined by young, so that by the time the mass

143

Yellowlegs and other shore birds return to Delta from their breeding grounds in early summer.

southward migration takes place, there is a heavy mixture of birds-of-the-year with the adults. This mixture, however, may not be taken as a rule for all kinds. In the Golden Plover most adults are said to go south along the Atlantic seaboard, whereas the young, and some adults, travel south in a broad movement across the prairie regions of the continent (Rowan, 1926).

There are many other kinds of birds, such as Catbird, Baltimore Oriole and Yellow Warbler, which remain solitary near the breeding territory, quietly inconspicuous during the molt, but announcing their presence in late August with autumnal song.

The primary wandering of juveniles

The urge to roam must be innate in young birds, and the random nature of their travel indicates no awareness of geographic direction (Figure 20). Thorpe (1944:77) suggests that such juvenile explorations lead to "latent learning," and he remarks that this is "especially characteristic of animals which explore their environment without the satisfaction of any immediate reward, but by their explorations secure information which may afterwards be of use to them in a number of contexts, for example, in food-getting, in escape from enemies, or in finding their way home." Such wandering serves to give the young bird a familiarity with a wide area beyond the birthplace, and this geographical experience must be an important factor in the homing orientation of the following spring.

Williams (1944), speaking especially of juvenile Redheads, says that "the available evidence indicates a vagabond existence for the birds until they concentrate on the wintering grounds." The extent of the youthful

144

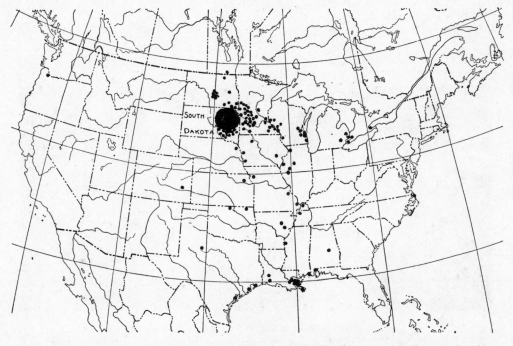

Figure 20. Dispersal of young ducks of seven species (Mallard, Gadwall, Pintail, Blue-winged Teal, Shoveller, Redhead, and Canvasback) from the pothole breeding grounds of South Dakota. During the summer of 1954 flightless ducklings were banded on their home marshes. Spots show where they were shot during October and November of their first autumn. Ray Murdy, who supervised this banding program, points out that although the dispersal is random, there is a bias toward the north, east, and south, where the habitat is more favorable than on the dry plains to the west. Not all birds cleared away from their birthplaces by the opening of the shooting season, and about one-half of the returns are from youngsters killed in their home country (large black circle).

(This figure is presented through the courtesy of the South Dakota
Department of Game, Fish, and Parks.)

wanderings hinges, of course, on the time and the latitude of birth. Young Pintails, some of which are on the wing at Delta by the last week in June, have more time to explore than young Delta Canvasbacks or Redheads, which seldom are in the air before August. Redheads hatched in Utah have far more time to roam than their kin which enter the world in Yukon Territory. Some late-hatched young have no time at all to stray before the arrival of frost, and a few individuals, especially in the diving ducks, never reach flying stage before the arrival of ice.

No doubt one of the functions of juvenile travel is the refinement of

145

The first Pintails are on the wing long before the oldest
Canvasback youngsters take flight.

flight technique; another is the strengthening of the flight muscles. After
watching the young color-banded ducks at Delta, I am sure that at least
three or four weeks must pass before the youngsters lose their awkwardness
on the wing. And the effect of flight on the wing muscles themselves is
evidenced by the changes in size and in the color of the flesh.

There is a universal urge for juveniles to use their wings; and once in
the air, they move out and away from home in what Thorpe (1951a:24) considers a "general curiosity about the environment." There is among juveniles
"an aggressive behavior," says Kalela (1954:24), "commonly shown by birds
when they leave their parents, and this leads to the development of undirected wanderings . . ." Here, once more, we find an exception in the geese
and swans, and also in the cranes, in which the family remains united in its
first flights and there is no aimless wandering of the young. This family
grouping also holds with a few passerines. In Manitoba the Arkansas Kingbirds move away from the nesting locality in family units a few days after
the young can fly. For a short while afterward these family groups may be
seen scattered widely on roadside wires, the parents still attending the
young; then in two or three weeks they are all gone, not to be seen again

Several weeks pass before the young birds lose their
awkwardness on the wing.

until the following year. Manitoba Crow families likewise leave the nesting
places soon after the young are on the wing, young and old joining bands
which eventually make up the large migrant flocks.

By and large, however, the evidence suggests a random scattering of the
young of many species away from the natal range. The true nature of the
scattering is sometimes confused — by ecological barriers, which inhibit
movement in certain directions (e.g., the failure of sea birds to wander over
forested country); by human bias in band recoveries (e.g., as between settled
and unsettled districts); or by elements in the weather (e.g., the dominance
of certain air masses, spoken of on p. 208) that may give random travel a
geographic bias in the direction of the dominant flow of air.

Winter vagrancy

However direct the autumn migration, however ancient the wintering
locality, there is strong evidence of vagrant travels by both young and old
birds about the wintering grounds or from stopping places along the flyways of migration. These may be "explosive" movements in any direction,
like those of the Louisiana Ring-necked Ducks or the McGinnis Slough teal
described elsewhere (p. 112). They may be "weather movements" — south in

147

hard weather, like those of Canvasbacks from the Susquehanna to Curri-cuck, or north in unseasonably mild weather, like the massive travel of North Dakota Mallards back into Manitoba. Or they may be cross-country, from one flyway to another, like the "round-robin" type of movement of Pintails (Low, 1949).

Bandings show that adults as well as juveniles wander about the winter ranges in this way; and of Mallards making November arrivals at Delta from North Dakota, I found both adults and juveniles in hunters' bags. Such vagrancies, however, do not concern the whole of the wintering population, some individuals and some large aggregations staying in one place through-out the winter.

The winter vagrancy ends with the rise of the sexual cycle, when travel is directed toward the breeding range upon the start of homeward migration.

Homeward spring migration is the relentless drive to the nesting place. It may consume several or many weeks; there may be interruptions and lags, usually due to the weather; but it is a persistent and unalterable move-ment toward the geographic place of home.

On the other hand, in travel from the breeding range to the wintering grounds, some or many ducks undoubtedly follow vagrant movements be-fore or between the mass fall migrations. Vast segments of the population move directly and swiftly over long distances in mass fall migration, and probably all adult birds and most young waterfowl participate in at least one mass passage during the course of the autumn. But the random travel of the young birds (with an ecological and meteorological bias toward the south in autumn) and the vagrancies of adults are variables of autumn that are not found in spring.

"Nature is pleased with simplicity and effects not the pomp of superfluous causes." Sir Isaac Newton

"We are accustomed to regard as real those sense perceptions which are common to different individuals, and which therefore are, in a measure, impersonal." Albert Einstein

11

The Dimensions of Travel

THE problems of avian migration are often approached from the standpoint of human experience; gauged thus, the enigma of orientation is insurmountable. A major barrier to objective thinking about migration seems to be the great distances that birds travel, distances that we apprehend as human travelers. We have an understanding of a bird's movements about the narrow limits of its home range, but its manner of orientation in migration is unknown. Rowan (1947) has explained that "when a flicker or a bluebird returns from the south year after year to the same nesting box, there is no essential difference between this performance and the return to the same box after a feeding foray, except in the matter of scale; in the one case the bird travels hundreds (or thousands) of miles, in the other merely yards." The depth of the mystery of migrational orientation is in direct proportion to the distance traveled.

We think of migration, and talk and write about it, in terms of miles or kilometers. Yet a bird has no awareness of a mile as such; neither can a mile be the same for two species, nor equal for man and bird. *The distance of travel is relative to the traveler*: "all movement is relative" (Bergson, 1911b); "distance is relative to a particular velocity of the observer" (Eddington, 1930). A journey across a field for a Meadow Mouse is far greater than for a man, although by yardsticks the trip is precisely the same for both. The mile for a walking man is longer than for a flying Canvasback; this unit is simply an arbitrary term of convenience that should be regarded as a relative rather than absolute measure of travel.

All travel of mouse, man, or bird has three dimensions: *length*, or distance of travel; *height*, the elevation of the eyes that guide travel; *breadth*, the distance between the horizons on either side of the line of travel. These coordinates vary with every animal because of variations in structure; the elevation of the eyes is half an inch in mouse, about five and a half feet in man, and anywhere from a few inches to several thousand feet in the Canvasback. The breadth of each individual's travel is relative to its height.*
We are able to understand these values all the better if we contemplate a ten-mile trip from the level of a mouse, then step into a light aircraft to experience the same journey as a Canvasback.

There is still another travel coordinate: the motion of the traveler. Length, height, and breadth merely outline the space within which a journey takes place, just as the walls of a coop are the chickens' boundaries of movement therein. Coops may be built according to ten thousand plans, each with different dimensions. Travel likewise follows many patterns, but travel implies movement within its three dimensions, and length, height,

* Breadth of travel may be modified by ground haze or other meteorological factors limiting visibility. Breadth is also variable according to variations in acuity. Breadth of vision may be extended by mountain ranges; but in the absence of these, even under conditions of ideal visibility, recognizable detail at the horizon approaches zero because of tangential viewing. Thus, for these several reasons, the exact mathematical measurements of breadth of travel cannot be given. This, however, does not greatly detract from the importance of this dimension at elevations normally used by birds in migration.

and breadth have meaning only as they are relative to motion. Thus the fourth dimension of travel is the velocity of the traveler within the space of the other three coordinates: time in the space of travel, or *time-in-space*.

Velocity of travel is commonly measured against two kinds of interval, one of distance, the other of time. The term *miles per hour* gives an idea of the relation between distance and time, but does not relate to the height and breadth of travel. If we are to study animal movement in a truly objective manner, we must consider the whole structure of its four dimensions.

Let us now examine a specific problem in bird migration. Evidence suggests that the fall passage of Canvasbacks from Delta to Lake Christina is made in one flight, a trip of about 300 miles. Canvasbacks have been observed on this course at an elevation of 2,000 feet and at a measured ground-speed of 60 m.p.h. At this height the breadth of travel is about 118 miles, or 59 miles on either side of the line of flight. If a tail wind prevails throughout, the time-in-space of this journey is 5 hours. The dimensions of such a flight are thus: length, 300 miles; time-in-space, 5 hours; height, 2,000 feet; breadth, 118 miles. This equation for a Canvasback is compared with the travel coordinates of a man who walks at 4 m.p.h.,* at an eye elevation of 5½ feet, and a breadth of travel (in the absence of obstacles) of about 6 miles. Time-in-space, 5 hours, is the common denominator for drawing comparisons, with all other coordinates relative to this. With the time constant for man and bird, the relative value of the man's distance is 20; that is, 20 miles is to man as 300 miles is to Canvasback. We of course recognize this relativity in our daily movements. As I walk over the open prairie to the marsh a mile away, I see a duck flying in the same direction. The bird's absolute mile is the same as mine, but its relative distance is much shorter.

The foregoing considered only two coordinates: distance and time-in-space. These are relative to the height of travel, 2,000 feet for Canvasback, 5½ feet for man. Bear in mind that height is not an isolated point in space; it flows with the traveler's motion and is perceived by the eye as movement of the earth itself, an optical illusion in which the ground beneath the traveler seems to approach from ahead, pass underneath and to either side, then recede behind. The velocity of this apparent ground flow is relative to the height of motion. In human experience, for example, the ground seems to speed rapidly past in a blur when our aircraft leaves the runway, the velocity of this ground flow decreasing as the aircraft gains altitude. Air

* Four miles per hour is not an average walking speed for man, but an experienced walker in top condition can average this on an overland journey.

and ground speed may remain constant, but the ground flow is much slower at 2,000 feet. It is by this apparent motion of the earth that both man and bird perceive their progress, and the height of the eye is thus of great importance in travel orientation.

A man would find it impossible to direct his journey at 4 m.p.h. if his eyes were at mouse level. The more rapid the ground flow, the more difficult the problems of orientation, a fact we human beings acknowledge when we slow down (or gain altitude in an airplane) when traveling in strange surroundings. To walk at 4 m.p.h., at an eye level of 5½ feet, gives a man a keen and efficient awareness of motion through space. When a Canvasback flies at 60 m.p.h. at an elevation of 82½ feet, its apparent ground flow is precisely the same as for the walking man (Figure 21). In short, 4 m.p.h. at 5½ feet is to man as 60 m.p.h. at 82½ feet is to Canvasback; the 300 miles to Lake Christina in 5 hours at an elevation of 82½ feet are to a Canvasback as 20 miles in 5 hours at 5½ feet are to a man, the relative values of distance, time-in-space, and height being the same for man and bird. The Canvasback seldom flies so low as this, almost never in migration, and it is immediately apparent that its ability to gain altitude gives it a tremendous advantage over man. There is no need to resort to mathematical comparisons to show how the bird is favored at 2,000 feet, but we must understand that not only is the area seen from this altitude greater, but, because of the relative

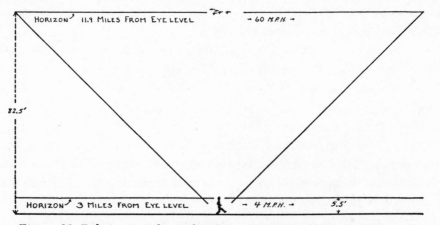

Figure 21. Relative travel equality for man and bird. At elevations and speeds shown above the relative velocity and the apparent ground flow are exactly the same for man and bird. The bird's relative velocity becomes less as it gains altitude, and it may rise so high that the apparent ground flow becomes almost imperceptible.

reduction in the velocity of apparent ground flow, the bird has much more time than the walking man for visual examination of any segment of the landscape over which it travels.

There remains the dimension of breadth. If the other three coordinates have relative equality, the values of breadth are the same for man and bird. But as the Canvasback rises above 82½ feet it gains a great superiority in its breadth of perception. Landscape patterns, such as lakes, rivers, and mountains, beyond sight at lower elevations come into view, and errors in course may be adjusted.[*] The increase in the breadth of vision reduces the requirement of precision in aerial navigation.

The four-dimensional comparison of man and Canvasback, then, may be shown as follows:

	Velocity (M.P.H.)	Travel Distance (Miles)	Altitude of Travel (Feet)	Breadth of Vision (Miles)
Man	4	20	5.5	6
Canvasback	60	300	82.5	24
Man	4	20	133.3	30
Canvasback	60	300	2,000	118

It is only fair, of course, to note that all Canvasback travel does not take place at 60 m.p.h. or at 2,000 feet, but we must apply the same four-dimensional examination for any speed or altitude if comparisons are to be valid. For example, if a head wind reduced the ground speed of the Canvasback to 30 m.p.h., the comparison would be:

	Velocity (M.P.H.)	Travel Distance (Miles)	Altitude of Travel (Feet)	Breadth of Vision (Miles)
Man	4	40	266.6	42
Canvasback	30	300	2,000	118

Although only the velocity has been changed for the Canvasback, the relative values of three other coordinates have thereby been altered for man; 40 miles are now to man as 300 to Canvasback, but the elevation of the eyes, in a fair comparison, is lifted to the 266.6 feet (as a man might travel at 4 m.p.h. in a helicopter), and the breadth of vision must be increased to 42 miles.

[*] "The formula for the distance, d, at which an object h feet above sea level is visible to an observer h' feet above sea level is approximately: $d = 1.317 \ (\sqrt{h} + \sqrt{h'})$ miles" (Griffin, 1940:65).

In a long migration, like the 3,000 miles from the Mackenzie Delta to the Gulf of Mexico, the relative values for man and Canvasback are:

	Velocity (M.P.H.)	Travel Distance (Miles)	Altitude of Travel (Feet)	Breadth of Vision (Miles)
Man................	4	200	133.3	30
Canvasback	60	3,000	2,000	118

Not all birds fly as high or as swiftly as waterfowl. In the Delta region, for example, blackbirds average 30 m.p.h. at approximately 200 feet, and in the table below a day's journey of 250 miles for a blackbird is compared with a man's walk:

	Velocity (M.P.H.)	Travel Distance (Miles)	Altitude of Travel (Feet)	Breadth of Vision (Miles)
Man................	4	33.3	27	14
Blackbird	30	250	200	38

The four dimensions of travel apply to all bird movement, but flight does not always have a relative advantage over walking. Some small birds, for example, are known to fly within three or four feet of the land or sea, and the Penguin migrates with its eyes at sea level.

The importance of the height and breadth of perception in travel is not always understood. At an elevation of 5½ feet, the eyes see a segment of earth, bounded by the horizon, that is slightly more than 6 miles in diameter. At an elevation of 2,000 feet the diameter between horizons is 118 miles. In terms of miles, the area encompassed by the horizon at 2,000 feet is nearly 20 times as wide as the circle of vision at 5½ feet. *But the relative size of this earth circle is the same at both (and at all) elevations.* The validity of this may be tested by pointing a finger at the horizon, which is always at eye level, regardless of altitude. No matter if one stands on the ground or in an airliner at 2,000 feet, the arc of vision between finger and feet is the same. The universe is divided into earth and sky at the horizon, and the proportion of the traveler's vision that includes the earth is constant regardless of his elevation, the relative size of the world remaining unchanged throughout travel.

We know, of course, that the higher one rises, the farther one sees. This extension of vision results from a relative shrinking of the earth's dimensions. As one goes up, the miles decrease in relative size as more miles come

The horizon is always at eye level.

into view. This phenomenon is so common to human experience that it needs no further elaboration except to emphasize the point that at higher elevations the eyes see farther because the relative values of the components of space become smaller. Thus all parts of the landscape — rivers, hills, fields, villages, and marshes — are seen in reduction as the eye climbs higher.

As the elevation of travel increases, the complexity of the visual field for the human air traveler undergoes little change, and, granting differences in acuity, I believe the same must hold for waterfowl. The details that concern the eye at ground level become reduced as the altitude is increased, and they are in the field of vision for a longer period of time. Flying at an elevation of 200 feet, one briefly sees individual trees standing out conspicuously, but at 2,000 feet each tree is lost in the arboreal pattern of the whole forest, which is viewed with leisure. This relativity of awareness was made clear to me in a flight with Robert H. Smith from The Pas, Manitoba, to Delta, in the "Grumman Widgeon" of the U.S. Fish and Wildlife Service. We left The Pas early on a bright August afternoon and followed the same course as taken by migrant waterfowl, southeast to the Delta Marsh. Coming down the maze of waterways of the Saskatchewan River, Bob flew at

200 feet, where we identified all species of ducks easily, as well as Crows, Coots, and Canada Jays. We could see the eyes of each Moose. Meadow and muskeg, spruce tree and waterfowl, were all perceived clearly. Awareness was of details within a limited landscape, each scene viewed for only an instant. We were lost, however, as regards exact geographical location. Bob then climbed to 2,000 feet, where we became precisely oriented. Now spruce trees were not seen individually; we were no longer aware of each duck, although there were many hundreds below. The plane drifted slowly over a world of green and blue, of forest and water, the patterns of which could be examined with leisure despite a ground speed of 120 m.p.h.

The cues or "landmarks" of aerial travel must be relative to height. In flying from The Pas to Delta at an altitude of 200 feet, there are perhaps a hundred or more key points in the landscape, identification of which is important to oriented travel. Miss two or three of these when flying low and the way is lost. At 2,000 feet, however, there are at most six landmarks that guide flight for the human pilot flying in reasonably good weather (Figure 22). Each new cue appears in the distance before the last one has receded from view behind, so that at this elevation the pilot is never beyond sight of such guiding features. It follows, then, that the number of cues required for memory is relative to the height of travel. It is much easier for the pilot to remember his way across Manitoba's lake country at 2,000 feet than at lower elevations. Were this not so, swift air travel would be impossible; no pilot (lacking instruments) could fly from Winnipeg to New Orleans if he had to obey as many cues to orientation as are followed by a man driving the same course in an automobile. Their behavior suggests that this same relation between height and landscape holds for ducks, for they precisely follow the patterns of creeks and channels, points and sloughs, in local movement at low altitude. In higher flights, these details, so important on the native area, are insignificant segments of the mosaic of the whole marsh, which the migrant, crossing at 2,000 feet, sees in its entirety as a single landmark along the way. I suspect that the cues to oriented travel about the Delta Marsh are no less numerous for the bird on its home range than are the landmarks required by a migrant during a day's journey at 2,000 feet.

The perceptual space of the traveler includes not only the surrounding world, but the sky above, with its sun, moon, and stars. These celestial bodies are so far from the eye that the traveler does not perceive them as

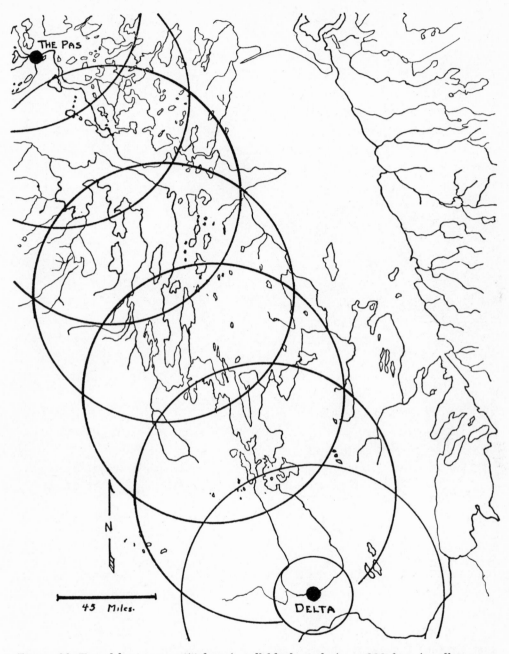

Figure 22. Travel horizons at 5½ feet (small black circles), at 200 feet (smallest open circle around Delta), and at 2,000 feet (largest circles). In clear weather no more than six landmarks would be required to guide the way from Delta to The Pas at 2,000 feet.

In local travel the sun serves as a compass. Both man and bird perceive it, like Joshua, as being relative to the earth and to time.

being relative to his movement. Instead, the sun, at any moment of travel, seems to move with the traveler at the same relative velocity. As the moments of travel become minutes and hours, however, the traveler (like Joshua) perceives the sun moving relative to the earth. It rises out of the east, crosses the sky in its arc, then disappears below the western horizon. When in view, the sun serves as a cue to compass direction regardless of its position in the sky. Moving about his home valley or along his village streets, man is guided by the familiar landscape; but as he travels

158

into strange places, the sun's function as a compass becomes ever more important. Kramer (1951, 1952) has shown how the sun functions as a compass for birds on the home range. With the sun as their only clue to direction in the experimental cages, Kramer's Starlings moved with a directional bias that held constant regardless of time of day. Without the sun, however, their movements were random, favoring no direction.

The daily change in the sun's position relative to earth and local time, the change by which the seasons ebb and flow, is too obvious and well known to merit discussion here. Let us merely recall that on any given day of the year, the position of the sun varies according to locality. A traveler who in autumn has moved several hundred miles toward the equator, for example, perceives that the sun rises at a steeper angle from the east, follows a higher arc across the sky, and drops more abruptly into the west. The interval between sunrise and sunset increases slightly, and the points where the sun strikes the horizon at sunrise and sunset approach more closely to due east and due west. Because of the more abrupt ascent to sunrise and the descent after sunset, the duration of twilight is shortened (Figure 23).

When a traveler moves across degrees of longitude, he perceives no change in the sun's arc and the length of day; but in eastward travel, sun-

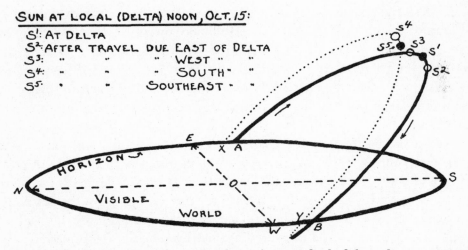

Figure 23. Travelers perceive changes in the sun's arc and schedule in direct proportion to the speed, distance, and direction of travel. A mid-October traveler going from Delta southeast to Lake Christina in one day would find the sun's arc higher (X–Y:A–B) and its position (S⁵) 12 minutes past zenith at Delta noon. From the dotted line it will be seen that the angle of descent becomes more abrupt as the traveler moves southward.

rise and sunset come earlier (relative to the time at home), and in westward movement, later. A traveler accustomed to breakfast at sunrise, dinner at high noon, and supper at sunset would find that if he went several
hundred miles due east overnight, the next day's sun would have topped
the horizon before breakfast, passed its noon peak by dinner time, and set
before supper. If he went west from home, breakfast would arrive before
sunrise, the stomach would call for its dinner before the sun had gained its
zenith, and supper would start with the sun still in the sky (Figure 23).

These changes in the sun are imperceptible, by men at least, in short
travels from home. It is only when they make long, swift journeys that they
are sensible of a change in the path of the sun relative to earth and time.
The sailor, with the wind behind his sails, was the first to understand how
sun position and schedule were related to his place in longitude and latitude. The Ancient Mariner observed, as his ship sailed southward:

> The sun came up upon the left
> Out of the sea came he!
> And he shone bright, and on the right
> Went down into the sea.
>
> Higher and higher every day
> Till over the mast at noon —

So it is, the sun serves man in two ways according to the distance and
velocity of travel. In short trips close to home, the sun is a cue to compass
direction. But if a man is lost, displaced from familiar surroundings, the
sun is not a guide to the direction home, even though it still serves as a
reference to north. A given direction may be followed, if the sun is in view;
but one must locate familiar surroundings before perceiving the direction
to home.

As a man goes farther, the change in the sun's position and schedule is
perceived; and awareness of this change is in direct proportion to the distance and velocity of movement. The farther and faster he goes, the more
keenly is he aware of the sun's changes relative to home. By the sun's arc,
one may tell whether he is north (arc lower) or south (arc higher) of
home. By its schedule, as measured against his clock or, more crudely, by
his metabolic stimuli, he must know the degree of his displacement east
(breakfast late by sun time) or west (breakfast early). By these cues a man,
suddenly shifted several hundred miles from his native range, might deduce
the direction home even when in unfamiliar surroundings.

Matthews (1951a, b; 1952; 1953a, b; 1955a, b)[*] and Kramer (1952, 1953) have shown in pigeons and (Matthews' studies) in several species of gull and shearwater that there is a pattern of orientation toward home when birds are given freedom in unfamiliar terrain. This direct orientation, Matthews demonstrated, functions only when the sun is in view, and Matthews has erected a hypothesis of sun navigation that hinges on the traveling bird's awareness of change in arc and schedule relative to arc and time at home. Moreover, with pigeons, Matthews (1955b:78) has shown how this ability to orient homeward from unfamiliar country varies according to the distance from home. At a distance of between 20 and 40 miles "there would seem to be a ring of country," Matthews observes, "in which birds would have no direct orientation and presumably have to fall back on random search methods. . . . Beyond 50 miles there is suggestive evidence that the accuracy of orientation increases with distance, though this is not so firmly established." This same "distance effect," as Matthews calls it, has puzzled other workers, like Wodzicki and Wojtusiak (1934) in a study of swallows, and Griffin (1943) in a study of terns and gulls. They noticed that birds released distantly tended to return home more rapidly than others set free in strange country within a shorter radius of home. This "distance effect" favors the idea of sun navigation. Although able to perceive direction from the sun on local range (like Kramer's caged Starlings), birds, like men, may have no awareness of the change of the sun arc relative to earth and time when close to home, and they must search for familiar surroundings if lost. But, so the evidence suggests, the farther birds travel from home, the more keen their awareness of the ever-increasing change of the sun's arc and schedule relative to home. Hence, we presume, the longer a bird's journey, the keener its awareness of the direction homeward even when displaced from familiar surroundings.

If birds are, indeed, able to navigate by the sun, as the pioneering studies of Matthews and Kramer suggest, and if awareness of the sun as a nagivational cue is directly proportionate to the distance and velocity of travel, then the swiftly flying Canvasback (traveling the 300 miles from Delta to Lake Christina in 5 hours) has in orienting itself a distinct advantage over a man on foot (walking 20 miles in 5 hours). Though for the purpose of an objective study of migration we may make comparisons based on the relative coordinates of travel, the additional element of sun-awareness, then,

[*] See Matthews (1955b) for the complete bibliography of Matthews and Kramer and for a discussion of sun navigation.

may give the migrating bird an advantage that the man going short distances on foot cannot even comprehend.

The sun, of course, is not always available for reference in travel. We know that some birds migrate through regions covered by cloud both by day and night, so that the success of migration may not hinge entirely on sun navigation. But from the evidence of Delta observations (mass migrations starting under clear sky), it appears that at the start, and at some periods during residence at the destination or at stopping places along the way, the sun is visible during segments of the long span of spring and fall migration and serves as a cue to the direction of home.

In summary, the discussion amounts to this: the distance of travel is relative to the height, breadth, and velocity of travel. We know this applies to our own human lives as between man on foot and man in an aircraft. Avian behavior suggests that this same relativity of motion applies to bird migration, but that distance is relative not only to height, breadth, and velocity of travel; problems of orientation and retentiveness are also relative to these coordinates. If the relativity of motion is applied to bird migration, the problems may be faced in a truly objective manner. A comparative examination makes it clear that the complexity of migrational orientation is not fairly judged by the miles of travel.

While the four coordinates of travel are always relative, men and birds may use the sun as a reference for compass direction in local travel, and as a reference for longitude and latitude in longer journeys. The traveler is cued by the arc and schedule of the sun and may appraise the general direction of home even when displaced from familiar surroundings. An awareness of the changes in the arc and schedule of the sun varies directly with the distance and velocity of travel; travelers moving swiftly over long distances could perceive these changes (hence their position relative to home) more keenly than those moving only short distances.

12

The Influence of Bad Weather

THERE persist some hallowed legends about migration carried from one generation to the next until by the authority of age they live unquestioned. One such is a belief that migrant birds are able to navigate through fog to their destinations. Lincoln (1950b) tells us that "we know that vision is not the sole reliance as some birds fly unerringly through the densest fog." He cites the observation of Cooke (1915), made when the latter was on a steamer "en route from Unalaska to Bogoslof Island in the Bering Sea, proceeding cautiously through fog so dense as to blot out all objects at a distance of 100 yards. About halfway across, flocks of murres, returning to their nests on Bogoslof, began to break through the wall of fog astern, fly parallel to the vessel and disappear into the mists ahead. The ship, with the aid of compass and chart, was headed directly toward the island, but its course was no more accurate than that followed by the birds."

Let us mark first that this was a *local* movement of sea birds in their native environment where they traveled from feeding grounds to nesting place. As they were within sight of the sea, their height was not more than 100 yards, while the breadth of travel was somewhat less than 200 yards. Unalaska is 60 miles from Bogoslof. The murres were encountered about halfway; hence their destination was 30 miles from the point where first seen. In fairness, as they came from behind, let us guess that the whole of their journey was at least 40 miles. If flying at about 40 miles an hour, their time on the wing would have been an hour. As such, the flight was comparable to a four-mile walk by a man through fog. While admittedly no "landmarks" were available to the murres, they started from their familiar feeding place toward the sexual goal at the nest and all the way were in sight of the water's surface, by which they might perceive velocity as well as wind drift. It is possible that there were ocean swells or waves, although the account does not tell about this; and when still some distance from their destination, the sound of bird voices and surf might aid navigation. Their objective was not a pinpoint of land, but a shoreline several miles broad which, when reached, could be followed to the nesting place. Perhaps these coordinates are not entirely accurate, but they are sufficiently in line to permit a more critical examination of this local travel. The object here is not to oversimplify such movements; the flight of murres through fog on their home range is indeed a complex performance. But it is not migration.

In spring the sky is sometimes clear over the Delta Marsh and the general weather situation ideal for migration, but over the ice-covered lake the blending of moist warm air and cold air brings a heavy fog. At such times I have seen ducks start out in migration, always to turn back upon striking the mist. When fog reigns at Delta, the passage of all species comes to a standstill. On the morning of April 27, 1951, Premier D. L. Campbell, Colonel Arthur Sullivan, and I, driving westward over the prairie from Winnipeg, saw many flocks of blackbirds and great numbers of Flickers flying northwest over the open country toward Lake Manitoba. When I left my companions at Portage la Prairie and drove north toward Delta, the migration was still so strong that I was never beyond sight of traveling birds. On reaching the south edge of the marsh, however, I came suddenly into a heavy fog that reduced visibility to a hundred yards. Near the north edge I saw a Flicker perched on a roadside telephone pole and I stopped to frighten it. At this point the road angled to the northwest and the Flicker launched north into the gray void. Just as it was about to disappear from my sight, it turned west to the road, where it alighted on another pole. The same performance was repeated, but the third time the bird gained sight of the ridge and flew on to the trees.

At Delta I found Flickers everywhere, perched singly or in clusters in maple and willow. When flushed, a bird moved only fifty or sixty yards to alight again. Many Robins and blackbirds were also sitting quietly in the trees. Peter Ward said that the visibility had been good in the early morning and that there had been no Flickers or other migrants on the ridge at 8:30 A.M. A strong passage had reached Delta about 9:00 A.M., but the flight stopped when the heavy fog had closed in soon after. All these birds remained stationary until the fog lifted in the afternoon, whereupon migration was resumed.

Fog brings migration to an abrupt stop, although local birds may fly about
their familiar home ranges except in the heaviest mist.

Though the migrants remained immobile this foggy morning, there was
some movement of local birds about the home range. Franklin's Gulls, which
had become established at Delta, were on the wing in small numbers,
always within sight of the marsh. Local waterfowl took flight at my approach, and a pair of nesting Crows flew back and forth between two clumps
of trees which were separated beyond the range of human visibility. In
short, local movements may continue except in the densest fog, but the
migrant delays its journey until the weather clears.

Trautman (1940:96), who watched the migrations so faithfully at Buckeye Lake, says that "the one climatic condition which caused birds to alight
was fog. Geese are apparently greatly disturbed or incapacitated for migration by fogs, and when a fog occurred as the main flight was passing through
the area, many of the birds were forced to earth. A notable example of this
occurred on the night of October 21–22, 1925. A mammoth flight of geese
was caught in a fog which apparently forced many or possibly all of the
birds to alight. On the morning of October 22, individuals and groups of
confused geese were scattered over eastern Ohio. Many had alighted in
cities, where some of the more bewildered ones were found wandering about
the streets, in the ponds of the city parks, and upon the roofs of buildings.
Various observers estimated that the Buckeye Lake area had between five
hundred and five thousand individuals. The geese remained in the area until

165

about 9:00 A.M. on October 22, when the fog disappeared, and they left. While in the area at least thirty, all Canada Geese, were shot by sportsmen. The flight consisted primarily of Canada Geese with some Blue Geese and a few Snow Geese."

Audubon (1840) said that when Canada Geese "are slowly advancing from south to north at an early period of the season, they fly much lower, alight more frequently, and are more likely to be bewildered by suddenly formed banks of fog, or by passing over cities or arms of the sea, where much shipping may be in sight. On such occasions great consternation prevails among them, they crowd together in a confused manner, wheel irregularly, and utter a constant cackling resembling the sounds from a disconcerted mob. Sometimes the flock separates, some individuals leave the rest, proceed in a direction contrary to that in which they came, and after awhile, as if confused, sail toward the ground, once alighted on which they appear to become almost stupefied, so as to suffer themselves to be shot with ease, or even knocked down with sticks. Heavy snowstorms also cause them great distress, and in the midst of them some have been known to fly against beacons and lighthouses, dashing their heads against the walls in the middle of the day. In the night they are attracted by the lights of these buildings, and now and then a whole flock is caught on such occasions."

Mr. J. H. Yerex, of Clair, Saskatchewan, reports * a weather accident described to him by a farmer friend, Don Knox. "We had a week of very foggy weather Nov. 12 to 18 and the trees and fields of stubble were coated with hoar-frost. The sun was hidden for days and at times it was difficult to see more than ten feet ahead in daytime. On the evening of the 15th Mr. Knox decided it would be a good time to burn an old straw stack, so set it afire about 7:30 P.M. Next morning as he was driving along the road, he noticed a few dead ducks scattered here and there but thought little about them as ducks often strike the telephone lines and kill themselves, but a little later he noticed something unusual going on in his stubble field and went over to investigate. Mr. Knox was amazed to find hundreds of dead and dying ducks, some with smashed bodies, some with broken legs and wings, and others less seriously injured but apparently dazed and unable to navigate properly. The stubble was so tall and heavily frosted that unharmed birds could not take off, but when they were lifted out of the stubble and thrown into the air, they were able to continue their flight southward. . . . The ducks were identified as Lesser Scaups, the bluebill

* In "Chickadee Notes," by A. G. Lawrence, *Winnipeg Free Press*, December 15, 1944.

of the sportsmen. Mr. Knox carefully estimated the loss and figures between five and six thousand ducks perished."

Warrant Officer Clayton Baldwin, of No. 8 Repair Depot, Winnipeg, writes: "In the fall of 1943, while I was stationed at No. 12 S.F.T.S. at Brandon, a similar duck disaster occurred. A heavy ground fog had settled over the area and aircraft were grounded. In the morning, as airmen proceeded to work, ducks, mostly Lesser Scaups, with I believe a sprinkling of other diving ducks, were found dead, dazed or haphazardly wandering around the Station roads. The Station is at all times brightly lit up and in this instance the ducks, in all probability flying very low, piled into hangers (which extended from east to west), and those striking head on killed themselves while the others were more fortunate." *

Such accidents happen in the spring as well, and a passage of diving ducks meeting fog after dark on April 28, 1955, dashed into buildings, trees, and wires at McCreary, Manitoba. Some of these were shown to me by Game Guardian A. M. Lundy: Redhead, Canvasback, Lesser Scaup, and Greater Scaup, most of them terribly smashed, but two of the scaup with only their wings broken.

A different kind of tragedy overtook migrating Whistling Swans, Canada Geese, and ducks in Clarke and Dunn counties, Wisconsin, in early April 1954. These travelers encountered torrential rains and hail: many were killed, some apparently by hail while they were still awing; and waterfowl were found dead far and wide over the countryside after the storm. At least thirty-five dead Whistling Swans were retrieved for examination by the Wisconsin Conservation Department. "The inspection shows definitely that they met violent deaths," said Cy Kabat, Chief of Wildlife Research for the Conservation Department. "They had broken necks, burst livers and hearts, lung hemorrhages and many bruises all over their bodies and heads where they evidently had been pelted by big hailstones. We'd guess from what we know that the hail caught them up high—very high." †

The meteorological factors responsible for the icing of airplane wings, a severe hazard to human flight, may also act upon birds. Dr. William G. Sheldon (letter) says that near "Quincy, Massachusetts, I was attracted at dusk by the chatter of hundreds of Starlings. These birds were scattered about the ground close to the south shore of Boston Harbor. Approaching them, I found they had lost the power of flight and were easily caught by

* "Chickadee Notes," *Winnipeg Free Press*, January 2, 1945.
† News story by Gordon MacQuarrie, *Milwaukee Journal*, April 23, 1954.

hand. Although there was no precipitation, the birds' feathers were heavily iced. Apparently they had been flying at a higher altitude where there was sufficient moisture to cause icing."

By and large, most of us think of birds in migration as invincible (except at lighthouses), like the Persian messengers of Herodotus for whom "neither snow, nor rain, nor heat, nor darkness, are permitted to obstruct their speed." One or two more examples of tragedy in other species will emphasize the everlasting threat of weather. Roberts (1932:446) tells the fate of migrating Lapland Longspurs on the night of March 13–14, 1904, which "was very dark but not cold, and a heavy, wet snow was falling with but little wind stirring. Migrating Longspurs came from the Iowa prairies in a vast horde, and from 11 P.M. until morning, incredible numbers met their deaths in and about villages by flying against buildings, electric light poles and wires, and by dashing themselves forcibly onto the frozen ground and ice." In Worthington, Minnesota, an attempt was made to compute the numbers lying dead on two lakes with an aggregate area of about two square miles. "A conservative estimate showed that there were at least 750,000 dead Longspurs lying on the two lakes alone!" The total area on which dead migrants were found covered approximately 1,500 square miles.

In Nevada, Cottam (1929:80) describes a "shower of grebes." "During an early morning hour (about 2 A.M.) of December 13, 1928, residents of Caliente, Nevada, were awakened by a heavy thumping of something falling on the roofs of their houses. Those who were curious enough to step outside and investigate the unusual occurrence found scores of water birds in the new fallen snow. The next morning, several thousand Eared Grebes were found on the ground and on flat roofs of business houses throughout the city." Mr. E. C. D. Marriage, of Caliente, wrote Cottam that "literally thousands of these birds were found in every portion of the town and outskirts . . . they were forced out of the air by the heavy density of the snow . . . Caliente had the main bunch, but they were scattered for twenty miles every way." Several hundred grebes dropped in the streets of Enterprise, Utah, about forty-five miles east and north of Caliente, and several hundred more were found in the snow at Uvada and Modena, Utah. "The evening of December 12," says Cottam, "the air was comparatively warm and still. By midnight a general and heavy snowstorm set in. The birds appeared to be in large flocks and were probably following the Meadow Valley Wash on their way to the Pacific Coast of southern California or to some inland lake near there."

In all these catastrophes the migrants probably started out in fair weather, but moving faster than the weather itself, they overtook storm. Once the flight is started, the members of mass migrations seem compelled to continue on, as if set for a journey of a certain time and length, not to be cut short by storm. Even where they might stop, as at Delta, they often continue their flight. The local birds, as we have seen, do not join these travelers passing over in storm, and I have never known mass migrations to leave Delta except under fair sky.

On their local range, ducks prefer not to fly in the rain, and a rainy day is generally a poor one for gunning. A very heavy influx of ducks, mostly Blue-winged Teal and Baldpate, arrived at Delta during a torrential downpour in the late afternoon of September 28, 1954; and then, as these new arrivals scurried about in search of a resting place, the few wet gunners on the marsh had fine gunning and bags were filled quickly.

The gyrations of migrants reaching Delta in storm or under heavy cloud overcast, suggest that the sun or the sun's light (such as the glow of sunset) may be important by way of directional reorientation; but we know that birds do carry on into weather situations in which there is no possibility of their gaining directional cues from any celestial source. It likewise holds that migrants may and do travel over cloud, so that they have no reference to terrestial cues. On the evening of October 17, 1952, Trans Canada Airlines personnel reported Blue and Lesser Snow Geese migrating heavily over North Bay, Ontario, the birds coming from the direction of James Bay and traveling south. Mr. K. R. Esselmont, T.C.A. Station Manager at North Bay, writes (letter) that the geese "were first spotted by the Department of Transport Met. Observer on duty, who saw them approach from the northeast, flying in a southerly direction. There were three separate flocks at intervals of perhaps 5 to 10 minutes. The weather was clear from our station north, and the overcast, consisting of alto cumulus, began just over head and extended south. The first flock, estimated at close to 200, approached the station in formation and immediately above they broke formation, flying in all directions, then reassembling just prior to entering the overcast, estimated at 8,000 feet. This first group was not seen again. The second and third groups, not so large in numbers, reacted in the same manner in that, directly over the station, they broke formation and then reassembled. Both these flocks, however, remained below the overcast. There were two notams on the DOT teletype advising that geese were flying at

6,000 to 8,000 feet. These were considered necessary because an RCAF Mitchell Bomber flew into a flock, damaging the aircraft."

This is a part of a migration which Cooch (1955) traced in nonstop flight from James Bay, Ontario, to Louisiana, a 1,700 mile trip which consumed about 60 hours. Those electing to go above the overcast would be aware of the direction and velocity of their travel by reference to the cloud below. In short trips over cloud, the course of travel would not be greatly altered; but if they went many miles with cloud as reference, the birds must become geographically displaced because the clouds themselves are moving. In this instance the weather records show that the sky was clear over Ohio and Lake Erie, so that the geese had not more than 200 miles of cloud ahead.

Captain Earl D. Sherman, T.C.A. pilot, tells me that several times he has observed geese flying above cloud and that late in 1952 a companion pilot, Captain Don Patry, saw thirteen or fourteen Canada Geese flying south at an elevation of 7,000 feet between cloud layers near North Bay, Ontario. In this case clear sky was in sight to the north, but not to the south. R. C. Hanson, of the U.S. Fish and Wildlife Service, wrote me that at about 10 A.M. on March 12, 1953, he saw Mallards and Pintails migrating over a layer of cloud that was 300 feet above the ground at the bottom and 1,000 feet above at the top. The ducks were flying northwest up the Mississippi Valley between Burlington and Muscatine, Iowa. Alvin P. Noltemaier, also of the Fish and Wildlife Service, has told me that in the process of herding Canada Geese away from concentration areas with an aircraft, he has seen them rise to disappear into the overcast above.

Such abundant evidence of above-cloud travel makes it clear that waterfowl do at times migrate without visual reference to the earth and that, as in the observation of Captain Patry, they may move between cloud layers without reference to either earthly or celestial guides. We must not conclude from this, however, that such individuals are possessed of the ability to navigate precisely overland without reference to it. If the birds moved with the weather, as is usual in migration, their displacement by movement relative to cloud might not be great. But migration, we know, does not always carry the travelers unerringly to their destinations, and above-cloud passage may be one cause of displaced migrants.

Though both spring and fall migrations of waterfowl generally occur with a favoring wind, they do not always do so. The Lesser Snow and Blue Geese, going to the northeast, are often seen migrating with a cross wind at the same time that many other migrants are traveling northwest with the southeast wind on their tails. I have seen both ducks and geese flying against winds of fifteen to twenty miles an hour. At such times the slower-flying passerines generally remain grounded, but I have watched Crows and blackbirds migrating against winds of such velocity as to make their ground speed almost nil.

On April 15, 1954, with Aldo Missio, Weather Forecaster for the R.C.A.F. MacDonald Weather Station, I departed by car at 10 A.M., going northwest to Minnedosa, Manitoba. Missio, who had just left his weather charts, advised me of the approach of a cold front from the northwest; and, indeed, we could see the long line of cloud ahead that marked the edge of the front. The wind was from the northwest at about 20 m.p.h. A dozen Red-tailed Hawks, three flocks of blackbirds, and one flock of Golden Plover were seen migrating to the northwest between Macdonald and Neepawa, where we met the front at 11:30 A.M. There was a sudden drop in temperature from 45° to 30° F., a rise in wind velocity to 35–40 m.p.h., reaching 45 m.p.h. in gusts, with light snow flurries. These conditions of wind and temperature remained the same all afternoon till dusk. After the front had passed, we noticed much more activity among blackbirds, Crows, and hawks. In some this seemed restlessness, as in the blackbirds that rose from a field, settled, then rose, flying around the brow of a hill, settled again, only to take wing once more. This restlessness soon resolved into a migration into the northwest; and as we ranged about the rolling country south of Minnedosa from noon until 3 P.M. there was a light but steady passage of Red-tailed Hawks, blackbirds, Crows, and a few Robins. The hawks were lower than we usually see them; they seemed to take advantage of hills and bluffs of trees, and often were seen to make their greatest headway against the wind in long dives, by which they gained speed as they lost altitude. The recorded velocity of the wind was greater than the ground speed of blackbirds, Crows, or Robins; and yet they gained ground against the wind by flying close to the earth, sometimes only a foot or two high, swinging behind clumps of trees, around hills and up gullies, reaching an objective, such as a group of trees, then stopping briefly, only to start on again. Their movements, however roundabout, always carried them into the northwest. Waterfowl were seen flying to sheltered situations, but none migrated.

It is not always possible, of course, to judge the relation of wind to migration. On April 13, 1954, there was a grand arrival of waterfowl from the south and southeast from 7 A.M. until noon, the birds reaching Delta at elevations estimated at 1,000 to 1,500 feet. Throughout the morning we were aware of a steady flow of wind from the northwest at about 10 m.p.h.; and yet the weather records of Macdonald, Manitoba, close by, showed that at the elevation the birds traveled, the wind was from the southeast.

Birds migrate higher with the wind behind than with the wind in face, just as in local travel (Deelder and Tinbergen, 1947). It is agreed that ground friction may reduce the wind near the earth so that in facing the weather, it is an advantage for the traveler to fly low. I'm sure, however, that this is not the whole story. I believe that the apparent ground flow has something to do with the elevation of travel. For example, at an air speed of 45 m.p.h., the bird with a tail wind of 15 m.p.h. has an awareness of ground flow at an elevation of 2,000 feet that is precisely the same as that of a bird at 1,000 feet moving at the same air speed against a 15 m.p.h. wind. This relativity of awareness may establish the height of the "ceiling" of migratory flights, for a bird may rise to elevations (as transcontinental air passengers know) where there is virtually no perception of ground flow, no awareness of velocity or wind drift. In this respect we note that, with the exception of soaring species, the slow fliers, like blackbirds, Crows, and Flickers, migrate much closer to the ground than swift fliers, like waterfowl and shore birds.

Weather favorable for diurnal travelers is good for night migrants, and often, after a heavy daytime passage of blackbirds, Flickers, and others at Delta, the night sky is alive with the voices of those species that choose to make their way homeward in darkness. Lincoln (1950a:29) has pointed out, as is evident to all who have taken night passage by plane, that "the nights are rarely so dark that all terrestrial objects are totally obscured, and such features as coastlines and rivers are just those that are most likely to be seen in the faintest light, particularly by the acute vision of the bird and its aerial points of observation." At Delta most waterfowl migration, spring and fall, begins late in the day. In spring, twilight lingers so long after sunset on the northern prairies that in late April and early May there is only a short period when there is not a sunglow in the sky. In autumn, however, ducks departing close to sundown strike complete darkness before they are long on their way.

Lowery (1951) has developed a program for plotting the night migrations of birds by watching their movements against the moon with telescopes. Moon-watching has been followed for years, but this work brings new techniques for recording and interpreting such observations. This type

172

Nights are rarely so dark that terrestrial objects
are totally obscured.

of study, of course, is limited to fine weather and to periods of the moon.
Lowery reports that "night migrants fly singly more often than in flocks,
creating a remarkably uniform dispersion on a local scale, quite unlike the
scattered distributions observable in the daytime." All our evidence for
ducks, geese, and swans, however, suggests that they hold their flock formations after nightfall, and that mass movements of flocks remain cohesive
after dark. There are many species which, like the Coot, travel singly; but
these individual birds, nevertheless, make up aggregations of migrants that
apparently fly within hearing distance of one another. The Nevada catastrophe of grebes testifies to the grand formations of night migrants; and
once at Ithaca, New York, during an autumn dawn, I saw an armada of
Common Loons coming out of the north, a loose formation of birds that

173

passed for half an hour, a vast aggregation that surely must have traveled so through the night from some distant starting place in Canada.

By the voices overhead, the contact calls of passerines, I have marked the migrations of small birds over Delta on spring evenings when there was no moon and the dark overcast obscured all sunglow in the northwest. I believe such birds turn west, judging by the drift of their voices, and, like the daytime travelers, they must be visually aware of the lakeshore to make this shift. On the evening of April 30, 1951, the moon (but not its glow) was hidden by an overcast that produced a fine drizzle of rain. It seemed a poor night for passage, yet not long after twilight had failed, there developed a heavy Coot migration, made evident by the flight calls of the travelers. I climbed to the observation platform of the Kirchoffer Lodge, where my eyes, at twenty-five feet, probably were about one-quarter as high as those of the migrating Coots. From that vantage point, despite the overcast and the rain, I could see the road four hundred yards away, and such details as individual trees and buildings were visible more than half a mile beyond. The south edge of Cadham Bay, two miles distant, was clearly outlined, and I could see bluffs of trees and the horizon. Many of these Coots apparently were arriving at Delta from the south; when they reached the lakeshore they were heard turning back, then alighting on the marsh.

One October evening, about two hours after dark and in the midst of a driving snowstorm, I heard a flock of small birds, by their voices Snow Buntings, fly past apparently a few yards above the trees. I cannot believe this could have been an oriented flight. Another night, jet with overcast and lack of moon, I was brought out of doors by the yelp of Richardson's Geese flying very low. Soon their voices told me that they had alighted on the lake not far from the lights of the village store. The Snow Buntings in the snowstorm, the geese in pitch darkness, represent movements such as are all too often considered to be oriented travel; yet the "note" sections of the ornithological journals in almost every issue carry reports of "accidentals," misplaced birds that have turned up far from their regular beats to delight the bird-watcher and send him quickly to print with his discovery. "Hold-ups, side-slips into cul-de-sac, losses of contact will happen. The birds that settle on the rigging of a ship miles out at sea; fog-bound stragglers around a light-house; storm-driven seabirds inland; exhausted migrants dropping in — all these are evidence of this. These are the unfortunates, the lost, the grim reminders of the perils and the cost . . ." (Ennion, 1943:63).

Whereas we note such regularities in waterfowl migration as the mid-

August departure of Pintail drakes, the mid-October travel of Canvasback and Redhead from the prairies, and the freeze-up passage of Mallard and Lesser Scaup, every hunter on the southern ranges knows that some years waterfowl do not come in their regular volume or at their usual time. In spring, too, there are years when the homeward passage is many days later than normal.

Major changes in the weather will alter the time, the place, and the volume of migration. During periods of drought, main flights of birds may shift to country more abundantly watered, and an unseasonably wet year may bring concentrations of ducks unusual to a certain region. In 1946 and 1947 there were heavy flights of White-fronted Geese through central Manitoba where the species had been uncommon. Hunters farther west in Saskatchewan, where the region was drier than usual, reported below-normal flights of white-fronts. In 1940 winds blew steadily from the southeast at Delta throughout late September and early October. Arrivals from the north during this period were so few that the success of the local hunters was greatly reduced and the small bag was the outstanding feature of the season. In 1943 south wind was unrelenting during the middle of October when the Canvasback and Redhead generally leave Delta, and these species were common until the twenty-second, when the wind abated and the birds moved southward.

Flights may be deflected by bad weather, as in 1949, when there was almost no spring migration through Delta, but at the Lower Souris Refuge, in North Dakota, there was a heavy passage. McCreary (1934) tells how a change in the normal pattern of winds caused a major shift in the spring movement of migrants, mostly small birds, in Wyoming. In England, Clarke (1912) observed that migration from Scandinavia was blocked by northwest wind, but winds from the southeast were followed by heavy migration. Over land the direction of migration may follow leading lines, such as rivers or shorelines or mountain ranges, hence continue its normal course despite adverse winds. Williamson (1952), however, considers that birds at sea, especially at night, are far less able to adjust for their wind drift, and then overseas movements may drift far from the regular course.

After the 1954 avalanche of spring migrants, April 8 to April 10 (see above, p. 119), the weather in Manitoba was dominated by the Polar Continental air mass, with a strong high-pressure area in northern Canada and a stationary Arctic front that held its mean position through the northern part of Lake Manitoba from April 10 to April 17. Then, for the balance of the month and until May 4, it moved well south of Delta. On May 4 the front retreated rapidly northward, and on the following days the Arctic air was pushed beyond the northern boundary of Manitoba. Between April 10 and May 4 there was very little migration of waterfowl or other birds northward from Delta. There were some massive arrivals from the south, as on the morning of April 13; and there were times when scattered flocks, especially of hawks, blackbirds, and Crows, were seen moving northwest against hard winds. But the whole period was one when there were no great movements of any kind away from Delta, when scattered travelers were seen only in small numbers. Through this period of Arctic air dominance, there was much north wind; the weather was stormy, with occasional rain and snow squalls. But there were also fine days of blue sky, rising temperatures, and little or no wind. During such fair periods we watched for a northward movement of ducks, but none passed through. Waterfowl remained in their great concentrations on the marsh and on the flooded fields in such numbers and so much later than usual that it was the subject of much comment by local farmers and sportsmen. With the retreat of the Arctic air on May 4, however, there began an avalanche of northbound waterfowl and many other travelers, the first heavy passage we had seen since April 9.

What did these waterfowl perceive in the weather that inhibited their northward travel during the fine days between April 10 and May 4? Had they gone north of Delta in April, they would soon have reached country still in the grip of frost. Surely on April's bright days they must have been aware of some subtile character in the local weather that discouraged their migration into the frigid region beyond.

"Treacherous in calm, and terrible in storm,
Who shall put forth on thee,
Unfathomable Sea?"   Percy Bysshe Shelley

13

Overseas Migration

Iт is one thing to measure the flight of a duck from Delta, Manitoba, to Lake Christina, Minnesota, and yet quite another to appraise the migration of Pintail, Shoveller, and other waterfowl from North America to the Hawaiian Islands. The shortest distance to the first landfall is at least 2,000 miles over the unbroken ocean, a passage equal to a flight from Delta to central Mexico. The first step in studying such overseas migrations is to quantify the flight distance in terms relative to the movement of man, the puzzled observer. In doing this it is only fair to use the most conservative combination of travel coordinates. Canvasback and other ducks have been seen migrating overland at Delta at ground speeds of 60 miles per hour, and faster; but on the open Pacific, Buss (1946) timed Pintails at approximately 33 m.p.h. At this rate of travel Pintails might cover the 2,000 miles from the Aleutians to the Hawaiian Islands in 60 hours of flight, which in relative terms is comparable to a journey of 240 miles for a man going at a speed of 4 m.p.h. (Figure 24).

The Hawaiian Archipelago, as Griffin and Hock (1949) point out, spreads over 1,600 miles of the Pacific, from Hawaii to Midway, while the knot of major islands is about 400 miles across. It is thus obvious that migrants are not obliged to navigate precisely to a pinpoint in the middle of the vast Pacific. Wide errors in course could be allowed and still permit a landfall upon one part or another of the archipelago, from which travel to the exact place of previous experience might be made over much lesser stretches of open water. With relative values of height and breadth of travel not differing greatly for man and bird, the problem fairly stated is directly comparable to that involved in a man's journey at 4 m.p.h. going 240 miles toward a region that has a total width of about 190 miles.

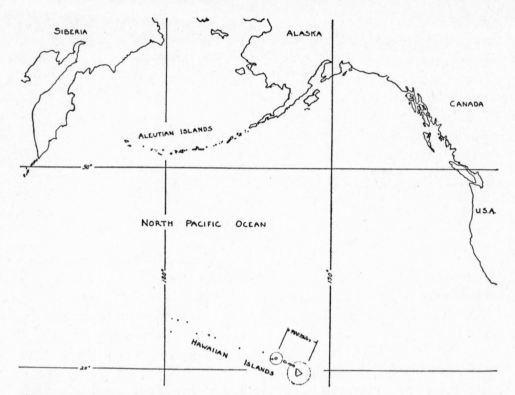

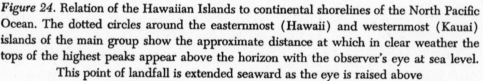

Figure 24. Relation of the Hawaiian Islands to continental shorelines of the North Pacific Ocean. The dotted circles around the easternmost (Hawaii) and westernmost (Kauai) islands of the main group show the approximate distance at which in clear weather the tops of the highest peaks appear above the horizon with the observer's eye at sea level. This point of landfall is extended seaward as the eye is raised above sea level and as cloud caps rise above the mountains.

Not only is the archipelago broad; the major islands are mountainous. On Hawaii, at the eastern edge of the group, are Mauna Loa, rising 13,675 feet, and Mauna Kea, 13,825 feet above the sea. In good weather the top of Mauna Kea is to be seen more than 100 miles to sea, extending the width of the landfall by so much. On the west the mountains of Kauai rise to above 5,000 feet, extending the fair-weather landfall at least 60 miles in that direction. The peaks of islands between lessen the possibility of travelers passing through without sighting land. To be sure, the sight of the peaks is not a constant aid to navigation, and, indeed, especially in the northwest, heavy cloud and rain obscure the islands for long periods of time. The rain, however, comes from the moist air striking the mountains; hence the clouds

178

themselves give evidence of land. J. Donald Smith, who traveled about the archipelago a great deal in his light aircraft, writes me that "Kauai Island, the northernmost of the main islands, is covered by clouds at one point most of the year. In fact, Mt. Waielele is supposed to be the wettest spot on earth. I have no idea how far this can been seen, but I have noted the cloud cover of Kauai from a distance of 100 miles when flying at 3,000 feet. I would not consider it reliable for precise navigation, but usable as a general indicator of land."

In long overseas journeys there is no physical advantage to be gained by high-altitude flying, and it seems to hold for waterfowl as well as for many other sea travelers that passages are made at low elevations. The Mallards and Pintails that Buss observed were 150 to 200 feet above the water; and since his original observation, he writes (letter) that he has watched the ocean travel of many more ducks on the open Pacific and their flights have always been below 400 feet. J. Donald Smith has written me of a flock of about two hundred and fifty Pintails which he watched depart in northward migration from Oahu, in January 1951. The birds, bunched and swimming nervously in close formation, "arose in a mass, circled the pond once, and took out over the ocean which is separated from the pond only by a beach ridge. They established a north course and continued on it until I lost them from sight. They flew just above the water and sometimes disappeared from sight in the trough." Yocom (1947) presents an interesting account of Pintails on the Pacific, and, while he does not give the actual elevations of the birds, they apparently were flying much lower than is the rule for overland migrations.

In their trans-Pacific migrations, then, waterfowl sometimes, perhaps usually, travel slower and lower than is their custom when moving over land; but even so, we seriously distort the problem by stating it in terms of absolute miles. The application of the relativity of motion to such passages renders the long overseas journeys somewhat less amazing, as the complexities are appraised by the mind of the human observer.

Besides distance, of course, directional cues are an aspect of the mystery of overseas migration. What do these birds follow as guides to orientation in a perceptual space that holds only sky and water? Many writers on bird navigation have considered the sea to be "trackless," without "landmarks"; and their readers, often without ocean experience, are easily led to accept this point uncritically. "The sea has no landmarks," so the reasoning goes; "hence birds must have some yet unknown sense that guides them over the

179

trackless monotony." Yeagley (1947) concluded that "since there are no 'sign posts' of any kind over the ocean wastes, the flights must involve true navigation."

Yet, however monotonous the seascape, every sailor knows that the ocean is not wholly a region of sameness. Some of its variations, as where currents meet, are nearly as stable and well marked as geologic formations on land. There are differences in color, salinity, air and water temperatures, plant and animal life, all to be perceived. There is a vast array of evidence to show how the birds of the sea are aware of these variations even when they are many miles beyond sight of shore. Murphy (1936:81) shows how "currents affect every sort of life in at least the upper layers and, in turn, exercise large control over the numbers and distribution of sea birds." Miller (1940) tells how the Blackfooted Albatross off the coast of California concentrates its numbers over a cold "tongue" of ocean, apparently attracted there by the abundant food. Carson (1951) describes the response of some birds to the movements of fish or plankton. "Capelin gather in the deep, cold waters of the Barents Sea, their shoals followed and preyed upon by flocks of auks, fulmars and kitiwicks . . . Out over the plankton meadows of the North Atlantic the dry twitter of phalaropes, small brown birds, wheeling and turning, dipping and rising, is heard for the first time since early spring. The phalaropes have nested on the arctic tundras, reared their young, and now the first of them are returning to the sea. Most of them will continue south over the open water far from land, crossing the equator into the South Atlantic. Here they will follow where the whales lead, for where the whales are, there also are swarms of plankton on which these strange birds grow fat."

The border of the Gulf Stream is obvious to the most casual eye; the water is drab green on one side, richly blue on the other. "The dark blue water of the open sea far from land is the color of emptiness and barrenness," writes Carson (1951); "the green water of the coastal areas, with all its varying hues, is the color of life. The sea is blue because the sunlight is reflected back to our eyes from the water molecules or from very minute particles suspended in the sea. In the journey of the light rays downward into the water and back to our eyes, all the red rays of the spectrum and most of the yellow have been absorbed, so it is chiefly the cool, blue light that we see. Where the water is rich in plankton, it loses the glassy transparency that permits this deep penetration of the light rays. The yellow and brown and green hues of the coastal waters are derived from the minute algae and other micro-organisms so abundant there. Seasonal abundance of certain forms containing reddish or brown pigments may cause the 'red water' known from ancient time in many parts of the world, and so common is this condition in some enclosed seas that they owe their names to it — the Red Sea and the Vermilion Sea are examples. The colors of the sea are only the indirect signs of the presence or absence of conditions needed to support the surface life; other zones, invisible to the eye, are the ones that largely determine where marine creatures may live. For the sea is by no means a uniform solution of water; parts of it are more salty than others, and parts are warmer or colder . . . And whenever two currents meet, especially if they differ sharply in temperature or salinity, there are zones of great turbulence and unrest, with water sinking or rising up from the depth and with shifting eddies and foam lines on the surface. At such places the richness and abundance of marine life reveals itself most strikingly."

Brooks (1934) says that when one's ship comes "within a few degrees of the equator the scattered cumulus clouds become thicker and grayer, a confused swell makes up, rain squalls come and go, and birds appear. At first there is only a greater abundance of storm petrels, with here and there petrels of other kinds hunting along utterly indifferent to the ship, or small groups of tropic birds flying along with the ship, off to one side or overhead. Then scattered groups of various petrels appear, and finally for an hour or two there are birds on every hand. If one is not too far from land, a few hundred miles perhaps, as in the case of the south equatorial drift north of the Marquesas, one may also see multitudes of sooty or crested terns. Occasionally one sees the grayish blue form of a shark gliding along, or a big purplish-brown hammerhead lazily twisting around as though trying to get a better view of the ship. Flying fish, while not so closely localized as the birds, are breaking the water every few seconds, and bewitch the beholder by their myriad sizes, shapes and antics, and their bewildering patterns and shades of deep brown, opal blue, yellow and purple. Then the sun comes out again, the sea takes on its deep tropical blue, the birds become more and more scarce and gradually, as the ship moves on, the ocean resumes its desert aspect . . . In the North Atlantic ship lanes the same play is staged with different actors. Instead of the equatorial currents there are the Gulf Stream and its continuation, the North Atlantic Drift, and the Arctic Current; instead of confused swells and squalls of rain there are slicks and fogs. Tropic-birds are replaced by jaegers and skuas; and different species of the petrel group, usually here spoken of as shearwaters and fulmars, are flying or swimming about, often in great flocks . . . One may pass from the blue water of the Stream, with floating gulf weed (Sargassum), and perhaps here and there the iridescent float of a Portuguese man-of-war, into the gray-green water of the Arctic Current with its thousands of jelly fish, and in a few hours back again into the Stream. Each time, at the margin, one is likely to see the surface display of that great abundance of life which has made the Grand Banks one of the great fisheries of the world."

Preston (1949) points to cloud formations as being constant during some periods of the year, hence possible cues to ocean travelers. He utters "a word of warning against the assumption that the ocean is featureless, merely because it is so shown on a map." Since we men do perceive some of this variety in the oceanic world, it is within reason to believe that the bird, so much closer to its wild environment, is aware of these things. Sutton (1934) speaks of the "Sheenah-cloud" of the North, "a gray cloud that gathers over open water at the ice-edge." This is a guide to the native Eskimo; it might be a cue for birds. Wetmore (1926) points out that the green lagoon water of reefed atolls throws a reflection high above that may be visible before the land itself is seen. Heyerdahl (1950) likewise speaks of this, saying that "as the sun rose straight up over the sky astern of us we could see a clear green glimmer high up towards the misty sky over the island. It was the reflection of the still, green lagoon on the inside of the surrounding reef. Some of the low atolls throw up mirages of this kind for many thousand feet into the air, so that they show their position to primitive seafarers many days before the island itself is visible from the horizon."

Heyerdahl also writes of the island cloud cap which identifies land long before it is seen. "With each day that passed, larger flocks of sea birds came and circled over us aimlessly in all directions. One evening, when the sun was about to sink into the sea, we noticed that the birds had received a violent impetus. They were flying away in a westerly direction without paying any attention to us or the flying fish beneath them. From the mast we

could see that, as they came over, they flew straight on exactly the same course . . . We twisted the steering gear and set our course exactly in the direction in which the birds had disappeared. Even after it was dark, we heard the cries of stragglers flying over us against the starry sky on the same course as that which we were following . . . Next day there were still more birds over us, but we did not wait for them to show us our way again in the evening. This time we had detected a curious stationary cloud above the horizon. The other clouds were small feathery wisps of wool which came up in the south and passed across the vault of the sky with the trade wind until they disappeared over the horizon to the west . . . But the lonely cloud on the horizon to the southwest did not move; it just rose like a motionless column of smoke while the trade winds drifted by. The Polynesians knew land lay under such clouds. For, when the tropical sun bakes the hot sand, a stream of warm air is created which rises and causes its vapor to condense up a colder stratum of air."

One might go on for many more pages, drawing from the literature of the sea a strong document, evidencing its variation in the eyes of man. Aware of these characters as we are, we still are not birds. Much more closely in tune with their environment, they may be far more keenly perceptive of environmental cues than we men.

If the height of overseas travel is truly lower than for overland migrations, I feel there must be good reasons why birds, such as ducks, reduce their height of travel. There are exceptions, to be sure, especially as ocean travelers start their journeys. Deelder (1949), for example, observed a tendency for the Chaffinch to increase its altitude when going out to sea. Henshaw (1910) gives evidence that the Pacific Golden Plover may rise to great heights in its departure from the Hawaiian Islands. By and large, however, the evidence in the literature suggests the regularity of low ocean crossings. Wetmore (1926), for example, says that he has "observed autumn flights of sandpipers crossing the Gulf of Alaska, south of Kodiak Island and the Kenai Peninsula, at heights of not more than 500 feet above the sea, with many at only a few yards above the waves. In fact, a Peale's falcon remained with our ship for a day, perching on a masthead and flying out at intervals to seize some poor sandpiper that came swinging up to examine our vessel. . . . Numerous recorders of migrants crossing stretches of open water note them frequently as passing barely above the waves."

In flying just above the water surface, migrants going into the wind might benefit as the air current is slowed by friction with the sea; and, as

Wynne-Edwards (1935) suggests, the waves breaking the surface might cause an air swell to the travelers' profit. Such advantages, however, would not be so keenly enjoyed at elevations of 100 feet or so. I believe that the consistency of low-level flying is also related to the bird's requirement to perceive its relative velocity. Thomson (1942) points out that in over-water passages, flight "without landmarks . . . seems to leave birds without any means of estimating their lateral drift." Odum (1948), however, believes that birds perceive their ground speed over water, explaining that ripples, swells, and whitecaps, although in motion themselves, give a texture to the water surface that is reference for accurate perception of velocity. "That this is true is known from the standard procedure of aviation over the ocean whereby the wing velocity of the air mass in which the plane is imbedded is told from 'double drift' measurements in reference to the sea surface." An awareness of velocity and drift from the water depends upon the speed and height of flight as well as the texture of the surface water. An aircraft can rise so high that perception of velocity and drift is impossible, in which case the navigator must drop a smoke flare by which to measure his drift. And in a complete calm, the air passenger does not perceive relative velocity until the plane is almost touching the water surface. Birds, without instruments or flares, must keep low enough to the water surface for visual perception of velocity. The Pintail flying at 33 m.p.h. at 200 feet would be keenly aware of its relative movement, but at 2,000 feet over the ocean, its perception of velocity and drift would be reduced to nil. If the sun is an aid to navigation, as Kramer and Matthews suggest, then sun-awareness and perception of velocity and drift will be very important cues for the ocean migrant; but an awareness of the sun without perception of velocity and drift will make it much more difficult to pursue an established direction.

That overseas travelers do hold to a line of flight is evidenced by the observations of Paynter (1953), who found a neat consistency of direction in migrants passing over the Campeche Bank of the Gulf of Mexico. And Siebenaler (1954), also studying migration over the Gulf of Mexico, made an extremely important observation of birds adjusting their line of flight to the wind. "At 10:59 A.M. on October 3, 1952," he writes, "the 'Oregon' was 160 miles north of Yucatán, and it was traveling a true course of 180 degrees at a speed of 10 knots. At this time heavy flights of warblers and other land birds were noticed overhead. The wind was from the northeast at speeds of 15 to 18 miles per hour. The birds were not traveling at a uniform altitude, but those that came near enough to be seen well with the naked eye or binoculars were all observed to be compensating for the wind speed and direction by angling their flight and heading approximately 30 degrees to the east of south. This carried the birds on a true southward course at an estimated speed of 30 miles per hour. The largest flights were made up of from 50 to 100 individuals flying in close formation."

Wynne-Edwards (1935) found that the spring migration of the Arctic Tern across the North Atlantic had a definite trend to the west-northwest, and he felt that he had evidence that these birds returned over the same route in the fall. Regarding the fidelity of birds to regular migration paths over the ocean, Lloyd (1954) observed on May 10, 1950, a remarkable flight of Long-tailed Jaegers in migration at 53° 19′ N., 26° 45′ W., in the North Atlantic. This location is only 200 miles from that where seventeen years earlier, on May 23, 1933, Wynne-Edwards (1935) encountered a migrating flock of the same species. By such deliberate attempts as those of Paynter and Wynne-Edwards to search out birds at sea for a study of their movements, and through the alertness of ornithologists like Lloyd, Yocom, and Buss during ocean crossings, we shall accumulate, bit by bit, much more information to explain the travels of the overseas migrants.

No problems of ocean passage have been solved here, no explanations established. But it seems certain that some of the mysteries of sea migrations (as these are mysterious to the inquiring mind of man) are generously diluted when certain fundamentals are marshaled for open-minded appraisal. Surely the complexity of pelagic journeys has been deepened by our human evaluation of distance and by our sense of the monotony of the ocean. The problem is faced in a much more rational manner when distances are approached as relative and when ecological variations at sea are critically assayed as possible avian cues for travel.

"There is recent evidence that many birds find their way not by relying on a special 'sense of direction' or other unique sensory mechanism, but rather by an ability to perceive environmental cues which are within the scope of the receptors common to all higher vertebrates." Donald R. Griffin and Raymond J. Hock (1949)

14

Magnetic and Radio Fields

SINCE the twelfth century man has depended so on the compass that some students quite naturally have attempted to explain the homing of birds as a biological awareness of the magnetic pole (Viguier, 1882). Thomson (1942:176) points out that "no evidence of any magnetic sense has ever been obtained, however, despite a good deal of experiment." Rowan (1931:84) remarks that "magnetic sensibility is an intriguing hypothesis, but the best we can say for it is that it never has been disproved. There is no evidence in its favor." Griffin's attempts (1944:25) "to train three homing pigeons to respond to a magnetic field were entirely negative, although the field was of considerably greater intensity than the earth's field." Henderson (1948) serving on a Canadian minesweeper during the last war, had abundant opportunity critically to observe the behavior of gulls, ducks, and other migratory birds exposed to intense magnetic fields set up by the vessel, and he found that "birds appeared to be supremely indifferent to magnetic field, even at the sudden beginning of magnetic pulsing." Yeagley (1947, 1951) conducted experiments testing the homing ability of pigeons wearing small wing magnets but found no "indication that the experimentally induced pulsing magnetic field moving across the birds' bodies in flight confused them insofar as navigation was concerned." Van Riper and Kalmbach (1952), in a meticulously planned experiment, found homing pigeons unaffected by wing magnets. Matthews (1951a) and Kramer (1949, 1950) likewise had negative results with magnetic tests, as did Gordon (1948) in his earlier studies.

Besides the lack of evidence in favor of a magnetic awareness, there is another circumstance making the theory less attractive. Even if a bird could sense magnetic force, successful orientation would still have to depend heavily upon visual geographic orientation. A Canvasback traveling to Delta from the Chesapeake Bay, for instance, directs its flight first to intermediate points such as Lake Erie and Lake Christina. Migrants from the Atlantic Coast would be obliged to appraise magnetic force in terms of directions relative to Lake Erie and each of the other stopping places on the long route homeward.

A more elaborate theory has been set forth by Ising (1945) and Yeagley (1947), who propose that birds may be aware of the Coriolis force. Yeagley's hypothesis implies an avian sensitivity "to the effect of motion through the vertical components of the earth's magnetic field and to the effort exerted to overcome the Coriolis forces due to the earth's rotation. Each of these influences provides a set of lines joining points of equal intensity and together forming a navigational gridwork. The theory is that by correlating its instantaneous land speed with the two effects, a bird can fly to its home which is a unique point in this gridwork, or to related conjugate points existing in the gridwork, at a position other than its home" (Thorpe, 1949:92). While Yeagley believes that this theory clarifies the "age-old mystery of bird migration" and considers it "the first working hypothesis to explain homing pigeon navigation," his experiments seem most important because their results appear to be essentially negative.[*]

Watching the homing behavior of his pigeons from an aircraft, Yeagley (1951:755) observed that they often detoured to fly over towns, usually circling the larger towns several times. He suggested that this town-interest might be due to the birds' response to power stations located there. Even before electricity arrived in Delta, however, and when the greatest electrical force was in automobile batteries, racing pigeons were seen each year over the village, the birds usually dropping down to alight on a house or barn. A displaced pigeon might be expected to react positively to a town as a lost duck turns to a lake or marsh.

Griffin (1944:25), in his classic discussions of the sensory basis of bird navigation, remarks that "there has recently been much rumor in popular publications about interference with the homing of pigeons and migrations of wild birds by radio stations (Brown, 1938; Casamajor, 1927; Darling, 1940; Aymar, 1935; and Maurain, 1926). The writer knows of no statistically

[*] For reviews of the Yeagley studies, see Slepian, 1948; Varian, 1948; Davis, 1948; Odum, 1948; Thorpe, 1949; Wilkinson, 1949; Drost, 1951; Matthews, 1955.

187

significant data supporting such opinions, and it seems appropriate to neglect them until they are adequately tested." From the radar research of the armed services come casual reports of birds, especially waterfowl, responding to radar pulsations. Poor (1946:631), reporting on the work of W. H. Doherty, of the Bell Telephone laboratories, says "he had noticed that when a radar transmitter was directed at a flock of flying birds, the birds appeared to become confused, with the flock often breaking up and the birds wandering aimlessly. Single birds also seemed to be disturbed." I have permission to quote from a letter written by Brigadier General Homer Case, of the U.S. Army, to Mr. Frederic C. Lincoln, of the U.S. Fish and Wildlife Service: "The antiaircraft units of this command are equipped with high power radars with a wave length of 10 centimeters. They conduct target practices near Bethany Beach, Delaware, and flights of wild geese frequently pass over that area. It is an interesting fact that when the beam of a radar is aimed at a flight of geese, the 'V' or other formation breaks up and the geese fly off in all directions. As soon as the beam is moved away the geese return to their original formation."

"In the fall of 1943," writes Knorr (1954), "I was in charge of a group of military personnel engaged in tracking aircraft over the ocean off the east coast of the United States. The radar set was emplaced in the dunes not far from the high tide line. During a lull in operation, a large flock of scaup (*Aythya sp.*) and scoters (species?) was seen flying parallel to the coastline a few hundred yards off shore and approaching our position. Having nothing better to do at the moment, we idly swung the parabolic antenna around and pointed it directly at the flock. The result was immediate and dramatic. The once orderly group of birds became a bewildered mass of individuals which flew in circles, missed wingbeats, and performed many unbirdlike gyrations. Some observers later insisted that a few birds accomplished loops and rolls, although I never observed this. As the beam was diverted by elevating the antenna, the flock regrouped and proceeded down the coast in the original direction. To verify this unusual behavior as being caused by radar, the experiment was repeated several times on subsequent occasions. In each case the result was essentially the same, the response of the stimulated flock coinciding with the incidence of the beam upon the birds, the cessation of response coinciding with the diversion of the beam."

I hoped that we might study the problem at Delta,* and a radar set was

* Our interest was stimulated by Dr. R. B. Roberts, of the Carnegie Institution, who observed what appeared to be avian responses to radar during his wartime researches.

established there, from April 21 to May 1, 1949, through the cooperation of the Royal Canadian Air Force.* This was a small aircraft type ADS operating on a 3-cm. band with a peak output of 50 kw. The scanner was set up on the roof of a garage at the edge of the Station, with the rest of the equipment inside, except for the generator operating beside the building.

The location was under a heavily used migration pass, and the calendar period was for the usual peak of the spring migration. It so happened, however, that the weather was unfavorable for waterfowl migration throughout the test, and fewer ducks passed over during the whole period than would be expected in one evening. During the eleven days, the radar was directed at only fourteen flocks of ducks migrating over the pass. These bands of Mallard, Pintail, and Lesser Scaup arrived from the southeast, crossed over at an elevation of 150 to 300 feet in swift, direct flight into the northwest. The radar was directed at these oncoming flocks when they were 100 to 300 yards away.

Twelve times out of the fourteen opportunities with migrants we observed unexplained actions that took place the instant the radar was aimed at an approaching flock: there was a marked quickening of wingbeat, the birds abruptly altered their direction, and the formation was disrupted. In each instance the disturbance lasted but an instant, then the flock reformed and continued on its way. The radar scanner could be swung around, the ducks held in its beam, but no further responses were noticed as the disturbed flock flew past. The behavior of the birds was hardly different from that of a flock fired upon with a shotgun, and I have never seen ducks behave in this manner except under gunfire. The noise of the generator might have disturbed them, as might the movements of observers. But migrating ducks have not before nor since been abruptly frightened by people or motors in the village. There was little wind throughout the tests and on several evenings, no wind at all, hence air currents were not responsible. Four migrant flocks passed directly over the radar when the generator was running, but the radar not operating; these birds showed no variation in their direct passage over the equipment. Unfortunately, no observations were made with the radar operating and the generator silent; and there were not enough birds to check on disturbed and undisturbed flights with and without radar.

In one instance, however, all other influences seemed to be ruled out. On

---

* I am especially grateful to Squadron Leader J. Hudson, who arranged for this test, and to Leading Aircraftsmen Douglas Hudson and Robert Stamm, who set up the radar at Delta and operated it throughout.

the evening of May 1 at 7 P.M. a pair of Shovellers flying at about 100 feet came directly toward the radar, and when they were at a distance of about 150 feet, the radar was directed upon them. The birds literally collapsed in midair, dropping at least twenty feet as if shot; then, regaining flight, they altered their direction to go away at right angles to the original course. This was a dead-calm evening, and the observers were well hidden. In any event, had the birds been disturbed by the watchers they should have swung upward rather than dropping. The same evening a band of four Shovellers flying toward the scanner dropped nearly fifty feet out of the sky the moment the radar was directed at them, almost reaching the ground before regaining controlled flight.

All the foregoing observations were made of ducks coming toward the radar and flying over it. There were many daily opportunities to direct the radar at local ducks going east or west along the shoreline of Cadham Bay, but no response was ever observed in any of these waterfowl crossing the beam. Nor did we detect any response in the wild and tame ducks and geese at rest in the Station enclosure to suggest that they were aware when the radar was directed at them, as it was for many minutes at a time.

Although few waterfowl crossed over the radar, hundreds of the four species of blackbirds migrated toward and over as they traveled west along the ridge. The radar was aimed at every crossing flock, such birds sometimes coming within fifty feet; but there was never a single response in more than a hundred tests. The same held true for heavy numbers of Tree Swallows, Franklin's Gulls, Juncos, and Flickers that crossed close to the scanner beamed in their direction. Drost (1949) also found specific variations in the response to radar; Kramer (1951) reported negative results with Red-backed Shrike; Matthews (1951a) saw no evidence of awareness in homing pigeons released in a radar beam. We do not understand the reasons for these differences, much less how the radar pulsations are perceived by some waterfowl. The whole subject offers an interesting and important field for continued research.

So far we know only that some birds, such as ducks, under certain situations apparently respond to radar pulsations in much the same manner as they do to a shotgun blast. But, as Drost explains (1951), "we do not suggest that birds are guided by waves, if we mention the fact that migrants show a positive reaction to ultra-shortwave (radar) transmission (Drost, 1949); we shall only mention that birds are able to react in cases where men are unable to do so." In his recent review of the studies of bird navigation Griffin (1952a:368) says that the "responses of birds to pulsed, high frequency, radio waves (from radar transmitters) have been observed both in the United States and in Europe (Drost, 1949), and these observations are cited by Yeagley as 'rapidly increasing evidence' for theories of bird navigation based on electromagnetic phenomena. As Schwartzkopf (1950) has pointed out, however, the density of the energy flux in a pulsed radar beam is probably sufficient to exceed known thresholds for biological effects of electromagnetic radiation. One such effect, described by Barlow, Kohn & Walsh (1947a, b), is the production of visual sensations when the human eye is stimulated either by weak alternating currents (O.2 mA. at 60 c.p.s.) or by the electric current induced by an alternating magnetic field of 500 gauss at 60 c.p.s. This magnetic-field strength is approximately 1000 times that of the earth's field. In fact both the radar beams and the artificial magnetic fields employed by Barlow *et al.* greatly exceed any known intensity of terrestrial magnetism or its electrical by-products. On quantitative grounds it thus appears most unsound to erect theories of bird navigation based upon these observed responses of birds or men to intense electromagnetic stimuli."

Let us not be dissuaded from the continuation of intensive studies of the influence of radio and radar waves on the behavior of birds; the subject demands further investigation. In the light of current knowledge, however, any electrostatic sensitivity in birds appears to be no more useful to regional orientation than sound waves from a shotgun, to which they respond in a similar manner.

"It is curious that although human navigators have for centuries been obtaining their position in unknown areas from the sun's co-ordinates, it is only in the last few years that the possibility of birds doing likewise has been considered." G. V. T. Matthews, *Bird Navigation*

15

Awareness of Direction

THE manner in which birds find their way in migration is one of the oldest mysteries to mankind. With each migrant is the secret, discoverable because it is there, yet undiscovered. Many like to believe this ability stems from a special sense — a "sixth sense," writes Chapman (1916:138), that "has been called a sense of direction. The sense of sight we know to exist in the eye, and the sense of hearing in the ear, and in the nerves leading from these organs to the brain. But no one knows where the sense of direction is situated."

While a few modern ornithologists still believe with Chapman in this undiscovered sense, we now realize, of course, that the so-called five senses are not discrete, that sensory awareness of the outer world is not separable into special components of perception. It is thus "a confused gesture of despair to dispose of the problem by calling for a sixth sense — or a sixteenth" (Griffin, 1953:215).

Some have turned to the travels of man to find evidence of a sense of direction, like Lincoln (1950a:28), who says that "man recognizes this sense in himself, though usually it is imperfect and frequently at fault." To be sure, there are abundant testimonials in favor of a human sense of direction, these offered by or concerning people who found their way home or to camp under adverse conditions. But the subjects seldom are aware of how such orientation is accomplished; the best Hudson could offer (1922) by way of explaining his homeward "hunches" was "a nerve in the brain," which he considered to be active in animals but usually latent in man. There seems to be no scientific evidence of such a sense in man. Indeed, man has spent far more time and money studying the orientation of birds than of the prob-

192

lem in his own human race. Gregg (1939) made a wide review of the literature to find that there have been very few studies of spatial orientation in humans. More recently (1953) Witkin said that "despite its importance to human adaptation, orientation has not been extensively studied at the human level. . . . It is particularly noteworthy that the specific way in which sensory factors contribute to human orientation has been given relatively little attention, even though in many instances the relevant sensory mechanisms have received considerable study."

Those crediting human beings with a special sense contend that it is more highly developed in native aborigines, guides, or woodsmen. Jaccard (1931), however, who reviewed many accounts of homing in man, concluded that all possess the same endowment for orientation, regardless of their station in life; there is no appreciable difference between the sensory capacities of different human races or occupations. Dwellers of the city are amazed at the Indian who travels so effortlessly about his wilderness; yet he, in turn, does not understand how a child can enter the subway in New York or London and emerge minutes later to find its way home through the maze of streets and buildings all so alike. "Admittedly in ordinary speech," says Thomson (1942:177) "we often talk of a person as having a 'good sense of direction' (or perhaps 'bump of locality') but by this, however, we merely mean that the individual has his wits about him in the particular respect of finding his way, and that he is observant and has good conscious or unconscious memory for places seen, distances covered and turns taken. If we stop to think about it, we realize that we have no intention of crediting him with possession of any special sense unknown to physiology."

Some students have referred to a "magnetic sense," an "inherited memory," or a "hereditary knowledge" by which birds are guided; and it is often implied (if not clearly stated) that in young birds there must be an innate foreknowledge of the *geographic* destination. The term "instinct" has been very loosely used in the literature on migration, there being implied an inborn awareness of the geographic destination and the direction thereto. And now Huxley (1954:106) tells us that "several zoologists have recently begun to consider psi as a possible explanation for the . . . extraordinary and hitherto inexplicable performances of migrating birds and fish." * But "if we concede it a scientifically legitimate sort of proceeding," writes Lorenz (1950:231), "to bridge any arbitrarily chosen gap in our present knowl-

* *Psi* is the term used by parapsychologists in reference to a paranormal faculty.

edge by an obliging little wonder, then all scientific research becomes a pure farce."

All through the ages of wondering, man has conceived the idea that the answer to this mystery of avian orientation might be found in a single explanation, like a magnetic awareness, a compass-like sense, a delicate perception of the Coriolis force, or some other discrete sensory capacity by which the geographic direction to home is perceived. This insistence on the complete efficiency of one directive source is set forth by Huxley (1954) as he dismisses the idea that birds may rely on the sun as a guide to their travel. "There is," he says, "the hypothesis that pigeons navigate by the sun. If they do, they must possess, built into their nervous systems, the equivalents of a chronometer, a sextant, navigational tables and a calculating machine for correlating the solar data observed at the point of release with those at the loft. . . . All in all, solar navigation seems just as untenable as the canal theory or the magnetic theory."

But neither Matthews nor Kramer claims the sun to be the sole factor in orientation. Matthews (1955:98), after having discovered that his pigeons, gulls, and shearwaters had a direct homeward orientation when released at an unfamiliar place on a sunny day, and having shown that this direct homeward orientation broke down when the sun was hidden behind cloud overcast, demonstrated "that when Pigeons are very familiar with a release point, after six previous releases there, overcast conditions have no effect at all on initial orientation." In short, Matthews' work shows that experimental birds orientate directly homeward from strange regions with the sun in view, are confused in strange regions with the sun hidden, but can orientate homeward without the sun on familiar range. The sun may thus play a role in the travels of birds as it does with men: if the way is familiar by previous experience, the sun is not necessary to homeward orientation, but if the way is not familiar, the sun is fundamental.

Griffin (1952a, 1953) has described three types of homing, these applying to experimental birds set free by students of avian navigation and also to free birds in the wild:

Type I. Reliance on visual landmarks within familiar territory and the use of exploration or some form of undirected wandering in unfamiliar territory.

Type II. The ability to fly in a particular direction, even in unfamiliar territory.

Type III. The ability to head for the home locality even when released in unknown territory and when the correct direction of the homing flight bears no relation to directions that have been previously adhered to in training flights or migrations.

Type I navigation is "contact" flying, the bird being guided by visual reference to the earth. Such orientation on the local range is commonly considered to be within our comprehension; we wonder only how birds find their way on the longer journeys. Watson and Lashley (1915), among others, have distinguished between *proximate orientation,* as where the goal itself directly and immediately stimulates the animal, and *distant orientation,* as where the goal is beyond the perception of any known receptors.

But in Type I navigation, where the bird orientates itself entirely by visual contact with the world over which it travels, I feel that it is misleading to judge the complexity of the problem in terms of distance. If we disregard the relative values of the travel coordinates, then the artificial problem in the mind of the human investigator must become vastly more complex than it can ever be to the bird in passage. We must not make a clear-cut distinction between proximate and distant orientation, for in all travel, whether of bird in migration or of human child to kindergarten, the distant, unperceived objective is attained only by passing through a series of proximate situations. In our human travel we "cross our bridges" as they are reached. Brown (Gregg, 1939:69), who studied human behavior in a maze, tells us that "few subjects, when they are able to tread the maze correctly, can recount the turns as 'right,' 'left,' 'right,' etc. Almost invariably, after giving a few turns thus verbally, the subject will say, 'I don't know what comes next; *I have to be there* before I can tell you.'" I suspect it may be the same with ducks and other birds. As Mallards cross the passes day after day en route to stubble, or return to the home marsh spring after spring, they may be ever aware of the proximate situations as these make the path to the distant and unseen goals.

At two or three weeks of age, the duckling travels in an oriented manner about its slough, where the forest of reeds stretching far above its head extends in all ways in confusing monotony. The grain fields to this bird are a world unknown, as unreachable as the moon itself, as far beyond comprehension as America was to Aristotle. Eight weeks later, however, when the youngster takes wing, relative distances become shorter, and prairie farms are soon a part of a wide, familiar realm. First to near fields, then to far, until the young Mallard is feeding many miles from home by mid-August. Come October and it has reached Minnesota or North Dakota or

The grain fields are a world unknown to these young Mallards,
as unreachable as the moon.

some other distant land; by the end of its first year it has experienced half
a continent. Where, as this circle of experience grows outward from the
natal slough, is the dividing line between proximate and distant orientation?

So, as its life develops, the young duck gains within a few weeks after
birth a traveler's perspective of the world that man could not achieve
through all the eons of his existence until this present moment of history.
Not until he understood the relativity of motion, nor until he had viewed
the earth as an airman, could man comprehend the world as a bird awing,
or understand how the realm of migration, like the narrow home range, becomes familiar through the experience of travel.

Although a bird comes and goes about a range that is familiar to it,
there is evidence of Type II navigation, where a direct course is followed
in the absence of landmarks to guide the way. Kramer (1951, 1952) has
shown how the sun serves as a cue to compass direction. Studying the activity of caged Starlings, he found that during the migration season, their
movements had a strong bias in one direction, and this orientation depended upon the sun. Such solar influence was tested by manipulation of

196

sunlight with mirrors and by an artificial sun; and it was demonstrated that with the sun obscured, as by overcast of cloud, the cage movements were random, without directional bias. Kramer's Starlings were not merely aware of the sun as division between night and day, nor simply as the cue to east and west, morning and evening. These experimental birds related their position to the sun in both time and space as it moved in its arc across the sky.

So convincing are Kramer's experiments that we must conclude that wild birds, like his caged Starlings, perceive the sun as a cue to direction. Santschi (1923) has shown how the sun is used as a compass by ants, and in a wonderful little book Von Frisch (1950) tells us of the role of the sun in the orientation of bees. Ants, bees, birds, and men perceive the sun only as an accessory guide when traveling about their homes; but when they are following a course beyond the limits of familiar surroundings, the sun becomes a primary cue to direction.

In the absence of the sun or of landmarks, as in overseas passages, the texture of the water may serve as a cue to direction. Because of their great inertia, waves may continue in a certain direction long after the wind has changed. "Once the flight direction relative to this rather long-lived system of parallel lines is established (from the bearing provided by the sun, or by some other means), it is possible to use them over a period of many hours as an indicator of direction." * Clouds may serve as a cue to direction, either by their texture overhead or on the horizon where cloud caps show above islands or mountain peaks. Flying above cloud, birds may perceive their velocity and wind drift relative to cloud texture, but of course they must become displaced over the land to the extent of the cloud movement.

Hitchcock (1950, 1952) has succeeded in training pigeons to fly in certain directions, which were followed by some of his trained birds when released in strange territory. Kramer observed that, besides maintaining their standard migrational direction in captivity, his Starlings could be trained to move in certain ways. This suggests not only a retentiveness for direction, but that such awareness may develop from a learning process.

The ability to hold a course accounts for the migration of waterfowl along standard directions during periods of heavy overcast. But the gyrations of travelers over Delta during unfavorable weather suggests that they seek some cue to direction to continue with a movement under adverse condi-

* Robert L. Lillestrand, "The Flight of Birds in the Wind" (unpublished manuscript).

tions of visibility. And of course the great waves of misplaced birds, as reported by Williamson (1952), make it clear that migrants cannot invariably hold a track throughout a journey in bad weather.

Banding records demonstrate that birds come back again and again to the same stopping places and winter destinations every year; and we gather that migrants are familiar with these regions of annual return. But it must not be assumed that every bird homing in spring flies every mile of the way by retracing a route learned in the fall. Like Pintails going south via California and homing north through the Mississippi Valley, or ducks flying part of the way over cloud, or birds of many kinds blown far off course by unseasonable wind, or migrants obliged to cross vast stretches of open water, there are many individuals which annually must rely on an awareness of the direction home for at least a part of spring migration. In short, Type III navigation, where the traveler in strange surroundings perceives the direction toward home, must be fundamental in spring migration. Such homeward awareness in strange regions has been observed with many kinds of birds released under experimental conditions: Noddy and Sooty Tern (Watson and Lashley, 1915), Swallow (Wodzicki and Wojtusiak, 1934), Song Sparrow (Manwell, 1936), Alpine Swift (Schifferli, 1942), Homing Pigeon (Matthews, 1951a; Griffin, 1952b; Hitchcock, 1952; Kramer, 1952), Herring Gull, Lesser Black-backed Gull, and Manx Shearwater (Matthews, 1952, 1953a).

With Swallows, Wodzicki and Wojtusiak (Wojtusiak, 1949) found that in many of their experiments "there was noticeable a characteristic behavior of the birds at the moment of their release. The Swallows soared up into the air, described one circle or several, and then started to fly in a direct line toward their nesting site." Griffin's pigeons, when released at points 72 and 100 miles from their loft, "took the correct initial direction within two miles of the release point." Kramer (1952:284), after studying the direct homing of his pigeons, concluded that "some sort of astronomical navigation is suggested by the fact that the pigeons seem to be orientated even before starting." Matthews (1955b:94) found that this initial orientation* toward home functioned only when the sun was in view: the "homeward orientation shown by pigeons in critical releases in sunny weather deteriorates markedly in conditions of heavy cloud and breaks down com-

---

* "Initial orientation" is that observed at the point of release. Not all individuals making initial orientation homeward have equal success in reaching home. See Matthews (1955b:26) for a summary of homing success.

pletely with overcast skies. . . . The homeward orientation of Lesser Black-backed Gulls in sunny conditions gave place to disoriented scatter in heavily clouded and overcast conditions." Matthews found disorientation under cloud in the Manx Shearwater, and he says that "it was possible to show, further, that the same individuals which gave good orientation in sunny conditions would scatter at random with overcast, and vice versa."

This initial orientation does not hinge on the bird's familiarity with the range about its home. Matthews (1953b) observed an awareness of the direction home in untrained young pigeons which had been allowed to fly only in the immediate neighborhood of their loft. Set free one by one at distances of 50 to 75 miles from home, they showed an awareness of the direction home that was but little inferior to that of experienced birds, although their success in returning was not so high as that of birds with training. Kramer and Saint-Paul (1954) went a step further, keeping their pigeons in large aviaries within which they had limited flight experience. Given their freedom 320 kilometers (about 200 miles) from home, these inexperienced birds showed a direct homeward orientation at the point of release, although, like Matthews' birds, their homing success was not so great as that of trained individuals.

There is before us, then, the evidence that some birds are able to orientate directly homeward from strange locations and that such direct initial orientation operates only when the sky is not hidden by cloud. The implication is clear that the sun serves as a cue to the direction toward home. If this is so, the displaced bird must be aware of the arc angle and schedule of the sun as these are relative to the situation at home.

It has been observed in many homing experiments that some birds released in strange country, far from home, orientate homeward more precisely and return at a greater rate of speed than others set free at lesser distances from home. Wojtusiak (1949) felt that the birds that were closer came back at a proportionately slower rate because of their self-confidence within the range of familiar surroundings. Griffin (1943), noting the poor homing of Herring Gulls when released close to home, said that "if this is a consistent effect it might conceivably offer a clue to the fundamental problems of homing." In the light of Matthews' sun-navigation hypothesis this failure of birds to return from strange but near places might be due to their inability to perceive changes in the arc angle and schedule of the sun close to home. Perhaps birds, like men, must travel some distance before they become aware of the sun's changes. Until they have been carried past this critical distance in homing experiments, they must search randomly* for familiar cues, consuming their time in wandering rather than in loitering.

When they have passed this critical point, birds may perceive the changes in the sun's position, then becoming aware of the direction home, which they adopt at once. Using two teams of experienced pigeons, Matthews (1955b:77) found that: (1) In birds released 10 miles from home, "a coarse orientation resulted which could be clearly attributed to memory of landmarks since it became generally better at closer distances." (2) In birds released 35 miles from home, there was a "near random scatter, associated as in the other nonorientated releases with slow returns." (3) When released at 50 miles from home, "good orientation has been achieved by these and many other pigeons." Perhaps 50 miles is near the critical point in this "distance effect" for pigeons. In the Swallow, Wodzicki and Wojtusiak (Wojtusiak, 1949:101) determined that 120 kilometers (74.5 miles) was the critical point. Griffin's homing experiments with Leach's Petrel (1940:72) showed that birds released at 65 miles and 85 miles from their nesting places came home much less efficiently than those set free 135 miles away. No doubt the critical point may vary with the species, with seasons, and with latitude, but the evidence suggests that it may rest roughly between 50 and 100 miles from home.

One wonders why migrants, such as petrels and swallows, if they find their way home to a familiar range in spring, become lost only 30 or 50 miles away when artificially displaced. We must remember that the displacement in the homing experiment breaks the thread of continuity linking past with present. For birds released at a great distance, the direction home in terms of the sun is perceived, and they approach home in the same manner as migrants. Those set free at closer range may be cued only to compass direction and, without awareness of the way home, must wander. In our own human experience, the whole of a range is often more familiar than its parts. Regardless of how I approach the vast Delta marsh from a distance, I can always perceive the way home. But more than once I have become lost within the marsh, not far from familiar landmarks.

Hitchcock (1952:285) points out that this distance effect may support the Coriolis theory of navigation. "If one makes the assumption that a homing bird wants to return at once," he says, "poor homing performance at short distances is difficult to explain on the basis of visual orientation

---

* See Griffin (1952a) and Wilkinson (1952) for a discussion of random movements.

involving recognition of landmarks. Such performance is not incompatible with theories of homing based on terrestrial magnetism or Coriolis force. According to these theories the stimuli for orientation at nearby points would be too similar to those at the loft to be differentiated, but those at a distance could be differentiated clearly." The distance effect is certainly evidence of a type of "grid navigation," but it does not obtain without the sun. The experiments of Kramer and Matthews are so amenable to quantitative analysis and tie in so closely with observations of wild migratory behavior that, in the face of present evidence, this distance effect favors the case for sun navigation. The challenge now is for other workers with other species in other places to repeat and test.

In one of the few orientation experiments human beings have conducted upon their own kind, Gregg (1939) found that a man will move in the direction of his thoughts without being aware of doing so. His experiments were set up very much like those of Kramer's with birds. Instead of being caged, the human subjects sat within an enclosure encircled by curtain. When a man, with motion-recording devices attached to his head or to certain muscles, was instructed to think of "north" or "sunset" or some other point of the compass, there was bodily motion or muscular activity (of which the subject was unaware) in that direction. "To entertain a thought of geographic location," concluded Gregg, "is to make *overt* or *covert* response in the perceived direction." When Gregg's human subjects were disoriented by being turned back and forth on their turn-table platform—when they were "lost" within their curtained enclosure—they showed no directional bias in their movements. Like Kramer's Starlings without the sun, their actions showed a random pattern.

We may step from Gregg's experiments into our daily lives to understand how a man directs his actions with his whole being. Here I sit comfortably in the parlor reading, until hunger sensations impel me to walk to the kitchen for a snack. Back to the easy chair for a while, then a yawn or two and off I go to bed. These actions are conducted thoughtlessly, yet precisely, so that I do not go to the bedroom when the stomach signals hunger, nor to the kitchen or bathroom when I am tired.

Such travel to kitchen and bedroom must be on a level of activity similar to that of a female duck with distended oviduct moving to her nest, or of hungry stubble Mallards flighting out to the grain fields. For both man and bird there is a pattern of appetitive behavior. For the man, the way to the bedroom is a learned route; he is directed there by the whole body to satisfy the appetites arising from inner stimuli. The appetite is not for the bed, but for the instinctive act of sleep. In the same way the hen moves to her nest, not hungering for the nest itself, but to complete the act of egg-laying. By the same pattern, man goes to kitchen or bedroom, bird to slough or gravel bar, neither hungering so much for the geographic place as for the completion there of instinctive acts.

In man, for all his intelligence, this orientation within the home environment is conducted without conscious organization; oriented movements develop with the same spontaneity as words flowing together to make the spoken sentence. "We seldom think of this experience with space," says Katz (1953:99), "except when we have some special reason to be aware of it. . . . This mechanism of orientation is easy to use when one does not think about it, but seems to resist deliberate manipulation."

Gregg's experiment concerned only compass direction. We know very little about man's awareness of the sun or other celestial bodies, except as their place in navigation is taught to him. The early mariners relied heavily on the sun and the stars in their voyages. In modern celestial navigation, computation of a "line of position" from the stars is a complicated process involving spherical trigonometry (if prepared tables are not at hand), and, besides, there must be a sextant and a chronometer set to Greenwich Mean Time. Yet, with no understanding of trigonometry, without charts, without sextant or chronometer, the Polynesians followed the stars in their travels about the South Pacific, the navigational techniques delivered from one generation to the next by tradition. They "considered the stars as moving bands of light that passed across the inverted pit of the sky, and they sailed toward the stars which they knew passed over the islands of their destination" (Carson, 1951:211).

We human beings are so concerned with the paraphernalia of civilization that it is difficult to appraise our awareness of the sun with respect to regional orientation. Two of my children, at the ages of seven and nine, independently observed and commented upon the change in the sun's schedule and position after a five-day trip from Delta, Manitoba, to Washington, D.C., in November. I find myself always conscious of the sun's change of position and schedule when traveling away from Delta, and I maintain an awareness of the location of Delta which I believe to be related to the sun. I also find it difficult to adjust immediately to "daylight saving time," clinging for several days to the sun's rather than the clock's signal for bed time. But we should test human beings in displacement experiments as Matthews has done with shearwaters, gulls, and Pigeons.

Robert H. Smith and Edward G. Wellein, pilot biologists for the U.S. Fish and Wildlife Service, have had much experience with low-level flying over the Arctic, where charts are often in error, the compass unreliable, and the landscape monotonous. Both contend that the sun is an important cue to navigation and that they are aware of the variation in arc and schedule as they move across degrees of latitude and longitude, so that by the sun they maintain an awareness of their relation to their base of operations. Wellein tells me that on several occasions he has sensed his position relative to the sun but followed his compass — and has found that his own awareness of position was the truer guide to position.

But the sun, especially in some regions of the Arctic during the summer, is not always available as a cue, and men, like birds, must make reference to the world about them. Robert H. Smith says (letter): "An inexperienced pilot is frequently lost because he can't pinpoint himself on the map at a given time. As experience is acquired, he worries less about the exact position, and is more concerned with the broad features of the terrain — drainage patterns, mountain ranges, large lakes, coastlines and distinctive features of culture. There is hardly any place where one is not bracketed in by a combination of these — and this is all that is really important on long cross-country flights. I believe I could fly from Aklavik, Northwest Territories, to Mexico City by following my usual routes, without charts, radio or compass, using my knowledge of details of terrain and culture near places where I must land for fuel, and relying on broad landmarks for the areas between. To do this would require flying at a reasonable height with good visibility."

Home, in all its individual and geographic varieties, means the same thing to every man in terms of his inborn appetites for those acts and stimuli of parenthood (or childhood) that for each human being can be satisfied at only one place: this territory of home. Wherever he is, however modern his age, the home, grand or humble, is the ultimate goal in the travels of all mankind.

As with birds, the circle of geographic learning extends outward from the home. The corner store is the edge of the universe for the two-year-old who cannot comprehend the father's travels. And yet in due course, in the natural way of life that no elder can ever explain to a child, the wide unknown becomes familiar. Modern transportation methods, guiding instru-

203

ments, books, maps, all have modified the problem of human orientation, but there is always the awareness of and the inborn hunger for home.

Man is impressed by the superiority of his intelligence to that of birds and mammals; and yet this homeward orientation — which had to be efficient in the dark, unknown ages before man began his climb up the intellectual ladder — may still be at a primitive level. However much we have learned to improve our homes and the trails leading there, the organization of our activities relative to home is apparently very close to the homing behavior of the lower animals. At dusk the bird flies home, the dog trots home, and the man drives home, perhaps listening to the radio all the way. Wherein lies the essential difference?

In man, orientation on his home range is fundamental. Surely such behavior must have developed early in his evolution; and upon this ability to find his way about is built the higher level of activity upon which civilized behavior is established, both in the evolutionary scale for the human race, and in the life story of each individual.

For the bird the satisfaction of innate hungers is life itself — but no less or more so than for man. And at this level of behavior where movement in space assists in the satisfaction of innate appetites, man and bird have much in common. To study the homing behavior of one is inevitably to learn something of the other.

Instead of a "sense of direction" in man, there appears to be an *awareness of direction*. This does not result from the function of one sense but is probably a product of all the sensory apparatus, with the eyes, no doubt, most important. This awareness exists without the requirement for a knowledge of its existence; it functions as long as a man maintains continuity with his environment. It ceases to have reality the instant the present is disconnected from the past; then a man is lost. Awareness of direction is thus not inborn but hinges on personal experience with the environment.

In birds there appears to be a similar awareness of direction, effective as long as the continuity of life's flow remains unbroken, ineffective when the continuous sensory contact with the surroundings is disrupted and the bird is displaced from all environmental cues. In birds and in men the sun is the basic cue to orientation. In local travel it serves as a guide to direction; beyond a certain point from home, changes in its position and its time may be cues to the direction of home. In the absence of the sun, man and bird must read their position in terms of the world about them, wandering if displaced from familiar surroundings.

204

In the flow of life, a bird faces familiar places on all sides. The direction in which the bird moves, that with the greatest valence, depends upon the appetites impelling travel. On the local range the bird may go toward nest, gravel bar, or slough according to the stimuli of oviduct, gizzard, or crop. In the same manner, the Manitoba Mallard hen wintering in Texas must be driven by her newly awakened sexual appetites to respond to her awareness of the direction toward Manitoba. We do not know what appetites awaken an awareness of familiar wintering places in autumn. But in each of these situations where migration is concerned, the valence of certain directions depends upon appetitive behavior, and the travel of migration differs from movement on the home range only by the relative measures of time and space.

Where waterfowl migrate homeward along flight lines of standard direction, we see great numbers going the same way; but the travel is not to a common destination. The spring navigation homeward (except for the mated drake, or the young of geese and swans) is an individual problem which must be faced separately by each bird. The female duck may start from Texas with many others of her kind, but eventually there comes a time when she, like each companion, must bend away from the direction of the group and take her own course to the familiar nesting place. Leadership in spring migration cannot be entrusted to casual companions, or else the arrival home would be a remote chance indeed.

In the same way, molting movements of adults and the swift, direct passage of mass fall migration hinge upon an awareness of direction toward destinations that have been visited before. But in these nonsexual migrations, the whole body of birds moves together as a social group to the common destination without the requirement of individual separation.

To understand this awareness of direction, as it is cued by the sun and by the surrounding world, would be to understand how the duckling learns to know its mother, or how it so rapidly takes its familiar place within the complex range of its natal slough. The evidence suggests that each bird gains familiarity with its mother, with its home pond, and with the great, wide world beyond, by virtue of its experience; but to explain this process of rapid learning and retentiveness would be to unravel the whole mystery of memory itself.

Such awareness of direction founded upon experience is, of course, thin soup for those who fail to distinguish between the orientation of adults and juveniles or who cherish the oldest and fondest of all migration mysteries, the idea of an inborn awareness of the direction and the route to the wintering grounds.

In any analysis of migrational orientation, I am sure we must distinguish between experienced adults and inexperienced juveniles just learning their place in the world. The primary dispersals of ducks from the natal ranges carry youngsters toward rendezvous areas where they gather together, not only with many of their own age, but with adults as well. As already discussed in Chapters 8 and 10, vast numbers of juvenile ducks make part or all of their final autumn journey to the wintering grounds with experienced adults in the traditional mass migrations. Juveniles that accompany their elders, whether they are children, as in geese and swans, or merely companions, as in ducks, may learn the flyways and standard directions, which thus become traditional.* But however many young reach the wintering grounds in this way, some juvenile waterfowl (and in some species of birds, perhaps all young-of-the-year) gain the wintering places without the companionship of experienced adults.

An analysis of juvenile travel in autumn must first distinguish between an ecological and geographical goal. Because the immature bird arrives at an ecologically suitable situation on its winter range, the literature often assumes an innate awareness of that place. When a young duck finds a sago bed on the far side of its natal pond, nobody claims there is an inborn guidance to that special location, nor to the stubble fields ten miles south of the home marsh, nor even to another marsh in the home province. When the juvenile eventually arrives in Minnesota or North Dakota, we credit it with no innate tie to these places. But somehow, when a young bird finally attains a wintering area a thousand miles or more from its birthplace, this feat is often explained by assuming an innate bond to that geographic location.†

* In ducks I found the existence of mass migrations poorly documented in the literature, and I believe this holds for many other species. While it may be true that in some kinds all young-of-the-year arrive on the wintering grounds independently of adults, I believe that mass autumn migrations are greatly underrated as the vehicle for the autumn travels of inexperienced juveniles. Simmons (1951:406), discussing raptor migration, says, "I feel the significance of socially-facilitated behavior has been under-estimated. There is a definite tendency for the birds to follow the movements of their companions, thus effecting general movement in the same direction." To show that large numbers of young in many species regularly travel part or all of the way to the wintering grounds en masse with adult companions is not to explain all juvenile travel. But this type of movement must account for the winterward passage of great numbers of young birds in many species.

† In some European species, like the Stork, European Sparrow Hawk, Starling, and Hooded Crow (Mayr, 1952), and in the American Crow (Rowan, 1946), certain experiments have been

Such assumptions are often embellished with the suggestion that the young bird went with precision to this place. If the wintering area has been used by a particular species for many years, or if the adults have arrived earlier, some by a different route, these circumstances are given as further evidence that the tie between bird and place is innate. Science has yet to describe an inborn awareness of a proximate geographic location, and it seems unreasonable to believe that such an awareness exists for some *distant* place beyond the realm of experience. A female may have an inborn urge to nest in a rather narrow ecological pattern of environment; but each and every female must explore to find the geographic place of her nest. In the same way young waterfowl and juveniles of many other species apparently have an innate awareness of environmental patterns, but the exact locations of these places they use their first autumn and winter must be found in the course of their juvenile explorations.

Some young ducks reach the wintering range in their primary wanderings, getting there before many adults have arrived. Other vagabonds, at the same time, find their way north or east or west. As long as these youngsters have no experience of the land over which they wander, they are under certain environmental influences. By their innate response to water, the early movements carry the young ducks from one lake or marsh to another. They follow rivers and shorelines; and when they move overland, their stopping places are marshes and lakes. In this random travel the wind inevitably is a major influence on the pattern of their wanderings. Without geographic goals the over-all trend of nomadic flight will be in the direction of the air flow, and it is most important that we understand the relation of the wind to the wandering juvenile. When a bird, young or old, moves about on its familiar range, flying to and from familiar objectives, the wind modifies the timing but not the direction of these move-

carried out which have produced results accepted by some as evidence of an inborn awareness of the direction of autumn migration. In several of these studies, pure groups of young birds were used, but there was no analysis of the weather prevailing during the period of study. Others studied the weather, but could not rule out the possibility of young meeting experienced adults. Nor has the role of tradition been thoroughly examined, as where local birds moved by tradition, while the experimentals, released later, might have been influenced by major air mass flow. When we assume something so vastly fundamental as genetic influence on geographic direction, I believe experimental investigations must insist on: (1) Studies to be carried out only with birds in which the history is known from birth. (2) A thorough assay of "ecological factors in the broadest sense, including air mass characteristics, wind direction, the apparent structure assumed by convection currents in the air, ocean currents, ocean wave patterns and the possibility that the sun or resulting sky-brightness pattern could serve as a directional cue" (Griffin and Hock, 1949:196). (3) No opportunity for experimental birds to join experienced wild companions. (4) A study of the role of tradition in the migration of the wild stock against which the experiments are being compared.

In their juvenile wanderings, young ducks move from one marsh to another.

ments, as discussed in Chapter 5. Once the bird leaves the familiar range, once it has no geographical goal, *once it wanders at random*, the over-all trend will be in the direction of the wind (Figure 25). In their explorations, the juveniles may travel part of the time against the wind, sometimes for prolonged periods, for the bird is not passively at the mercy of the wind as a leaf or wisp of spider's web. But as long as the travel is random, the total product of a day's or a week's wandering will be in the direction in which the air mass flows, just as surely as a ship *wandering* in the Gulf Stream moves with the ocean currents.

This is a small matter when the flow of air in any one direction is of short duration. But with the advent of September in central Canada and the north central United States, the flow of air, when measured by weeks, is predominantly from the northwest. There are periods of calm, days when the warm autumn air moves up from the southeast; but when the whole of the air movement from mid-September through November is measured for any year, the major trend across the heart of the continent is from the northwest (U.S. Weather Bureau, 1952) (Figure 26).* However far northward the inexperienced juveniles may have wandered in August, the domi-

* Although the dominant November flow of air over the main waterfowl breeding range is from the northwest, the patterns of high- and low-pressure areas give some interesting variations. Winds moving counterclockwise around the Aleutian low (Figure 26) create a westerly flow over the Pacific Ocean from the Aleutian Islands to the continent; and there is evidence here (such as that presented by Yocom, 1947) of an oceanic migration of waterfowl and other northern birds in autumn. The eastward flow of winds from the Greenland low suggests a reason behind the autumn migration of Greenland birds toward Europe; and it may be with this same current that the Arctic Tern takes its flight across the North Atlantic in the first leg of its long autumn migration. The intercontinental flow of wind around the Aleutian and the Greenland lows may be the medium of transportation by which North American waterfowl regularly drift to Siberia and to Europe.

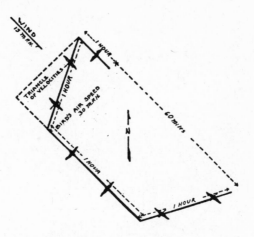

Figure 25. When a bird flies at random, it must inevitably move in the direction of the wind. Here the speed of the wind is 15 m.p.h. from the northwest. The air speed of the bird is 30 m.p.h. If it flew one hour directly northwest into the wind, one hour southwest, one hour southeast, and one hour northeast, the product of the four hours' travel would be 60 miles southeast of the starting place.

nance of the Polar Continental Air Mass in September and October must make for a southeasterly movement of these young birds, just as the blindfolded bird, flying in circles, drifts downwind. I believe that all young waterfowl which do not join mass migrations are inevitably destined to travel toward the equator in autumn by the dominant flow of the air mass in which they move. Williamson (1953) explains "that in the case of Greenland-Iceland populations down-wind drift, without dependence on an innate sense of orientation, provides the surest method of reaching the western sea-board of Europe in autumn."

We find evidence of this influence of the wind in other places with other birds. In summer there is a flow of air to the northeast along the Atlantic Coast (Trewartha, 1937:88). Young herons of several species, wandering aimlessly from their birth range in the southern United States, arrive in regions far to the north in August and September. Broley (1947), studying the movements of immature Bald Eagles he banded in their natal state of Florida, found a similar trend northward along the Atlantic Coast.

Hoar (1953:440) has shown how the Chum Salmon fry move with the current during the night when in darkness they lose their visual orientation,* and he points out that "it is not necessary to assume that fish transported in this way will move at the same rate as floating objects." He goes on to say that "the downstream movement of juvenile and spent fish, emphasized by Russell (1937), is recognized as a part of the migratory behavior of a great many fish. Cod, salmon, herring, mackerel and flatfish may be mentioned as a few of the important species showing such be-

* See p. 69.

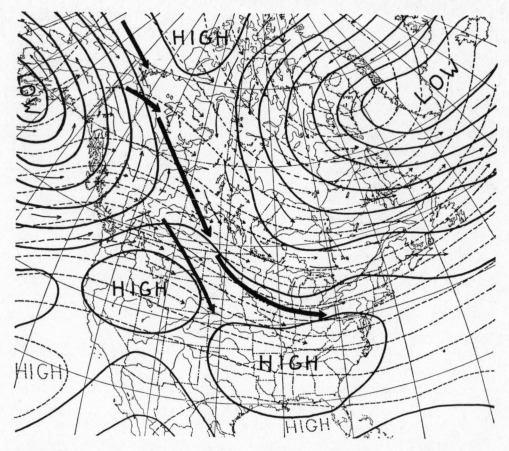

Figure 26. Normal weather chart for November (U.S. Weather Bureau, 1952). The solid lines show the pattern of sea-level air pressures (millibars), and the thin solid arrows mark the flow of winds near the earth's surface. The weather for the whole of November, of course, does not remain stable on a day-to-day basis, there being a regular progression of migratory lows from the northwest to the southeast across the continent. Behind each mobile low there follows a ridge of high pressure, usually starting just east of the Canadian Rocky Mountains (see the weather map for November 7, 1947, on page 105). The tracks of these high-pressure cells flow almost exclusively from the northwest to the southeast, as shown by the heavy black arrows (Berry, Owens, and Wilson, 1952). The broken lines and arrows indicate the contour and wind flow at the 700 millibar surface (approximately 10,000 feet above sea level). At this height, where weather is less under the influence of surface variations, the predominance of November's northwesterly movement of wind over the whole of North America becomes more apparent.

210

The rock and spruce country of the Pre-Cambrian Shield
is avoided by most migrant waterfowl.

havior." Whether the current is of air or water, the animal moving randomly must travel with the flow of the medium in which it wanders.

Just as a boatman in a great current may avoid shoals by steering around them, so juvenile birds are ecologically selective in their travel within the air mass. If the movements of waterfowl were in complete obedience to the flow of air, there would be a mass passage of western ducks over the inhospitable spruce forests of the Pre-Cambrian Shield, for this vast region is southeast of important duck-breeding grounds. While there is, indeed, some crossing of the Shield, we find the major trend of movement holding to the prairies. Sigurd Olson, who has lived many years within the Spruce Forest of northern Minnesota, writes me that he has "observed the flight of ducks in the Pre-Cambrian Shield from the Lake of the Woods to Lake Superior for 35 years and can say that there is no comparison with the flight over the prairies to the west. Along the western edge of the Shield there is a transition area where the flight may be fairly heavy, but as one penetrates more deeply into the Shield country, the numbers become appreciably less." In the same way, autumn juveniles may avoid drought areas or congregate in regions abundantly supplied with water or where there is a profusion of preferred food.

However the young waterfowl arrives on its wintering grounds — in company with experienced companions, or in the course of its wanderings — the juvenile's vernal return to the nesting place is to the familiar range of youthful experience. In view of the return of the young to the marsh of their first liberation (as in the experiments of Välikangas, 1933;

211

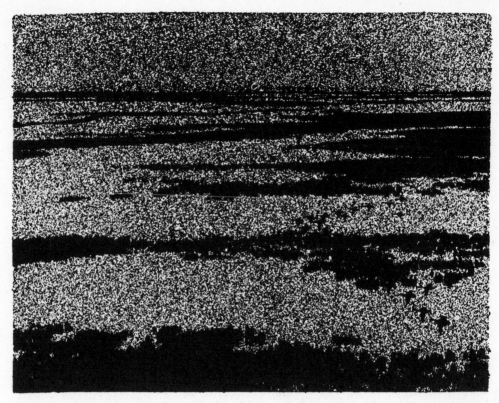

Long journeys are carried out in the absence of the sun or other celestial guides.

Williams and Kalmbach, 1943; McCabe, 1947; Foley, 1954b) there can be no inborn awareness in waterfowl of the direction of home. The course of homeward migration must be founded on experience of the world.

This discussion is not presented as an explanation of migrational orientation, but merely attempts to organize the problem, especially with respect to waterfowl. The evidence at hand suggests that adult waterfowl travel as experienced birds over a familiar range. By reference to the sun, as to a compass, or to environmental patterns, like those presented by waves, they may hold a direct course for some distance without visual reference to a familiar landscape. The studies of Matthews and Kramer (yet to be repeated with waterfowl) suggest that the sun may serve as the cue to the direction of home when the bird is displaced from familiar surroundings, but that such awareness hinges on the bird's distance from home. Long journeys are carried out in the absence of the sun or other celestial guides, but the gyrations in stormy weather suggest that ducks seek re-orientation when traveling under adverse weather conditions. There is ample evidence that migration does not always carry migrants to their destinations; in bad weather they may be blown far from their course or meet their destruction by accident. In the fall migration of juveniles toward the wintering grounds, vast numbers travel with experienced adults. Other young birds, still wandering randomly, gain temperate regions and wintering companions under the influence of the air mass in which they travel, such air flow showing a southward trend in autumn; and some few each year drift to Europe or to Siberia, carried there by the streams of wind flowing around the Greenland and the Aleutian low-pressure areas, the transoceanic air currents linking North America with the continents to its east and its west.

PART III

Traditions of Waterfowl

"It is by means of a sort of tradition that the migratory birds transmit to each other from generation to generation the knowledge of the airy paths they follow."

G. Reynaud, *The Laws of Orientation among Animals*

> "The role of tradition in evolution should not be so lightly dismissed without better evidence, for such dismissal tends to discourage further attempts to learn the facts of the case." John E. Cushing (1944)

16

Biological Traditions

IN THE summer of 1951 a crate of young Pintails traveled to New York State by rail. These ducklings had been hatched at Delta from eggs taken from wild nests in nearby stubble and meadowland. They were half-grown when they left Delta and had seen no countryside beyond the narrow view from the hatchery window. Their travels ended in central New York, where they were banded and released on Spicer's Marsh. Next spring, a survivor of the first autumn and winter, identified by her leg band, migrated back from the southland to nest and rear her young on Spicer's Marsh. This place had not known nesting Pintails in modern times. With all the wide northland to visit, she was faithful to the marsh of her maidenhood.

All week the wild geese passed over Delta, each flock going beyond the horizon to destinations we knew not where. Then, on the evening of the eighth day of April, there came thirty-six birds flying straight for the Station pond. They circled only once before alighting on their home waters. These were birds we had raised and to which we had presented freedom the November previous. The parents came back to their home; their children were with them.

I live on the prairies, but when I dream it is of mountains. Often, when there is a dark cloud bank in the west, I squint my eyes and pretend it is the Rockies. When soft spring winds blow, they feel like Chinooks to me. My parents are from Illinois, but I was born within sight of Long's Peak; and, however wonderful the prairie sunsets, I think of the mountains beyond.

217

Often when there is a dark cloud bank in the west, I squint my eyes
and pretend it is the Rocky Mountains.

Many songs are of places for which some men have great attachment:
songs of the prairies, the hills and the rivers of home. Homeland has been
inspiration for the poet; the artist paints this land he knows best. When
a man hears the melodies, reads the poetry, or sees pictures of home, he
cannot suppress nostalgia; for no matter where this place may be, all mankind has an inborn attachment to the region of early experience.

Crossing the Susquehanna at Havre de Grace was always the highlight
of my ride home from college at the Christmas holidays. Usually some
Canvasback were in sight of the bridge, and once they were strewn down
the river as far as I could see. Every wildfowler knows of the Susquehanna's Canvasback, and Heilner (1939) says that in the old days they sometimes "looked like plumes of smoke when they got up." A century earlier

218

(1831) Alexander Wilson had written that "on the first arrival of these birds in the Susquehanna near Havre de Grace, they are generally lean; but such is the abundance of their favorite food, that toward the beginning of November they are in pretty good order. They are excellent divers, and swim with great speed and agility. They sometimes assemble in such multitudes as to cover several acres of the river, and when they rise suddenly, produce a noise resembling thunder. They float about these shoals, diving and tearing up the grass by the roots which is the only part they eat. They are extremely shy, and can rarely be approached unless by strategy." In those days, as now, the Susquehanna was a major wintering place for the Canvasback; then, as now, it gave the best of Canvasback gunning. In Wilson's time the Chesapeake market gunners claimed that their bird was of a finer breed and "boldly asserted that only their waters were favored by this species, and all other ducks, which seemed to claim affinity, were a spurious race, unworthy of consanguinity. Hence at the same time when a pair of legitimate Canvasbacks, proudly exhibited from the mail coach, from Havre de Grace, readily sold for two dollars and fifty cents, a pair of the identical species, as fat, as heavy, as delicious, but which had been unfortunately killed in Delaware, brought only one dollar." *

The regularity of the Canvasbacks' return to the Susquehanna is but one example of the tie between waterfowl and their wintering grounds. As surely as the arrival of frost, the Greater Snow Geese come each year to Cap Tormente, Quebec, until all their worldly numbers are together there. Every autumn finds thousands of Redheads settling down on the Laguna Madre off the east coast of Mexico. The coming of Greater Scaups to Cayuga Lake in New York is an event of annual interest to upstate waterfowlers. Earlier in the discussions I have dwelt upon the return of ducks to McGinnis Slough, and there is no reason to burden this chapter with further testimony to the fact that ducks, geese, and many other birds come back to the same wintering places year after year, generation after generation.

What link ties them to their wintering quarters? To be sure, they have selected a habitat that provides suitable food and rest, the kind of environment to which we believe they have some innate attachment. With respect to the geographical location, however, there can be no genetic bond; the Canvasbacks have no inborn guidance to the Susquehanna, nor

* Mr. Glenn Martin told me that many Maryland wildfowlers still consider the Susquehanna Canvasbacks distinct — heavier and better eating than Canvasback shot elsewhere.

the Blue-winged Teal to McGinnis Slough. Our present understanding of innate behavior accounts for no inherited relation between a bird and a special geographic place. I believe that once a Canvasback has come to the Susquehanna, a Redhead to the Laguna Madre, or a Snow Goose to Cap Tormente, these same birds must find their way there again during another fall migration. And when juveniles travel southward in company with experienced adults, the Susquehanna, the Laguna Madre, and Cap Tormente are delivered from one generation to the next as traditions. True, some young stray; some do not go directly; some travel without the company of adults. But where such neophytes chance upon birds that have come to use a place regularly, they take this into the realm of their experience. In this way, the link between the Susquehanna River and the Canvasbacks that use it lives in the action of experienced birds, a tradition that ties the wintering behavior of modern birds to their ancestors of Wilson's time and long before.

In our everyday use of the word, *tradition* refers to story or verse or rule of family and community that has been handed down from our ancestors. Essentially, tradition is the delivery from father to son or from ancestors to posterity of knowledge, experience, and custom, carried through the years without written memorial. Many songs have come to us this way; tales of the frontier have reached us by word of mouth. On sidewalks and in schoolyards we listen to children repeating doggerel that no child ever reads.

We generally think of traditions as carried vocally, yet it is clear that the verbal link is not essential. For example, some rituals, such as the handshake or the tipped hat, survive in action alone. To be sure, some mothers must prompt their children, but instruction is often absent. Neophytes follow the actions of the experienced as when rising for the hymn in church; all do the same thing at the same time with no cues other than the direct movements of companions. Other human traditions are carried by symbol, as the lapel buttonhole and cuff buttons on a man's suit. Without a word, the young accept the customs of the fathers, eventually to see their own progeny following the same traditions, so that no son ever asks for cuff buttons, nor does he order a coat without these ornaments. The paths of our pioneers were followed by others, and the original routes have become traditional; many trails of the frontiersman are the roadways of today. In cities we follow by walk and curb the traditions of generations gone. Surely our daily lives are ruled far more closely by tradition than we generally realize. Although ancestors have not consciously directed us and we have not sought their guidance, we the moderns cannot escape the force of the traditional influences in the actions of living from day to day, from youth to old age.

The welfare of our daily lives is broadly influenced by this social inheritance. Health measures, safety procedures, the design of our homes, live by tradition. So it is that most North Americans own a toothbrush, and automobiles keep to one side of the road. Many traditions are of biological importance to the human race, and the pattern of social life is essentially a nongenetic inheritance passed from father to son or from elders to young. We realize the strength of this force on our lives when examining the mating behavior of human beings in different parts of the world. Monogamy is traditional for a large segment of the human race, but it is by no means universal; there are numerous patterns of marriage customs according to race and region. "No man ever looks at the world with pristine eyes. He sees it edited by a definite set of customs and institutions and ways of thinking. Even in his philosophical probings he cannot go behind these stereotypes; his very concepts of the true and the false will still have reference to his particular traditional customs . . . The life history of the individual is first and foremost an accommodation to the patterns and standards traditionally handed down in his community. From the moment of his birth, the customs into which he is born shape his experience and behavior. By the time he can talk, he is the little creature of his culture, and by the time he is grown and able to take part in its activities, its habits are his habits, its beliefs his beliefs, its impossibilities his impossibilities" (Benedict, 1946:4). These customs from the cradle onward have no biological transmission; they are nongenetic; they are a part of our heritage, but they are not genetically heritable.

Any study of human behavior, any searching investigation into our ethology, must give deep and careful examination to tradition. So too, in the animal world, where there is learned behavior, where individuals live in companionship, where there are communities and biological societies, there is the nongenetic link of intelligent action between one generation and the next. This being the case, it may be said that *tradition* is a proper biological term of special reference to behavior that is delivered by ancestors to progeny nongenetically.

When a bird learns from the behavior of its experienced companions, the objects, places or actions thus learned become traditional. Cushing

(1944) discusses the role of tradition in the feeding habits of birds and comes to the conclusion "that all evidence so far available favors the contention that the differences in specific food habits of various species of raptors are maintained much more through non-heritable factors passed on by the interaction of parental behavior with that of the offspring than they are through specifically heritable factors." He goes on to say that "there is abundant evidence that tradition may play an important role in the food habits of a great variety of birds besides raptors."

When a wild bird feeds on a cultivated domestic crop, there must be some link of tradition that carries this new food habit from one generation to the next. In the Mallard and Pintail, the habit of eating cereal grains is certainly traditional, and this likewise holds for ducks that feed on lettuce fields in the Far West or on rice in the southland. More obviously traditional, perhaps, is the acquired habit of opening milk bottles in the Great Tit and at least ten other British birds. Fisher and Hinde (1949) show how this milk-robbing has "become widespread in many parts of England and some parts of Wales, Scotland, and even Ireland." These authors concluded, after careful study, that "this source of food was actually discovered de novo by only a small proportion of the tit population, and was then passed on in some manner to other individuals." In such feeding traditions pioneers discover new sources of food by trial-and-error learning, perhaps as some human beings first learned to relish tomatoes. Companions eventually repeat their actions until the habit is acquired by many. Miller (1942) says that "habits and associations with respect to environment and particular landmarks are passed on nongenetically from generation to generation. Cultures or societies are formed in the higher vertebrates, as indeed in humans, and temporary barriers set up. Perhaps the hill-dwelling Song Sparrows of San Francisco Bay do not associate with those of the salt flats, figuratively and literally on the other side of the railway tracks, because of their upbringing." Snyder (1948), who discussed avian traditions in some detail, shows how a transplanted population of Mallards established a traditional breeding area in Ontario. Lorenz (1952), speaking of his beloved Jackdaws at Altenberg, tells how the modern birds "follow loyally all the traditions which reigned in the first colony, and which were transmitted to the present by Redgold."

Mayr (1942:53) speaks of the Yellow Wagtail of Europe, which "is nearly always a ground-nesting bird. About 1915 Schiermann (1939) found a little colony of these birds in which all individuals (eight or nine pairs) had built their nest off the ground on Artemisia plants. The birds came back year after year and built the same kind of nests, until the habitat was destroyed. It is extremely unlikely in this case (and many similar ones) that some sort of mutation had occurred which resulted in the changed habit. It is much more likely that one bird started the new fashion and others 'learned' from him, until the entire population had 'acquired' the new habit. Such new habits are usually lost as quickly as they are acquired, unless they add measurably to the survival value of the species." On the Delta Marsh, the Redhead usually nests over water in emergent vegetation, but some few individuals nest on dry land, sometimes quite far from water, in situations where one would expect to find Mallards. I have found such land nests of Redheads in loose groups, with more than one in the same restricted area. This looks like traditional nesting behavior.

Nice (1943:150) decided that in the Song Sparrow, the pattern of song "is innate, but the quality may be imitated. Particular songs may be improvised, or may be adopted from some other Song Sparrow." Mayr (1942:54) says that "it has been known to the field ornithologist for a long time that in some birds the song varies from district to district. . . . The most remarkable geographic variation of song and call-notes that has been described occurs in the European Chaffinch. Promptoff (1930) called attention to the fact that this species tends to break up into a number of geographic song races. Sick (1939), who gives a general survey of the literature on geographic variation of song, found that the so-called 'rain-call' of the Chaffinch is subject to an even more remarkable localization. This call, whose exact biological significance is still somewhat obscure, is uttered by the male within his breeding territory. In the township of Stuttgart, southern Germany, three sharply characterized rain-calls occur, of which one is restricted to the three-hundred-year-old park which extends along the valley floor for a distance of three kilometers. The second call is restricted to the hills to the west, and the third to the hills to the east of the town. A 'hybridzone' is found where two of these dialect districts meet, but distributional barriers, such as railroad yards, prevent such hybridization in other places, so that districts of pure call notes approach each other occasionally within a distance of only five hundred meters. Much circumstantial evidence indicates that these call notes are not genetically fixed, but conditioned. The young Chaffinch learns these call notes from his father and from the neighboring males and he either stays at or always returns to the locality where he was born. The exact history of the parks of Stuttgart is known, and it is evident that a period of three hundred years was available for the development of the striking 'park dialect.' The significance of such nongenetic changes as contributory factors to isolating mechanisms is evident (see also Cushing 1941)."

Thorpe (1954) studied the pattern of the Chaffinch song by means of the sound spectrograph and from this concluded that the normal song "has a very restricted inborn basis." Some learning of song takes place during the bird's early life, but the final song form is acquired during a period of a few weeks during the first spring.

Nice (1943:264) says that "apparently the Song Sparrow recognizes enemies by both inborn and learned patterns. In nature, the behavior of the adults must be of great importance in the forming of conditioned patterns in the young." She concludes that "experience may be handed down non-genetically from generation to generation particularly in matters regarding protection from enemies." All evidence suggests that wild ducks learn the nature of their relationship with man, fear or lack of fear being transmitted from the experienced to the inexperienced. Hunters claim the Mallard as the "wildest" of all ducks in autumn, the wariest, the most difficult to approach with gun. When young from wild eggs are reared in captivity, however, they are "tame" in the presence of man, showing no fear of him.[*] This awareness of man as a "friend" is transmitted from one bird to another, from flock to flock, until each year the number of fearless birds of wild origin in the Delta pond is increased. We note the companion influence when a small band of Blue-winged Teal alights near the tame ducks. As I approach these wild birds, they make departure movements. But when their companions, who know me as a friend, show no escape reactions, the wild birds remain; and although they are obviously more nervous, they usually do not take flight. In a few days they may be approached on the pond as closely as any of the old residents and are completely "settled down."

Surely some birds are tied traditionally to certain places. Not far from Delta are the dancing grounds of a band of Sharp-tailed Grouse, which local farmers recall as having been in regular use for at least sixty years. Although many generations of grouse have come and gone, the living link of action ties modern birds to the same plot of prairie as was used by their

[*] And yet there is such a thing as "heritable wildness" (Leopold, 1944) in waterfowl. When Mallard and Baldpate are hatched from wild eggs and reared by man in captivity, the Baldpate, according to my experience at Delta, never becomes as tame or fearless of man as the Mallard.

224

ancestors more than half a century ago. In New York State, Emlen (1938) found that in 1932 the locations and boundaries of winter Crow territories were essentially the same as those reported twenty-five, fifty, and, in one case, one hundred and twenty-five years before. Austin (1949) describes Japanese netting places that have been used by wild ducks from time immemorial. The ponds where the ducks rest are kept as sanctuary, the birds captured in cast nets at passes as they arrive and depart each morning and evening. At one pond, netting privileges are still held by a guild established more than a hundred years ago. One of the best known traditional ties is that of the Whooping Crane, with the last few coming back from the north each autumn to the Aransas Refuge in Texas. Cushing (1941b) discusses the regular return of Ravens to their roosting place and says that "it is probable that an individual acquires rather than inherits its special attachment for a particular roosting site, even though it probably inherits the ability to form this attachment." Hamerstrom (1942:35) believed that in the continuity of winter territories of the Chickadee "the key lies in tradition. Instead of repeating this random building up from a fresh start, the territory begins its second winter with a nucleus of old-timers." Moffitt (1937) tells of a group of Western Canada Geese that used the same wintering quarters in northwestern California for at least fifty years. Stresemann (1934) refers to Palmén's (1874) hypothesis that some birds hold strongly to certain migration routes that are handed from one generation to the next in a traditional manner.

In some mammals, certain traditions such as the game trail are handed down by record. An Elk need never see another to follow the traditional route that generations of its ancestors have taken out of the high country each autumn. At Delta the White-tailed Deer arrived in the late 1930s. Before this no big game trails had survived from pristine times, and the first deer pioneered their way about the marsh. Now, eighteen or twenty years later, with none of the original stock alive, the modern White-tails follow in the footsteps of their forefathers, and the main deer trails are those established by the first deer. Some birds leave records for tradition, such as the bulky nest of the Osprey, the chalkings of the Peregrine Falcon, or the mud workings of the Cliff Swallow. Mostly, however, avian traditions are carried in action alone. Such passing of experience by action may be local and brief, like the opening of milk bottles. Or the experience may be long and regional, like the flight of the Whooping Crane to Texas or the Canvasback to the Susquehanna. There is no intent upon the part of the elders to "teach" the

225

young or the inexperienced. Yet the directness of experienced behavior is the medium by which one bird learns a custom or a region that another bird has used, and by this unconscious delivery, the cultures and traditions, new and old, are handed down through the ages.

As we examine the traditions of food and place, we are aware of certain characteristics that distinguish this inheritance from the innate. Firstly, a tradition may have spontaneous beginning at any time in the life of any individual, as genetic mutations cannot. Secondly, as Mayr (1942) points out, traditions may be "lost as quickly as acquired." A tradition may have its beginning today and its ending next year, after delivery to but one generation; or a habit acquired this afternoon by an individual or a group may live for many years, perhaps for centuries. Traditions that have lived for unknown generations beyond the beginning of history may die forever overnight. Errington (1941:99) postulated for the Bob-white that "traditions die along with populations during periods of great mortality." The link is always in the actions of experienced individuals. When these are lost or killed or no longer active, the tradition is ended. It is this nonheritable spontaneity of tradition that permits the establishment of a breeding colony of Canada Geese almost anywhere a man may choose for the starting of young birds.

We observe that there are two ways of delivering avian traditions. There is, first, the direct tie between parent and offspring. In numerous species, like the ducks, the parent-child relationship is short and family traditions are thus weak. In others, such as the geese and cranes, where the family holds together for a long time, family traditions are strong. Second, there is the companion bond whereby group or community traditions are delivered from one experienced bird to another, although there may be no blood relationships. The use of a sanctuary and the feeding travel to grain fields are examples of such social inheritance. We of course are aware of these patterns of inheritance in our own human lives, how each family has its individual codes of behavior passed on from father to son, while every community maintains traditions of action that concern all its families. So it is that in man and in many of the lower animals, certain cultures, habits and actions are delivered nongenetically from one generation to the next and, as Cushing and others have suggested, we may properly refer to such nonheritable actions as traditions.

"The pioneer that carries the range a little further forward starts from a base where it has associated with companions and found food plentiful; and when the impulse to live in society again asserts itself, it not only repeats its former experience but hands on the habit thus acquired to those of the next generation that happen to accompany it." Eliot Howard (1920)

17

Building New Traditions

To THE Mission San Juan Capistrano, in California, come Cliff Swallows each March, returning to build their gourdlike nests under the Mission's eaves. The pastor, the Reverend Vincent Lloyd-Russell, wrote me that the pioneer swallows first took residence on the buildings in 1776. Originally, the Cliff or Eave Swallow was confined in its nesting to natural features of the land such as cliffs and overhanging walls. With the coming of civilization, the structures of man offered ideal nesting situations; barns and other buildings were quickly accepted so that, as Bent (1942: 465) points out, the swallows "multiplied and spread from place to place where they were never seen before." Far and wide over the land they claimed new homes, deep over the prairies, far into the woodlands, miles beyond their pristine nesting range. Lewis (1939a) tells of a Nova Scotia farmer who dates the history of a barnside colony back "ninety or a hundred years," and he mentions another colony with a history going back to at least sixty years. Grinnell (1937) believed that the pioneers were yearlings; and in the colony starting on the Life Sciences Building, in Berkeley, California, there was a span of six years between the completion of the building and the establishment of the first swallow nests thereon. At Assessippi, Manitoba, however, Thompson (1891:608) noted that "although the carpenters have scarcely finished the new mill, and hotel, over three hundred pairs of Cliff Swallows have begun to build under the eaves." Buss (1942) traced the history of a Wisconsin Cliff Swallow colony which started with one nest on the barn of Cory Bodeman in 1904; the birds returned each year in increasing numbers, until by 1942 there were 2,015 nests.

Equally interesting in its pioneering is the Arkansas Kingbird. This is not a member of the original fauna of Manitoba and is not mentioned in Thompson's (Seton) 1891 list "The Birds of Manitoba." The first record is from Oak Lake, Manitoba, in 1907; this kingbird reached Winnipeg in 1912, and by 1921 it was breeding commonly in southern Manitoba.[*] Now, forty-five years after its arrival, it is a typical bird of Manitoba's agricultural region; there is hardly a farmstead without at least one pair. In a similar way it has invaded Minnesota (Roberts, 1932) and Saskatchewan.

Such enlargements of range frequently go hand in hand with environmental changes.[†] In some species, such as the Cliff Swallow and the Arkansas Kingbird, the breeding area is occupied only during the spring and summer, the birds migrating back to their wintering grounds after the young are reared. In others, like the Prairie Chicken and the exotic English Sparrow, new ranges are held through the year. Many hunters think that this pinnated grouse is a native of Manitoba, but Coues (1874) said that "I have no reason to believe that it occurs at all in northwestern Minnesota or northern Dakota . . . I have met with no indication of its occurrence north of the United States boundary," an observation in which Thompson (1891) concurred. Leopold (1940) traced the spread of the Hungarian Partridge in Wisconsin, where it moved "by slow overflow into the vacant territory." Kessel (1953) has traced the far-flung pioneerings of the European Starling in North America. In Manitoba, where the Hungarian Partridge is a recent arrival, its spread now has covered the agricultural region of the province, and locally its coveys have developed traditional territories where the birds may be found in the same places year after year. That is to say, the history of a covey in a locality is older than any members of the band. Similar pioneerings are well known in the Cottontail Rabbit and in the White-tailed Deer.

In waterfowl, Hochbaum (1946) pointed out that the river ducks are the most rapid pioneers, the Canvasback, Redhead, and other diving ducks enlarging their ranges more slowly. In the Mallard, Pintail, and other river ducks, the young are on the wing by early summer, hence have time to gain broad geographical experience. Moreover, there is a wide tolerance of nesting situations in these species, so that as long as there is water, they may settle down to find nesting cover somewhere nearby. In the diving ducks,

[*] A. G. Lawrence, "Chickadee Notes," *Winnipeg Free Press*, May 30, 1952.
[†] Mayr (letter) points out that "range changes are sometimes due to changes of the habitat, sometimes independent of it, such as the fantastic range expansion of *Streptopelia decaocto*, the Collared Turtle Dove, in Europe."

228

In ducks the parent-child relationships are short, and family traditions are thus weak. Redhead ducklings, such as these, are often abandoned by the mother several weeks before they can fly.

the young mature later in the summer, thus enjoying a shorter period of breeding-ground experience their first year. Moreover, they are much less tolerant of variations in the nesting cover, and they do not pioneer into a region for several years because of the slower development of a suitable habitat. When water comes to the dry prairies of Saskatchewan, or when a new lake is established, Mallards and some other river ducks are often there as nesters the very next year, but the arrival of the diving ducks is delayed until their nesting cover has become established. In 1945 the surface water remained on the farmlands of the Portage Plains and Red River Valley through the spring and summer for the first time in at least a decade. Mallards and Pintails and, less frequently, Shovellers and Blue-winged Teal settled down on these areas, and breeding pairs were scattered over country that had seen no nesting ducks for several waterfowl generations. None of the diving ducks moved to these new waters, which were lacking in emergent vegetation. In the same way, large numbers of Pintails invaded southwestern Saskatchewan, where there was an abundance of new water in the spring of 1952 (Gollop, Lynch, and Hyska, 1952). Bue, Blankenship, and Marshall (1952) have shown how the waterfowl advanced to occupy the new stock-watering ponds of western South Dakota. In such range extensions there may be a previous history of waterfowl breeding in past years, but often the period of drought is longer than the life-expectancy of ducks; hence the regions are entirely new to the modern generation that moves in during a wet cycle.

New areas often remain wet for only a few years; then water and ducks are gone again. On the Portage Plains most of the sloughs of 1945 held water and nesting ducks each year until 1950, a span of six consecutive breeding seasons. By 1951 some had become dry and duckless; by 1952 most were dry. With ducks there is an ebb and flow of breeding populations at the edge of permanent ranges. Many large marshes, such as the Delta, never lose all their water or their ducks. The sloughs and potholes of the true prairie are relatively stable. But in the western mixed prairie, water and ducks, like agricultural crops, fluctuate severely.

The degree of pioneering in ducks, it seems to me, depends on the proximity of new areas to established nesting grounds. In the Dakotas and the prairie provinces of Canada there is a large and established breeding population in the marshes and smaller water areas of the true prairie. In years when the water comes to the shallow depressions of the western plains region, the shiftings of breeders originates from the dense population centers not far away. Farther south and east on less densely populated breeding grounds, there are fewer waterfowl centers of abundance from which birds may overflow. In the Delta region I have noticed that ducks pioneer more quickly and more abundantly to new ponds within ten miles of the marsh than to new waters beyond that range. I presume that most such pioneers are young birds approaching their first breeding season. Pioneering does not contradict the homing behavior of young females that may establish themselves near their natal marsh or in an area learned during juvenile wanderings.

The story of the Gadwall, on the other hand, shows breeding populations and probably recent pioneerings on the Atlantic Coast, far from the major nesting range, which lies northwest of the Mississippi Valley (Griffith, 1946). Certainly the new nesting groups of this species on Long Island (Sedwitz et al., 1948) and in Maryland (Springer and Stewart, 1950) are pioneerings. Most of these records are for refuge marshes, where nesting conditions have been made favorable for the species and where shooting has been controlled. Robert A. Wells writes me that there are recent pioneerings of the Ring-necked Duck in small lakes of the Adirondack Mountains, the bird now breeding on waters where it was unknown before.

In the Canada Goose there is not the same pioneering as in ducks, in breeding situations at least. The close family and group ties hold birds to given locations from which they expand slowly. Despite the existence of large regions of prime goose-breeding habitat, much of this is not occupied by geese. Such vacancies cannot be explained entirely in terms of ecology, for where we introduce a flock of Canada Geese, such as the plantings at Delta or the Lower Souris Refuge, the flocks thrive in the new locations. Hawkins, Wellein, and Crissey (1950) covered a large part of the West shore of the Hudson Bay in an aerial waterfowl survey during the breeding season, and they found that "goose ranges continued without interruption, so far as we could tell, from Wawa Lake southwest of Moosonee to Eskimo Point. Along this entire strip, however, the only place where Canadas appeared to be nesting in large numbers was on Akimiski Island. Otherwise, the population appeared to be widely scattered." I take it that faithfulness to the breeding place and reluctance to pioneer to new regions are evidence of the strength of family traditions in the Canada Goose.

Faithful as they are to their home range, however, geese are elastic in their use of migration routes and wintering quarters. Jack Miner's sanctuary, in southern Ontario, gives the history of a new goose tradition, the birds being few in the beginning and increasing in the lifetime of one man to many thousands more. Such also was the modest start of goose traditions at Horseshoe Lake, Illinois. "Originally, Horseshoe Lake was an Oxbow of the Mississippi River, but its present location is about two miles from the river channel," writes A. S. Hawkins (letter). "During floods, the river still spreads over it. More recently this was a swamp, which early in the present century became dry enough so that a fire burned deep holes in its bed. Horseshoe Lake resulted, and today a dam holds the water at a fairly constant level. Old-timers report that Horseshoe Lake used to offer good duck hunting but not good goose shooting. For at least 50 years, Horseshoe Lake Island has been farmed, although during one period, brush claimed it for a few years. Probably geese have fed on Horseshoe Lake Island as long as it has been farmed, but they did not use the lake until the dam was built. Formerly a hunting club, Horseshoe Lake became a refuge in 1927. The first estimate in wintering numbers places the 1928–29 population at between 1,000 and 1,900 (Leopold, 1931:206); by 1953 the mid-winter inventory of the flock showed a total of 143,000." Originally the feeding places around Horseshoe Lake had no superiority over other parts of the valley. When the refuge offered protected resting grounds, however, an element of advantage was added. Despite heavy and ever increasing gun-pressure between refuge and feeding places, the protected rest area attracted more and more geese till, as Hanson and Smith (1950) pointed out, about 50 per cent of the Mississippi Valley population came to roost on Horseshoe Lake.

At Jack Miner's and at Horseshoe Lake, formerly gooseless places have become the rendezvous of tens of thousands, the many following the trails of the original few. These famous gathering grounds continue to hold their numbers. Elsewhere are records of broken traditions. Grant's Lake, Manitoba, was the last stop of the Lesser Snow and Blue Geese before their long journey to James Bay. Here they gathered in such great numbers that Greshem (Soper, 1942) could describe flights where "the leading birds of the flock were dropping into the lake while the tail of the flock was still out of sight." Then suddenly all of this ended: Grant's Lake dwindled and dried; the geese came no more; where the clangor was once deafening, the land was now silent of wavies except in May, when they flew over en route to James Bay. The habit of unrecorded generations came to an abrupt close.°

The geese of Horseshoe Lake and Grant's Lake seem to offer firm evidence that there is no inborn tie of waterfowl to the geographic parts of their continental ranges. Here are the beginnings and the endings of traditions, built recently at Horseshoe Lake, dying over winter at Grant's Lake. Attachments to place live with the birds from generation to generation, growing as the advantages of use remain constant, ending when the places are no longer useful or tolerable.

Successful explorations and rapid extensions of the breeding range imply a constant population pressure. For centuries the force of this internal stress in the Cliff Swallow and the Arkansas Kingbird was met with inhospitable breeding conditions; but within a few years after man altered the face of the land in their favor, some individuals overflowed into new environments to take occupancy. So rapid were these invasions, sometimes, that human settlers believed the birds had always been there. A careful study reveals pioneerings of many kinds of birds which we now casually accept as part of the native fauna. In regions once forested, the opening of woodland for agriculture favored the Meadowlark, Bobolink, Vesper Sparrow, and many others that ventured into country which never before had held nesting populations. Where trees and thickets invaded prairies, woodland birds enlarged their ranges in the same way. For southern Wisconsin, Schor-

° There is local disagreement on this point, some contending that the geese abandoned the area in the face of the abundance of aircraft from wartime training centers.

ger (1941:105) says "it may be stated in general that the Crow was distributed sparsely in the State prior to 1855, became common in the southern portion by 1875, and abundant by 1890." As the land changed, pioneering Crows and Meadowlarks, Robins and Song Sparrows moved in to take residence in country their kind had never occupied before, migrating to and from these new places and delivering the traditions to their progeny,* so that now these regions are firmly established within the natural ranges of the species.

When the Arkansas Kingbird moved into Manitoba, it extended its migratory range northward by at least two hundred miles, to such an outpost as Lake St. Martin.† Even though this bird was not a member of the native fauna, it is now among the most regular of spring and fall migrants. Here, within the span of a few years, we have the evolution of a migration carrying many individuals hundreds of miles into land their race never used before. The urge of these Arkansas Kingbirds to migrate must be sexual and inborn, regardless of the newness of the places to which they migrate. The recent origin of the migration, however, seems to give further evidence that the route is learned; the short time these kingbirds have lived in Manitoba cannot have been sufficient to permit the establishment of inborn ties to their new geographic locations. This same thing, as suggested by Mayr and Meise (1930), must have taken place in response to the ecological changes in the wake of receding glaciers. As Allen (1880) wrote, "Such migration must have been at first 'incipient and gradual,' extending and strengthening as the cold-wave Ice Age receded and opened up a wider area within which existence in summer became possible." There is strong evidence, then, that the length of migrations was extended by ecological changes following the recession of glaciers in the same way as new migrations accompanied the changes wrought by man. In the first instance, the pioneerings of birds must have been slow; in the modern example of the Arkansas Kingbird, the deep advance into new migratory range has been accomplished in a twinkling of history. Probably both slow and rapid pioneerings became established in the same way, as the actions of experi-

* We must point out that there are some species, of limited number to be sure, that seem to have no ties to the land, birds that pioneer to new breeding places one year, never to appear there again for many seasons, wanderers such as the Pine Siskin, the crossbills, and the Evening Grosbeak, which, as Roberts (1932:365) points out, are possessed of a "gypsy-like wanderlust" that takes them "now here, now there and only irregularly and seemingly by chance back again to the same locality." These "eccentric creatures" are pioneers leaving behind no followers, explorers delivering no traditions except of wandering.

† A. G. Lawrence, in "Chicadee Notes," *Winnipeg Free Press*, May 29, 1953.

enced birds carried new traditions from one generation to the next. Many hundreds of years elapsed in the recession of glacial Lake Agassiz before the Upland Plover arrived on the prairie border of modern Lake Manitoba, and yet these plovers have traditional rather than genetic ties to this land in the same way as the Arkansas Kingbirds which arrived on the neighboring farmsteads only a few years ago.

Salomonsen (1951), among others, has presented evidence of the response to changes of climate taking place in our time. "Recent climatic change in the arctic and temperate zones of the Northern Hemisphere," he says, "has caused an amelioration of the conditions of life of many animals and plants. It is a well-known fact that the breeding-area of a number of birds belonging to the Mediterranean, European or the Siberian Taigoa fauna has been pushed to the north in the last decades." He describes in detail the immigration of the Fieldfare to Greenland; and Gudmundsson (1951) discusses the relation between climatic changes in Iceland and the arrival of pioneers establishing new breeding ranges there. It is interesting that the pioneers to Iceland and Greenland have come from Europe rather than from North America; and, indeed, Salomonsen (1951:519) shows how the movement of the Fieldfare to Greenland was related to the favorable flow of winds blowing from Europe around the "top" of the Greenland low-pressure area.[*]

Students of tradition will study the transplantings of game species to learn something of the artificial establishment of pioneers. Leopold (1933: 87) points out that "transplantation of game is as old as civilization," and with some kinds, such as the Pheasant in Great Britain, the originally exotic species has become established as a part of the native fauna, with a local history running back centuries. By and large, artificial introductions have been most successful with nonmigratory species, but Delacour (1954: 161) tells us that the Canada Goose was introduced into Europe from North America in the seventeenth century. "It soon became well established and hundreds are still living in a feral state in Great Britain today." Although not of themselves inclined to pioneer new breeding colonies, geese respond well to artificial transplantings. In North America there have been many successful "seedings" of Canada Geese, breeding colonies having been established on new ranges or in areas where the original populations were killed when the country was settled. New colonies of geese may be started

[*] For other discussions of pioneerings see Cowan (1937), Fisher (1951), Keve and Udvardy (1951), Salomonsen (1948), Svärdson and Durango (1951), and Välikangas (1951).

A Pintail hen, hatched at Delta, Manitoba, and released as a flightless duckling on a
New York marsh, returned to the New York range of her juvenile
experience, there to nest and raise her family.

with pinioned, hand-reared pairs whose progeny are allowed to migrate, or
with wild-trapped birds set free on a new range before they are fledged.
The object is to start with young birds that will have their first flight experience at the site of the new colony. Old birds used as breeding stock must
be fully pinioned, not simply wing-clipped; else they will fly home when
the next wing molt is completed, taking their young along with them.

The transplanting of ducks is a technique by which breeding populations of such species as Redhead or Gadwall may be restored as native
breeders to ranges where the original populations have been "burned out."
Young, hand-reared juveniles are released on new marshes before they are
able to fly, at five to seven weeks of age, and the females surviving the first
hunting season and fall migration may be expected to return in spring to
these places of first flight experience, there to rear their young, like the Spicer
Marsh Pintail mentioned on page 217 (Foley, 1954b). The success of such
plantings hinges on the willingness of local sportsmen to delay the opening
of their wildfowling season until the breeding females and young birds
have dispersed from their home marshes. "If there is practical value to be
derived from the release of hand-reared stock other than satisfying the local
gunner on an immediate basis," Brakhage says (1953:474), "it must be
realized through the return of birds to nest. If the surviving individuals return to their marshes of liberation to nest in the following years and thus

replace a 'burned out' breeding population or colonize a new area, a long term value may be realized. But it cannot be considered sound management to stock birds which do not survive long enough to reproduce."

In the Mallard, heredity apparently plays an important role in the success of plantings. The wild Mallard is the source stock from which the "call" ducks and most domestic varieties originated, and the mixing of wild and domestic blood may take place on game farm ranges. Such birds may fail to survive or to migrate when released in a wild environment, and the experience with such mixed strains prompted Lincoln (1934:81) to say that "efforts to restore marshes with artificially produced Mallards are doomed to failure." More recent investigations (Benson, 1939; Brakhage, 1953; Foley, 1954a; and Wells, 1954) suggest, however, that when hand-reared Mallards are planted on wild ranges, the survivors of the first hunting season may migrate in a pattern not different from that of wild-bred birds. At Delta we have found that hand-reared females return with unbanded, wild-bred drakes as their mates.

It is unfortunate that more attention has not been given in North America to the artificial re-establishment of breeding traditions in some of of the rarer species. The Trumpeter Swan, when reared by hand, breeds well in captivity, and young from such hand-reared stock might be used to repopulate locations where favorable breeding habitat still remains. The species was captive-bred for many years in Europe, but unfortunately in its own country there never has been a reservoir of hand-reared stock. And I feel that it is only through captive-breeding that the Whooping Crane can be saved from extinction, for the hazards of the long, traditional journey may be too dangerous for the few young that are produced each year. The old birds, of course, must be left to follow their migration to and from their northern breeding grounds, for adults would not breed in confinement. But some young stock of these wild birds must be brought to captivity at the earliest possible age and, under the care of trained "keepers," raised where they may grow to maturity in a favorable, yet protected, environment. If this is done in time — if, at the rate of two or three young each year, a captive breeding stock may develop in a protected situation — then eventually some full-winged progeny of these long-lived birds may be set free with the wild adults to learn from them the traditional flyways to and from their ancestral breeding grounds. By captive-breeding the Wildfowl Trust has given substantial increase to the numbers of the rare Hawaiian Goose (Scott and Boyd, 1951, 1954, 1955).

236

18

Tradition and Racial Isolation

ON EVERY hand is evidence that groups of animals isolated from each other will vary. Poultry, cattle, and hunting dogs have been divided into their many domestic varieties by the artificial isolation of selected breeding stock. In the same way, many kinds of barnyard ducks have stemmed from the wild Mallard. Similarly, over a vastly greater period of time, natural isolation has divided many species of wild animals into distinct races; and it was this that gave Darwin his inspiration concerning the pattern of evolution. Before Darwin a species was generally believed to be a distinct creation, with the specific characters showing no variation from a certain type. As specimens from many regions were examined, however, it was found that there often occurred differences in size and color, and this discovery led to the description of geographical races or subspecies. The Song Sparrow is a good example of this regional variation; the A.O.U. Committee on Classification and Nomenclature now recognizes thirty-one subspecies for North America (F. C. Lincoln, letter), ranging from the large, dark Aleutian Song Sparrow of the Alaskan islands to the small, pale Desert Song Sparrow of the southwestern United States.

Geographical isolation is the most widely recognized and probably the most important factor separating different units of population. Ford (1949: 92) reminds us that geographic isolation is established not only by "barriers such as water or land (to terrestrial or aquatic forms respectively), or those due to altitude, but that mere distance will prevent a free interchange of hereditary material between individuals at opposite extremes even of a continuous range." Mayr (1942:106) defines the subspecies as a "geographically localized subdivision of the species, which differs genetically and taxonomically from other subdivisions of the species."

In many birds, such as the Downy Woodpecker, Song Sparrow, Robin, and Yellow Warbler, to name only a few, there are numerous races which

237

are separated more by space than by sharp geographical barriers, and their many subspecies blend together from one region to another without abrupt divisions between two races. Where space is the major isolating factor, we have what Mayr (1942:244) calls "subspeciation by distance." "The formation of local races in the absence of distributional barriers will occur," Mayr tells us, "whenever the combined effects of recurrent local mutations and of selection pressure outweigh the effect of the interchange of individuals between local populations."

Free as the wind to fly wherever it will, a Song Sparrow wintering in Georgia could just as easily fly northeast to the Atlantic Coast as northwest to central Canada; but by force of experience it travels to its former breeding place in Manitoba, where it is geographically isolated from some winter companions that migrated to Maine. Its tie to Manitoba can hardly be considered a genetic bond. The return is to the place of experience; and this, as Nice (1937) has shown for the Song Sparrow, is the region of youth, often near the birthplace. Manitoba is the *birthright* of its Song Sparrows; their inheritance of Manitoba experiences is traditional. The homing behavior which brings the migrant back to traditional breeding grounds establishes the geographic isolation upon which racial subdivision depends. To put it another way: if Song Sparrows did not return to their home region year after year, if they spread their breeding ranges widely without regard to birthplace, there would not be the same degree of geographical isolation that now exists, and we could not expect the same racial variation. Cushing (1941a:107) observes that "if we are to consider the homing reaction as a potential isolating mechanism, it may be classifiable as on par with geographic isolation (see Dobzhansky, Genetics and Origin of Species, 1937: 230), although itself physiological in nature. Such non-genetic mechanisms, while presumably of a relatively temporary nature, theoretically precede the rise of genetic isolation within populations." So it may be that in some species the primary factor in isolation is the tie to the home breeding range.

In species with broad ranges we might expect those kinds possessing the strongest traditional ties to have the greatest racial variations. This holds with the geese. With their firm regional and family traditions, the geese follow a pattern of behavior which must encourage the development of variation. Mayr (1942:242) says that "no other arctic or subarctic bird breaks up into so many pronounced races as the geese. The Canada Geese of the genus *Branta* have some 6 to 9 geographic races in North America, some of which are so different that some authors propose to put them in 3 or 4 different species." Mayr (1951:97) notes further that in the Canada Geese "it occasionally happens that neighboring nesting colonies differ in body size, voice (honking vs. cackling), nesting site (sea-coast vs. island), nest (mound vs. scrape), migration season and other features." Delacour (1951) recognizes only one species, *Branta canadensis,* which, however, he divides into twelve subspecies. All of these have the white cheek patch, black head and neck "stocking," and similar body patterns; but they vary widely in size, voice, darkness of plumage, and behavior. The brant of North America show three distinct subspecies (Delacour 1954), while the Snow Goose and the White-fronted Goose each have two.

It is quite another story for North American game ducks.[*] Taxonomists recognize subspecific variation in only one species, the Florida Duck.[†] All the other game ducks show no racial divisions on this continent. Moreover, some North American species are quite the same as those of northern Europe, and Mayr (1942:241) says that "many of the Holarctic ducks, such as the Gadwall (*Anas strepera*), Shoveller (*Spatula clypeata*) and so forth, have no subspecies, or only one or two very slight ones, in spite of their wide circumpolar distribution." This monotypic pattern apparently stems from the absence of traditional ties in the male. In the gregarious societies of winter there is opportunity for the meeting of males and females from widely separated breeding places. In such matings, the male, faithful to his bride, follows her wherever she may go, spreading hereditary material widely, allowing no true isolation. Thus taxonomists cannot distinguish a Minnesota-bred Pintail from one hatched in Alaska.

This monotypic characteristic in ducks is evidence that the waterfowl flyways of North America, described by Lincoln (1935a), are not strictly isolated entities. There must be free genetic mixing of populations from different flyways, and evidence of this overlap is shown in the patterns of dispersal reported by Aldrich *et al.* (1949), such as the "round-robin" migration of the Pintail, and in the winter vagrancies of the Ring-necked Duck.

In the light of the wide winter movements of most ducks, the narrow range of the Florida Duck seems significant. This is not a migratory species, and, though there is a seasonal shift from one place to another, the breeding grounds and wintering range are approximately the same (Bent, 1923:72, 75). The eastern race of the Florida Duck, *Anas fulvigula fulvigula,* has

[*] All North American ducks except the eiders and tree ducks.

[†] The "Red-legged Black Duck" (*Anas rubripes rubripes*), once regarded as a distinct race, is now known to be the adult male of the Common Black Duck (Shortt, 1943).

both its breeding and wintering range in the state of Florida, whereas the western race, *A. f. maculosa*, lives the year round in Texas and Louisiana. Within these restrictions there is no wide dispersal of males in winter, hence little chance for the cross-mating of birds from widely separated breeding places. Consequently the geographic division between eastern and western birds has been sharp; the genetic changes recognizable to the taxonomist have developed from this spatial isolation.

Among the Eiders of the genus *Somateria*, four closely related kinds are recognized: the American Eider, the Hudson Bay Eider, the Northern Eider, and the Pacific Eider. The American, Hudson Bay, and Northern Eiders are so closely related as to be considered subspecies of one another, and the Pacific Eider is just enough different to be given specific recognition by some authorities. Bent (1925:94) points out that there is an overlapping of range in the American and Northern Eiders, but this is slight, and the main breeding and wintering places of the Northern Eider are well to the northeast of the ranges used by the American Eider. The Pacific Eider is still further separated in its winter and summer ranges; and despite the possibility of some overlapping with the summer range of the Northern Eider, matings with the American Eider could result only by rare chance.

In considering the distribution of the Florida Duck and the Eiders, the relation between geographic isolation and subspecific differences seems to be one of cause and effect. The variation could hardly occur if Florida Ducks mixed thoroughly on the winter ranges or if all Eiders shared the same wintering places. Whether or not this regional isolation is genetic or traditional, however, is a question we will not try to answer here; for in these instances it may be impossible to separate the genetic and traditional inheritances.

Tradition may have been a factor in establishing the geographic races in the crane family. Cranes, as already noted, are like geese in their strong family bonds during migration and in their firm regional traditions. Taxonomists recognize four subspecies of the brown crane of North America, the Little Brown Crane of the far north, the Sandhill Crane of the middle latitudes, the Florida Sandhill Crane, and the Cuban Sandhill Crane. The Coot, a close relative of the cranes, is more like the ducks in its habits. Its breeding range is spread widely over North America, being much the same as that of our game waterfowl; and it joins in large gregarious bands on the wintering grounds. Present evidence suggests that some Coots pair on the wintering grounds, thereby effecting the same genetic mixing as

The nesting habitat of Mallard and Pintail on the treeless plains is nothing
like the environment used by these species in Manitoba.

occurs in ducks. Taxonomists recognize the Coots nesting in Ontario as the
same race that breeds in California.

The weight of the discussion has been placed on waterfowl, which, it
must be acknowledged, have patterns of behavior quite different from those
of many other kinds of birds. For example, the family unity in migration,
which builds such strong traditions for the geese and cranes, is found only
in a few other groups. Not many species accomplish their pairing in gregarious winter companies, as do the ducks. More typical is the behavior
of the passerines, in which the family usually dissolves soon after the young
are able to take care of themselves and in which pairing takes place at or
near the nesting area, often on the territory proclaimed by the male before
the arrival of the female. The tradition of birthright is strong in such birds,
however, as both sexes migrate back to breed near the place of youthful
experiences. Thus a wide gene-flow from one region to another is prevented.

In these migratory perching birds there are only a few, such as the
Magpie and the Barn Swallow, that have one geographical race spread over

241

most of the continent. Most of the rest are divided into several subspecies, and some, like the Song Sparrow, show abundant racial variation. This point is important to our thesis because it appears that, within certain limits, ecological patterns as well as geographical locations are the traditional birthright of subspecies whose distribution is limited to certain habitats. Marshall (1948:252) says (in reference to races of the Song Sparrow in the San Francisco Bay area) that "habitat preferences, based merely on the impulse of the individual to stay in the kind of environment in which it was raised and with which it is familiar," may serve to effect the ecological isolation of a race; and that "it should be evident that such preference would be unlikely to be fixed genetically." It seems to me that Marshall has neatly expressed this fine difference between the inborn and the nonheritable response to the environment. At Delta some Song Sparrows live their whole reproductive lives in stands of *Phragmites* far from shrubby edges. But close by, and over much of the prairie country, other Song Sparrows (which taxonomists recognize as the same subspecies) nest in brushy edge cover. This local variation in breeding area I take to be the nonhereditary habitat preference to which Marshall refers. It is interesting to note that since there are no outstanding singing posts in the *Phragmites*, the males with marsh territories regularly make towering song-flights, which are not characteristic of nearby shrub-dwelling Song Sparrows.

The same sort of thing is seen in ducks. On the Delta Marsh the preferred nesting of the Canvasback is bulrush, but in the pothole country around Minnedosa many Canvasbacks nest in cover types entirely unlike anything used by the species at Delta. The nesting habitat of Pintail and Mallard in the farming country of Manitoba is quite different from the nesting environment of these species on the treeless plains of Alberta. In Manitoba the Canada Goose nests on fish boxes mounted on poles at Rennie, on open islands at Dog Lake, and on Muskrat houses at Delta.

Waterfowl and many other birds apparently have an inborn urge for the homeland of birth, where each individual selects the environmental patterns most closely meeting its innate breeding requirements. From this instinctive attachment to home may arise the isolation upon which morphological variations are founded, even in the absence of geographical barriers to the flow of genes. However innate the homing behavior, the geographic place of home is inherited, not genetically, but by birthright and experience.

"We may read indignantly of the Great Auk and the Passenger Pigeon and say complacently that such a thing could not happen nowadays, but only by the narrowest margin is the Trumpeter Swan of North America, the largest of all waterfowl, still included in the avifauna of the world." Peter Scott, *Wild Chorus*

19

Broken Traditions

THE Passenger Pigeon is gone beyond recall. Oaks live whose branches held their nests; much of the pigeon environment is still here on earth; but the last pigeon is long since dead.

The Canada Goose is a living part of our native fauna, a passage migrant with numbers strong enough to give the modern hunter a share in the annual harvest. On part of its range, however, it is as dead as the Passenger Pigeon. Many regions of the United States and Canada once knew the clarion call of the goose on its breeding territory. It bred in Illinois, Indiana, and Iowa (Cooke, 1906). In Minnesota, Roberts (1932) tells us that it was "formerly a common summer resident, nesting throughout the State." Manitoba old-timers, such as Stuart Criddle, of Treesbank, remember nesting geese where there are none today. Cooke, writing in 1906, said that "a hundred years ago the species bred commonly in all the northern third of the Mississippi Valley and not uncommonly to the latitude of St. Louis." McClanahan (1940) shows that its breeding range reached to northwestern Mississippi. Now this region is barren of its original stock; the native geese of the Mississippi Valley and their breeding traditions have vanished with the Passenger Pigeon.

Despite drainage, places still remain in the Middle West where geese might nest, marshes as fine for reproduction as are to be found in the north country. It must hold that the Canada Goose has left the Mississippi Valley as a breeder not simply because all its nesting habitat is gone, nor because of the encroachments of civilization, but because all geese with

Trumpeter Swans still raise their families in
some regions of the Northwest.

local breeding experience (like all Passenger Pigeons) are dead and gone. The breeding traditions for this region died with the geese that once nested there. No matter how many fly north along the Mississippi in spring, all modern geese have nesting or family experiences beyond the northern horizon; when the time comes, they continue on to their more distant homes. The Giant Canada Goose, which Delacour and Moffitt (Delacour, 1951) considered a distinct subspecies, is forever gone from the Mississippi Valley.*

The Trumpeter Swan tells another story of total regional losses. Roberts (1932:206) gives convincing evidence that this great bird of the prairies bred at Heron Lake, Everson Lake, Swan Lake, and other places in Minnesota until the 1880s. Bent (1925:293) says that "when the great Central West was wild and uncultivated it was known to breed in the uninhabited parts of many of our central states, even as far south as Missouri." It nested in Iowa as late as 1883. Trumpeters still raise their families in Wyoming, Montana, Alberta, and British Columbia; but their traditions of the Middle West are gone with the pigeons.

Why have the geese and swans departed from so much of their original

* Wild breeding flocks of Canada Geese have been re-established in several parts of the Middle West, as mentioned in Chapter 17, but this transplanted stock is not the same as the one that originally bred in the region.

But their traditions of the Middle West have
gone with the Passenger Pigeon.

range? Some, of course, left because their homelands were spoiled, but
this is not the whole story. Some say they left because civilization pressed
too closely upon the nesting places. If it is implied that these wildfowl
moved away because they could not tolerate the close presence of man and
his activities, this cannot be true, for today in some parts of their present
range, wild Trumpeter Swans and Canada Geese thrive within sight of
human dwellings. It must be that during settlement and in the lush days
of gunning, local breeders and their young were gradually taken. One by
one, pair by pair, family by family, the geese and swans of Minnesota and
the Middle West were used for food. An old-time resident of Heron Lake,
Minnesota, told Dr. Roberts (1932) that Trumpeter Swans "used to breed
there in fair numbers and that men from the east came to the lake, rounded
up the cygnets in the open water before they could fly, and shipped them
to eastern parts." Delacour (1944) points out that "Trumpeters used to nest
and to winter well within areas which became settled by man when the
country was opened up. Consequently they were slaughtered quickly and
easily." Unlike the Whistling Swan, which calls the Arctic its home, the
breeding places of the Trumpeter Swan were in lower latitudes early settled by man. When domestic duties held swans to a small locality, voice
and action soon disclosed their presence to men, who came to take what
they believed to be their rightful harvest.

Locally, the numbers of swans and geese killed probably were small. Here were a pair on this pond, there several at a nearby lake, a few more in waters beyond. In the settler's mind a modest harvest of local birds did not seem beyond reason in view of the great flights that passed through, spring and fall.* In a few years, however, such predation gradually thinned nesters down to widely scattered birds. When the last families were taken, their traditions were dead. The lakes, many of them, the rushy borders, and the muskrats upon whose houses these wildfowl nested, have survived to please the settlers' grandchildren; but the native geese and swans are gone.

In other species we find similar endings of breeding traditions — sometimes complete, as where the Carolina Paroquet and the Heath Hen have been exterminated, sometimes only regional, as where the Raven has gone from southern Wisconsin, the wild turkey from New England, or the Prairie Chicken and Sandhill Crane from many places. Some, like the Raven, disappeared in the face of intolerable environmental changes. For many kinds, however, favorable environment remains, but local breeders have been killed.

Tracing the histories of lost species, we note, as with the Trumpeter Swan and the Canada Goose, that the end came quickly for those that were vulnerable on their breeding range. For some, however, the nesting grounds were beyond the reach of man, and it was on the flyways and the wintering places that whole breeding populations were shot out, none surviving to go north. Forbush points out (1912:552) that where northern-breeding species are regularly over-shot along certain flyways, there may be no birds to return to their Arctic nesting places the following seasons. He suggests that, as in the olden days of shorebird gunning, a few families "reared in the same locality in the far north, start down the Atlantic coast in their migration. Gunners in the Bay of Fundy first decimate the birds, which then cross to Cape Cod, pass a blind occupied by an experienced gunner, who gets nearly all of them, and the next gunner a little farther down the beach kills what is left. There will be no more birds coming down the Atlantic coast from that nesting place for some time." Meinertzhagen (1935) saw the results of heavy shooting on the coast of Syria. "The stream of migrants which used to pass north up the coast no longer does so . . . which would indicate that particular communities of birds use especial mi-

* Owen Wister (1955), in the diary of his western trips, tells how the flightless young of Canada Geese were chased down as food for camp supper.

gratory routes, and that the persistent persecution of that community on that especial route will eventually exterminate that community."

This, no doubt is what happened to the Eskimo Curlew, which was killed heavily through much of its migratory and winter range. Carroll (1910) says that in Labrador, "the Hudson's Bay Company's people at Cartwright annually put up large numbers of hermetically sealed tins for the use of company's officials in London and Montreal. I have seen as many as 2,000 birds hung up in their store as the result of one day's shooting by some 25 or 30 guns." In Nebraska, as Swenk (1915) tells it, "hunters would drive out from Omaha and shoot the birds without mercy until they had literally slaughtered a wagonload of them, the wagons being actually filled, and often with sideboards on at that. Sometimes when the flight was unusually heavy and the hunters were well supplied with ammunition, their wagons were loaded too quickly and easily filled, so whole loads of the birds would be dumped on the prairie, their bodies forming piles as large as a couple of tons of coal, where they would be allowed to rot while hunters proceeded to refill their wagons."

Bogardus (1899), the great wing-shot of his time, says that when "two or three of the plover or curlew are crippled, the others will circle round them and often offer chances for capital shots. . . . On one such occasion I remembered having killed forty-two golden plover and curlew, all shot on the wing, before I picked up one of them. Many a time I have killed as many as fourteen or fifteen without lifting a bird, there being opportunities to load and fire again and again while the plover swept and circled over the dead and wounded of their own flock. . . . Of late years I have generally killed from fifty to two hundred plover and curlew a day." The days of Captain Bogardus are gone forever, and so are the great flocks of Eskimo Curlew.

The Golden Plover was spared, and so, too, has been the Upland Plover of our prairies. Roberts (1932:487) says that "to recite the history of the Upland Plover in Minnesota is to tell a sad tale of wanton destruction of a valuable and once abundant bird that resulted in its almost complete extermination. Sixty years ago it was present all through the summer everywhere in the open country in countless thousands. . . . In May, 1893, the writer visited Jackson and Pipestone counties, and the Upland Plover was present everywhere on the prairies. A return visit was made in 1899, and it was largely gone — the incessant and musical qua-a-aily, qua-a-aily of the hovering birds was a thing of the past." Roberts tells of the heavy market hunting that took place in southern Minnesota during the nesting season and he concluded that it was doubtful whether "the remnant can be saved even with careful protection." The passage of years has shown, however, that protective action came in time so that in Minnesota and many other prairie states and provinces, the Upland Plover is still a member of the native fauna, in some places showing steady increase.

Another story of the salvation of threatened birds, and perhaps the most remarkable one, is that of the American Egret and Snowy Egret. Brought so close to extinction early in this century by the plume-hunters, these herons are once more abundant on their breeding grounds, from which some wander each summer north to southern Canada.

Forbush (1912:516) concluded that "when North America was first settled, wildfowl bred more or less abundantly throughout most of the region now known as the United States." This still holds today, for a study of the summaries of the annual breeding ground surveys shows that at least sixteen states * claim to have from nine to sixteen breeding species of ducks within their boundaries. A dozen more have from four to eight, and each of the remaining states have two or three. Thus in terms of species, the roll call of breeding ducks in the United States may not have changed greatly since early times.

This shows the potential for waterfowl within the United States; but of course, while there may be a fine list of nesting species, state by state, some regions have lost most of their native ducks. Some populations have disappeared entirely with the rise of cities and intensive farming. As a young man, my Grandfather Hochbaum knew places, now deep within Chicago, where several kinds of ducks bred; and when marshes, like the great Kankakee, where he went wildfowling, were drained, large units of breeding range were lost. Far and wide across the Middle West, waters were spilled forever from marshes large and small, and these places were withdrawn from the realm of wildfowl. Even where water itself was not lost, certain agricultural practices so altered the reedy edges that they no longer served some kinds. Where grazing destroyed emergent vegetation and shoreline cover, some, like Canvasback and Redhead, could not stay on.

* Michigan, Wisconsin, Minnesota, North Dakota, South Dakota, Nebraska, Iowa, Colorado, Wyoming, Montana, Idaho, Utah, Nevada, California, Oregon, and Washington claim from nine to sixteen of the following species: Mallard, Black Duck, Gadwall, Baldpate, Pintail, Blue-winged Teal, Green-winged Teal, Cinnamon Teal, Shoveller, Wood Duck, Redhead, Ring-necked Duck, Canvasback, Lesser Scaup, American Golden-eye, Barrow's Golden-eye, Bufflehead, Harlequin Duck, Ruddy Duck (surveys published by many authors in Special Scientific Report — Wildlife No. 25, published jointly by the U.S. Fish and Wildlife Service and the Canadian Wildlife Service).

In the North American way of life, most of us are brought up with strong ideas of right and wrong, good and bad. We have been taught, for one thing, that it is not good for the country that water be drained too quickly into the valleys. This lesson, which most school children must still learn, is not taught entirely in the interest of preserving the fish, furbearers, or waterfowl. We learn that the upland waters must be held to protect the land and the people from drought and flood. And yet generation after generation sees the shrinkage of marshland. Having done away with many of the big marshes, the drainage programs now seek to empty the smaller places. The prairie land of eastern South Dakota and western Minnesota is spangled with sloughs and potholes, scattered here, there, and everywhere at the rate of five or six to more than a hundred per square mile, many thousands of them covering only a fraction of an acre. For mile after mile, traveling across this rolling prairie, one is seldom beyond sight of ducks or farmsteads. Here is some of the best farming country in the world; and here, also, is a part of the finest duck-breeding range in the whole of North America. Pintail and Gadwall nest close to main roads, Canvasback and Redhead in farmyard sloughs, Ruddy Duck and Blue-winged Teal in village ponds. This region produces well of both waterfowl and agricultural crops.

Drainage of these marshy places has been going on for many years, and by 1935 the loss of waterfowl habitat in some districts was severe. After World War II better machinery and more Federal funds made the drainage programs still more efficient. Conservationists set upon a steady program of protestation and deploration, and the subject has been raised at least ninety-three times before the annual meetings of the North American Wildlife Conference, often by some of our most distinguished citizens; but the argument for water conservation carries no weight with the ditching agencies. In 1949 Schoenfeld (1949) found that 1,400 potholes had been drained from Day County, South Dakota, "not simply due to the chance initiative of individual farmers, but also to calculated financial and technical aid from three Federal agencies. What is happening in Day County," said Schoenfeld, "is only a portion of what is going on in the 5,000 square miles of prize duck pothole country in eastern North and South Dakota." By 1952 Evans and Nord (1952) found an annual loss of 7 per cent of Day County's potholes; and from 1946 to 1950, Peterson tells us (1952:126), "at least 10,700 potholes were wiped out and habitat for an equal number of ducks

249

is gone forever" from South Dakota. The exclamations against the loss gained in vigor, but the drainage forges ahead.

As the marshlets lose their water, the waterfowl breeding traditions are broken forever. In another human generation, the people of the land, wildfowlers and farmers alike, will be unaware of this heritage lost, as unknowing of the legions of Canvasback and Pintail once nesting here as the present generation is unaware of swan and pigeon. The landplanners who advise and subsidize the farmers to spill the water from their holdings tell us their eyes are on the future, on the years ahead, when the human populations of the 1980s and 1990s will require the returns of a greater agricultural productivity. "Get the potholes out of the way now," they say, "and the land will be ready for the wheat and corn our children and grandchildren will need."

What about waterfowl for the grandchildren; what about wildfowling in 1990? The economists, if they are thinking of ducks at all, count on the north for the birds of the future. The north always has been the horn of plenty for the wildfowler. However badly the home marshes have fared, however thin local populations have become, there is the everlasting hope for a grand north flight. But we must understand that the north country cannot supply all the waterfowl now and forevermore. Despite the vast, pristine northland, much of the finest waterfowl-breeding grounds in all North America remains within the realm now used by man. This is especially true for many of our most important game species. Some of the best breeding grounds — particularly the true prairie country of eastern Saskatchewan, Manitoba, the Dakotas, Minnesota, and Wisconsin — is also some of the best farmland. In 1953 careful breeding-season estimates by transect sampling revealed that North and South Dakota together held nearly 2,500,000 breeding ducks.* These included some of our finest game species: Mallard, Gadwall, Baldpate, Blue-winged Teal, Pintail, Redhead, Canvasback, Lesser Scaup. In that same year another survey by experienced biologists flying transects over several thousand miles of the lake-studded wilds of western Ontario (which on a map looks like a waterfowl paradise) and northern Saskatchewan showed that on some 400,000 square miles of this north country, there were approximately 1,181,000 breeding ducks (Wellein and Newcomb, 1953a). The combined area of the two Dakotas is 147,712 square miles. Thus a parcel of Ontario and Saskatchewan wilderness al-

* The 1953 index figure for North Dakota waterfowl was 1,459,839 (Fashingbaur, 1953: 188). The 1953 index figure for South Dakota was 1,021,000 (Murdy and Anderson, 1953:192).

most three times as big as Dakota farmland accommodates less than half the Dakotas' supply of ducks. What is more, half these northern birds were mergansers or other nongame species.

We know, of course, that this spruce and muskeg country of Ontario and northern Saskatchewan is not the finest of the wilderness breeding grounds, hardly comparing with the Yukon's Old Crow Flats or the Mackenzie delta. A 1953 aerial survey of the finest waterfowl range in the Yukon and Northwest Territories of Canada gave an estimate of a breeding population of 2,267,000 ducks on 235,000 square miles (Smith and Sutton, 1953). Thus the best of the north country requires twice the area to accommodate the same number of ducks that breed in the Dakotas. There are vast regions of the Arctic — the Barren Grounds away from the seacoasts and the river valleys — where waterfowl numbers average less than one duck per square mile (Wellein and Newcomb, 1953b). It would take an area of such country ten or twelve times the size of the Dakotas to hold the same number of breeding ducks.

Take the potholes out of the Dakotas and Minnesota and we have cut a major slice from the wildfowling of the future. Schoenfeld (1949) pointed out that in Day County alone, the loss from drainage up to 1949 had destroyed a waterfowl range that was ten times as productive as Manitoba's famed Delta Marsh. Whichever side of the international border the drainage occurs on, both Canadian and American wildfowlers must mourn the loss together. And wildfowlers of the United States must realize that in Canada the waterfowl range "is more limited than would first appear. Many sites which provide accommodation for ducks also provide attractive areas for the growing of crops and, with continuing agricultural expansion, are being withdrawn from natural waterfowl habitat" (Colls, 1951). Speaking of the prairie and parkland region of Saskatchewan, Gavin (1953) says that "when settlers first moved into these areas, lakes, sloughs and potholes were in abundance. Loss of much of these breeding areas has been a major blow to waterfowl. . . . Traveling through these areas today and trying to compare them with the older large-scale maps provides a shock that cannot be adequately described."

Pothole country is the finest of all breeding ranges because the scattered water areas let the pairs spread far and wide over the land. Gregarious through most of the year, ducks isolate themselves, much in the same way as Robins and Song Sparrows, during the nesting season, each pair keeping separate from others of the same species. The small sloughs and pot-

The prairie land of Minnesota and the Dakotas is spangled with sloughs and potholes. Here is some of the finest waterfowl breeding range in North America.

holes create the ideal pattern for the kind of dispersal the breeding pairs like best. Farming country, spotted with marshlets, may hold as many ducks per square mile as do the great marshes like the Delta, or even more, and over vastly many more square miles. The big marshes function as gathering places, spring and fall, as molting areas and summer rendezvous; but they comprise but a fraction of the total nesting range.

Many regions, like the lake country of Ontario and parts of the Arctic, have a favorable spacing of small waters, but the acid or thin soils do not produce the food or nesting cover plants so attractive to the waterfowl of the prairies. Thus, while the lake country of Ontario or eastern Minnesota may have only two or three breeding ducks to a square mile, the prairie pothole range only a short distance west may attract a hundred or more breeding ducks per square mile. Years ago, Leopold (1931) pointed to this variation, showing how the duck breeding range is to be evaluated not so much by acreage as by quality. The quality breeding range for many of our finest game ducks is on rich land that is also good for man. The millions of acres of slum range can never supply the wildfowling of the future if today's potholes must grow wheat and barley for the next generation. To save this range is going to take better arguments than we have been able to put across during the past quarter-century. We who wish to keep these breeding grounds must act with the same conviction, with the same intelligent planning, as the drainage agents. For the wildfowler drainage is more than a matter of good or evil, drought or flood, feast or famine: drainage is the process by which succeeding generations, however rich in wheat and barley, must lose their heritage of Canvasback, Gadwall, or Redhead.

Man, of course, is not by any means the only force changing the face of the world. In the regular cyclic rise and fall of waters by which the levels of Lake Manitoba and the Delta Marsh vary, there are important changes in the marsh pattern, influencing waterfowl activity. In the most recent rise the water of the Lake Manitoba basin has reached record-breaking elevations. As a result the shallows at Archie's Point where the Whistling Swans fed through so many Aprils have flooded so deeply that the swans can no longer reach the bottom with their long necks, and they come there no more. Bergman (1951) tells how a traditional spring resting place of the Old Squaw was changed because of a variation in ice conditions. Either flood or drought may bring to a close nesting traditions of many generations.

Besides the loss of breeding range, waterfowl have suffered from the same kind of heavy gun pressure and market interests as shore birds. In Ohio, Trautman (1940:47) described the techniques of market hunters who combed "the swampy fields with dogs in order to capture the larger ducklings and adults in flapper stage." Richard Harker, a market gunner from Spirit Lake, Iowa, recalls that "the law on ducks was out about the 15th of August and we shot from then until freeze-up. . . . It seemed that when we were market hunting, every year ducks were just a little harder to get" (Musgrove, 1949:198).

The killing of local stock seemed unimportant in view of the vast numbers during migration. Even so great a conservationist as Theodore Roosevelt (1927:41) wrote that flightless young ducks were "as tender and delicious birds for the table as I know . . . In these small ponds with little cover round the edges the poor flappers are at a great disadvantage; we never shoot them unless we really need them for the table. But quite often, in August and September, if near the place, I have gone down to visit one or two of these pools, and have brought home half a dozen flappers." The tug of conscience was not strong enough to deter E. L. Brown, pioneer of northern Minnesota, who wrote that he "flushed a duck from her nest, but did not shoot her from a confused notion against shooting the females;

but afterwards went over where she lit and missed her when she rose, but dropped her with the second shot, a gray duck. The nest was prettily placed at the edge of the bank, seven eggs all clean and fresh." * When acted upon annually, the philosophy that to take only a few from the home marsh is harmless must surely have accounted for a considerable loss of breeding stock in some parts of the range. Ducks continued to pass aplenty in migration; but once the native birds with local breeding traditions were killed, flights went through each spring with few or none stopping to nest in some localities.

We speak with contempt of the carefree, heavy gun pressure of the past; yet even in our time, early-season wildfowling and careless gunning on the breeding marshes threaten some late-maturing waterfowl like Canvasback and Redhead. In some parts of the nesting range the season continues to open on marshes where many young diving ducks and adult females are still flightless or barely on the wing. Evidence of bag studies shows that in some early-season openings, more Canvasback and Redheads are killed in one or two days of gunning than are raised locally in a season (Sowls, 1946; Hochbaum, 1947). In such early-season shooting, the careless waste is sometimes quite unbelievable. On the opening day of the 1946 season on the Delta Marsh, a hot, windy September 16, it was estimated that about half of the 4,000-bird bag spoiled and was thrown aside. Kit Kitney, Winnipeg columnist, wrote that "heavy losses were due to the fact that birds carried all day in the car, spoiled and had to be discarded . . . We took only nine birds. This was fortunate, because we were too tired to do anything about our game when we arrived home Monday, and on Tuesday night they were too far gone and had to be thrown out." † On September 17, 1946, in routine bag study, I saw a pile of more than two hundred and fifty ducks, mostly Canvasback and Redhead, which were being thrown away as spoiled, these on the kitchen floor of an Indian woman who had contracted to process the birds for shipment.

Besides spoilage, the products of early-season gunning on breeding marshes are often cast away as too thin or pin-feathery. Frequently on the Delta Marsh young Redheads have been left behind by hunters as not worth taking home. The adult drake bagged in October is as fine and as wary a bird as any Canvasback; but the little Redheads just on the wing in September are thin-breasted, flabby birds, innocent of all experience

* Diaries of E. L. Brown, 1889–1901. Typed manuscript, Minnesota Historical Society.
† "Sportsmen Afield," *Winnipeg Tribune,* September 21, 1946.

with shot and gun, so different from the adult that some local gunners contend that they are of a separate species. Others believe that the light little birds are sickly, and for this reason do not keep them. In early season shooting, when birds are abundant and bag-limits small, it is a common practice, during the course of a day's shoot, to discard the smaller ducks, like Blue-winged Teal, or less desirable kinds, like Shoveller, replacing these with larger Mallards and Canvasbacks. Ducks scattered and lost in the reeds by novice hunters, or ducks thrown away by city shooters as spoiled or too small to take home, are just as dead as those the market hunter packed in ice.

Of course, one cannot wholly blame the hunter if his seasons are set so that he is likely to shoot birds so immature that they are all but worthless as food. To most hunters the young Redhead just on the wing is not readily distinguished from an adult until it is dead. I am sure that as we find out more about the life histories of waterfowl, there must stem from this understanding a new pattern of gunning regulations. At present all ducks are shot under a common plan. Even though many Canvasback and Redhead are not strongly on the wing until late September, their shooting season opens at the same time as it does for young Mallard and Pintail, which are flying by midsummer. Even though many adult females are still flightless on the breeding marsh at the start of autumn, gunning on the marsh starts on the same day as it does on upland fields or open lakes, where drakes and strongly-flying young have been feeding for many weeks. It is unreasonable to set laws which require the hunter to recognize the legality of killing one species but not another in the same environment. But by certain zoning regulations, hardly more complicated than now exist for upland game, the season might open early on grain fields for strong-winged Mallard and Pintail; shooting could be delayed on the breeding marshes, and the pressure there thus relieved, until after the young diving ducks and adult females had had a chance to become strong of wing and had dispersed from the home range.

This, of course, is no place to discuss the modern pattern of wildfowling, for it is a subject yet unstudied. We know almost nothing of the customs of hunters or of the impact of their practices on native populations of northern marshes. The throwing away of spoiled birds or the waste of young Redheads in September shooting may be of little consequence. The whole subject of the influence of the hunter on the waterfowl population awaits careful study and analysis. But it is the hunters themselves who say that some great Canadian marshes are already overshot and "burned out." The gunner is moving ever northward.

Shooting, when it begins before the close of summer, may be responsible for the existence of good marshes that lack breeding ducks. Where the young and adult females are killed heavily enough on their native range, local traditions may be broken to the point where, despite plenty of migrants passing through, there are not enough birds with local experience to fill some marshes. Leopol (1931), in his surveys of the North Central states, found that while "only 10 percent of the original marshlands remain in existence, possible only five percent are actually used to any extent."

During our most recent duck depression, in the middle 1940s, similar vacancies reached deep into Canada. In 1947 Soper (1948:54) found places where "numerous favorable small bodies of water were conspicuously underpopulated by waterfowl; and in many tracts, eight or nine sloughs out of every ten, though provided with plenty of water and duck food, had no ducks." In Manitoba's famous Minnedosa pothole region, less than half the water areas had breeding pairs in 1947 (Hawkins, 1948:44). Since the pothole country was not heavily shot (the young and adults most seasons having departed to larger waters before the advent of gunning) the thin nesting populations, as in the case of the shorebirds, may have resulted from overshooting on the flyways.

An important advantage held by waterfowl over the shorebirds and the Passenger Pigeon is the larger clutch. The Passenger Pigeon laid one, sometimes two eggs (Schorger, 1955), and the standard clutch size in the shorebirds is only four. While there is some variation between species, duck clutches range from eight to twelve eggs, the over-all average being perhaps ten. Thus in successful seasons these waterfowl are able to recover their numbers at a much faster rate than the shorebirds, and the pigeons were at a disadvantage greater still. Moreover, the evidence of Sowls's studies (1949) is that among the river ducks, at least, there is a persistent drive to renest in the face of early nest loss; and such renesting may carry the bird to a third attempt after a second catastrophe. The ability to recover numbers is shown in the surveys of the Newdale-Erickson district of Manitoba's Minnedosa pothole country, where the breeding population climbed from 26 ducks per square mile in 1947 (Hawkins, 1948) to 81 ducks per square mile in 1949 (Hawkins, 1949). By 1953 there were 100 ducks per square mile in this district (Kiel, 1953).

If the number of waterfowl of Minnedosa could be trebled in two years, it is possible that populations of more southern marshes might show a simi-lar capacity to expand when more ducks are available. In 1951 the Waubay pothole region of South Dakota held 124 ducks per square mile (Evans, Mann, and Black, 1951:162), a resident breeding population five times as dense as that of the similar Canadian pothole country in 1947. In 1950 the State of North Dakota held a nesting population averaging 19.7 ducks per square mile, a number greater than the over-all average for Alberta (11.5 ducks per square mile) (Hjelle, 1951:149; Smith, 1951:30). I suspect that the breeding grounds in the true prairie country of the Dakotas, Minnesota, Wisconsin, and Manitoba may serve as security range during seasons when parts of the more western plains dry out to the point of being untenable to nesting ducks. This does not imply that birds move east to breed success-fully the first year of a drought; but during dry periods lasting several years, the marshes of the true prairie hold water longer, then providing the main part of the breeding grounds in the middle latitudes.

I have spoken mainly of the United States breeding grounds of the north central region because they are potentially so fine and so immedi-ately threatened by drainage. There are other great breeding ranges in the United States, such as the sandhill country of Nebraska, the plains of Mon-tana, the Great Basin country of Utah and Idaho, and the marshes of the Klamath basin of California and Oregon, to mention only a few. Some of these western ranges not only have many species of game ducks, but are heavily productive of Canada Geese. If we are to plan for the wildfowling of the future as carefully as we plan for barley, we must count heavily on these breeding grounds within the settled regions of North America.

In token of the importance of this resource, a technical program for waterfowl investigations has been launched far and wide across the land. At last we have grasped the idea that we cannot manage waterfowl as a renewable resource unless we know more about ducks and geese, species by species, region by region. And during the past ten years we have learned more about these birds than in all our previous history. University gradu-ate departments, biological stations, provincial and state game branches, and central government agencies are studying waterfowl in many ways and in many places. Some seek to understand such fundamental problems as the natal range of ducklings in Manitoba (Dzubin, 1954), or the effect of spring rainfall on nesting Mallards in California (Mayhew, 1955). Others set about to find ways of restoring birds to new or empty ranges, as by transplanting flightless juveniles from old to new marshes (Wells, 1954;

Foley, 1954b). Bright young men in every corner of the land search for information aimed at a better understanding of this great resource. Annually an international team, composed of more than fifty biologists representing many different agencies, surveys the waterfowl breeding population from the central United States north to the Arctic Ocean and beyond, so that the pattern of the harvest may be fairly planned. Another team appraises waterfowl on their wintering grounds each January.

For all this new interest, however, for all the technical advancements, for all the many pounds of published facts about life histories, numbers, ranges, food habits, territorial requirements, for all the new dams and impoundments, we have not learned how to draw a compromise with the economists who are doing away with the breeding range faster than it can ever be restored. Perhaps we have learned more about the behavior and living requirements of ducks than of ourselves. The time when we start saving the prairie marshes may arrive when we somehow realize that we need these wetlands for our own human race, when we understand that the real concern is not for ducks, but for the people themselves: can we continue to be strong and healthy on this North America after we have let the gems of upland waters drain to the valleys?

The real concern is for us, the people. We who wish to keep marshes and their waterfowl must study ourselves and our human society. We are at the threshold of an era we cannot comprehend. But surely we know that each nation must find its strength in the land. The people of North America cannot remain always strong if the value of our prairie land is measured wholly in terms of wheat and barley.

Bibliography

THE following titles, all but a few of which are cited in the text, are those that I have used in writing this book. For anyone wishing to read further in the very extensive literature on bird migration, I suggest the excellent reviews by Drost (1951), Griffin (1944, 1952a), Matthews (1955b), and Schüz (1952), all of which contain fine bibliographies listing many important titles that I have been unable to include here.

In this book I have not dealt with the stimuli responsible for migration, and as an introduction to this subject one might start with Farner's careful review paper (1950) and the works of Rowan and Wolfson cited below.

Bagg, Imhof, Salomonsen, and Williamson, together with a few others mentioned in their papers, are making important observations on the relation of traveling birds to moving air masses; I consider their publications extremely important for all to read. Nor can the modern student of bird migration afford to overlook "Normal weather charts for the Northern Hemisphere" (U.S. Weather Bureau, 1952).

Concerning migration North American ornithologists have recorded many incidents and arrival dates. But there has been little attempt to study the behavior of birds, in the way that Lack, L. Tinbergen, and their colleagues in Europe have studied it, in the very act of passage. As an introduction to important papers and bibliographies on visible migration, the April 1953 issue of the Ibis (Volume 95), is a logical starting place. Matthews (1955b) has a full review and a bibliography of studies that have been made on avian relation to the sun, work that has been carried out almost entirely in Europe.

In regard to learning and instinct, the student may refer to Lorenz (1935, 1937), Thorpe (1951a), and N. Tinbergen (1951), studying at the same time the critique by Lehrman (1953). Although the important role of tradition has been suggested by numerous writers over a long period of years, such as Palmén (1874), Reynaud (1898), and Howard (1920), in the modern literature available to me the subject is treated only briefly and often self-consciously (with abundant apologies for anthropomorphic interpretations). But I found the work of Cushing to hold original, straightforward discussions of traditions, and Mayr (1942) and Nice (1943) have offered a number of stimulating ideas and observations.

All through my review of the literature on behavior and migration, I have found evidence of friendships between European and North American authors and of a broad exchange of ideas and observations that are bound to result in a fuller understanding of the subject.

Acworth, Bernard
  1946. The cuckoo and other bird mysteries. London: Eyre and Spottiswood.
Aldrich, John W., and others
  1949. Migration of some North American waterfowl. U.S. Fish and Wildlife Service, Special Scientific Report (Wildlife) No. 1, pp. 1–49.
Allee, Warder C.
  1951. Cooperation among animals. New York: Schuman.
———, and Karl P. Schmidt
  1937. Ecological animal geography. London: Wiley.
Allen, Arthur A.
  1914. The Red-winged Blackbird: A study in the ecology of a cat-tail marsh. Proc. Linnaean Soc. of New York No. 24–25, pp. 42–128.
  1931. The Canvasback. Bird-lore 33:347–360.
Allen, Francis H.
  1939. Effect of wind on flight speeds. Auk 56 (3):291–303.
Allen, J. A.
  1880. Origin of the instinct of migration in birds. Bull. Nutt. Ornith. Club 5:151–154.
Armstrong, Edward A.
  1947. Bird display and behaviour (rev. ed.). New York: Oxford.
  1954. The behavior of birds in continuous daylight. Ibis 96 (1):1–30.
Audubon, John James
  1840. Birds of America, from drawings made in the United States and their territories. Philadelphia: Chevalier.
Austin, Oliver L., Jr.
  1932. The breeding of the Blue-winged Teal in Maryland. Auk 49 (2):191–198.
  1949. Waterfowl of Japan. General Headquarters, Supreme Commander for the Allied Powers, Natural Resources Section, Report No. 118.
Aymar, Gordon C.
  1935. Bird flight. New York: Dodd, Mead.
Baerends, G. P.
  1950. Specializations in organs and movements with a releasing function. Symposia of Society for Experimental Biology No. 4, Physiological Mechanisms in Animal Behavior. Cambridge, England: Cambridge Univ. Press.
Bagg, Aaron Moore
  1948. Barometric pressure-patterns and spring migration. Auk 65 (1):147.
———, W. W. H. Gunn, D. S. Miller, J. T. Nichols, Winnifred Smith, F. P. Wolfarth
  1950. Barometric pressure-patterns and spring bird migration. Wilson Bull. 62 (1):5–19.
Balham, Ronald W.
  1954. The behavior of the Canada Goose (*Branta canadensis*) in Manitoba. Unpublished thesis, Univ. of Missouri.
Barlow, Horace B., Henry L. Kohn, and E. Geoffrey Walsh
  1947a. Visual sensations aroused by magnetic fields. Amer. J. Physiol. 148:372–375.

1947b. The effect of dark adaptation and of light upon the electric threshold of the human eye. Amer. J. Physiol. 148:376–381.

Barnett, Lincoln
1948. The universe and Dr. Einstein. Harpers 196:303–312 (April), 465–476 (May), 525–539 (June).

Bastock, M., D. Morris, and M. Moynihan
1953. Some comments on conflict and thwarting in animals. Behavior 6 (1):66–84.

Beecher, William J.
1951. A possible navigation sense in the ear of birds. Amer. Midland Naturalist 46 (2):367–384.
1952. The unexplained direction sense of vertebrates. Scientific Monthly 75 (1): 19–25.

Bellrose, Frank C.
1951. Waterfowl flight. Illinois Wildlife 6 (4):10–11.
1953. Housing for Wood Ducks. Illinois Natural History Survey Circular 45:1–47.

Benedict, Ruth F.
1946. Patterns of culture. New York: Pelican Books.

Bennett, Logan J.
1938. The Blue-winged Teal. Ames, Iowa: Collegiate Press.

Benson, Dirck
1939. Survival studies of Mallards liberated in New York State. Trans. 4th North Amer. Wildlife Conference, pp. 411–415.

Bent, Arthur Cleveland
1923. Life histories of North American wild fowl. U.S. National Museum Bull. 126.
1925. Life histories of North American wild fowl. U.S. National Museum Bull. 130.
1929. Life histories of North American shore birds. U.S. National Museum Bull. 146.
1942. Life histories of North American flycatchers, larks, swallows, and their allies. U.S. National Museum Bull. 179.

Bergman, Göran
1951. Om isförhållandenas inverken på anfågelns, *Clangula hymalis* (L.), rastvanor under våren. Ornis Fennica 28 (3):62–65.

Bergson, Henri
1911a. Creative evolution (tr. by Arthur Mitchell). New York: Holt.
1911b. Matter and Memory (tr. by Nancy Margaret Paul and W. Scott Palmer). New York: Macmillan.

Berry, F. A., George V. Owens, and H. P. Wilson
1952. United States Arctic weather maps. U.S. Naval Air Station, Norfolk, Va.

Bogardus, A. H.
1899. Field, cover, and trap shooting (3rd rev. ed.). New York: Forest and Stream Publ. Co.

Bossenmaier, Eugene F.
1953a. Field-feeding of waterfowl in the Whitewater Lake district of southwestern Manitoba. Unpublished thesis, Univ. of Minnesota.
1953b. Waterfowl investigations at Whitewater Lake, Manitoba. Unpublished thesis, Univ. of Minnesota.

Boughner, C. C., and M. K. Thomas
1948. Climatic summaries for selected meteorological stations in Canada, Newfoundland and Labrador. Canadian Dept. of Transport, Toronto, Ontario.

Brakhage, George K.
  1953. Migration and mortality of ducks hand-reared and wild-trapped at Delta, Manitoba. J. Wildlife Management 17 (4):465–476.
Broley, Charles L.
  1947. Migration and nesting of Florida Bald Eagles. Wilson Bull. 59 (1):3–20.
Brooks, S. C.
  1934. Oceanic currents and the migration of pelagic birds. Condor 36 (5):185–190.
Brown, J. E.
  1938. The "pigeon cooker." Radio News, April 1938:21, 60–61.
Bue, I. G., Lytle Blankenship, and William H. Marshall
  1952. The relationship of grazing practices to waterfowl breeding populations and production on stock ponds in western South Dakota. Trans. 17th North Amer. Wildlife Conference, pp. 396–414.
Bullough, W. S.
  1951. Vertebrate sexual cycles. New York: Wiley.
Buss, Irven O.
  1942. A managed Cliff Swallow colony in southern Wisconsin. Wilson Bull. 54 (3):153–161.
  1946. Bird detection by radar. Auk 63 (3):315–318.
Carrick, W. H.
  1949. Experiments on sensory perception in birds. Typed report, Delta Waterfowl Research Station.
Carroll, W. J.
  1910. The Eskimo Curlew or doughbird. Forest and Stream 74:372.
Carson, Rachel L.
  1951. The sea around us. New York: Oxford.
Cartwright, Bertram W., and Jean T. Law
  1952. Waterfowl banding 1939–1950 by Ducks Unlimited. Winnipeg, Manitoba: Ducks Unlimited.
Casamajor, Jean
  1926. Le mystérieux "sens de l'espace" chez les Pigeons voyageurs. La Nature No. 2748, pp. 366–376.
Chapman, Abel
  1896. First lessons in the art of wildfowling. London: Horace Cox.
Chapman, Frank M.
  1916. The travels of birds. New York: Appleton.
  1932. Handbook of birds of eastern North America (2nd rev. ed.). New York: Appleton-Century.
Clarke, W. Eagle
  1912. Studies in bird migration. 2 vols. London and Edinburgh.
Collias, N. E.
  1944. Aggressive behavior among vertebrate animals. Physiol. Zoology 17 (1):83–123.
  1950. Social life and the individual among vertebrate animals. Annals New York Acad. of Sciences 51, Art. 6, pp. 1074–1092.
  1952. The development of social behavior in birds. Auk 69 (2):127–159.
Colls, D. G.
  1951. The conflict between waterfowl and agriculture. Trans. 16th North Amer. Wildlife Conference, pp. 89–93.

Cooch, Graham
    1955. A note on autumn migration of Blue Geese. (Circulation draft.)
Cooke, May Thacher
    1937. Flight speed of birds. U.S.D.A. Circular No. 428.
Cooke, Wells W.
    1906. Distribution and migration of North American Ducks, Geese, and Swans. U.S.D.A. Biological Survey Bull. No. 26.
    1912. Distribution and migration of North American shorebirds. U.S.D.A. Biological Survey Bull. No. 35.
    1915. Bird migration, U.S.D.A. Bull. No. 185.
Coombes, Robert A. H.
    1950. The moult migration of the Sheld-duck. Ibis 95 (3):405–418.
Cottam, Clarence
    1929. A shower of grebes. Condor 31 (2):80–81.
————, Cecil S. Williams, and Clarence A. Sooter
    1942. Flight and running speeds of birds. Wilson Bull. 54 (2):121–131.
Coues, Elliott
    1874. Birds of the northwest. U.S.D.I., U.S. Geol. Survey of the Territories, Misc. Publ. No. 3.
Cowan, Ian McTaggart
    1937. The House Finch at Victoria, British Columbia. Condor 39 (5):225.
Craig, Wallace
    1908. The voices of pigeons regarded as a means of social control. Amer. J. Sociol. 14:86–100.
    1918. Appetites and aversions as constituents of instincts. Biol. Bull. 34:91–107.
Cullen, J. M.
    1954. The diurnal rhythm of birds in the Arctic summer. Ibis 96 (1):31–46.
Cushing, John E., Jr.
    1941a. Non-genetic mating preference as a factor in evolution. Condor 43 (5):233–236.
    1941b. Winter behavior of Ravens at Tomales Bay, California. Condor 43 (2):103–107.
    1944. The relation of non-heritable food habits to evolution. Condor 46 (6):265–271.
————, and A. O. Ramsey
    1949. The non-heritable aspects of family unity in birds. Condor 51 (2):82–87.
Darling, J. R.
    1940. Miracles on wings. Natural History 46:205–207, 240–243.
Darwin, Charles
    1859. On the origin of species by means of natural selection or the preservation of favored races in the struggle for life. London: Murray.
Davis, Leverett, Jr.
    1948. Remarks on "The physical basis of bird navigation." J. Allied Physics 19: 307–308.
Dawson, William L.
    1923. The birds of California, Vol. 4. San Francisco: South Moulton Co.
Day, Albert M.
    1949. North American waterfowl. Harrisburg: Stackpole and Heck.
Deelder, C. L.
    1949. On the autumn migration of the Scandinavian Chaffinch (*Fringilla c. coelebs* L.) Ardea 37:1–88.

————, and L. Tinbergen

1947. Waarnemingen over de vlieghoogte van trekkende vinken, *Fringilla coelebs* L., en spreeuwen, *Sturnus vulgaris* L. Ardea 35:45–78.

Delacour, Jean

1944. Government refuges are saving the Trumpeter Swan. Animal Kingdom 47 (6): 130–136.

1951. Preliminary note on the taxonomy of Canada Geese, *Branta canadensis*. Amer. Museum Novitates No. 1537.

1954. The waterfowl of the world, Vol. 1. London: Country Life.

————, and Ernst Mayr

1945. The Family Anatidae. Wilson Bull. 57 (1):3–55.

Dice, Lee R.

1940. Ecologic and genetic variability within species of *Peromyscus*. Amer. Naturalist 74 (752):212–221.

Dobben, W. H. van

1953. Bird migration in the Netherlands. Ibis 95 (2):212–234.

Dobzhansky, T.

1937. Genetics and the origin of species. New York: Columbia Univ. Press.

Dorer, Richard

1954. Save Minnesota's wetlands. Minnesota Naturalist, Sept., pp. 1–5.

Drost, Rudolf

1949. Zugvögel perzipieren Ultrakurzwellen. Vogelwarte 2:57–59.

1951. Study of bird migration 1938–1950. Proc. 10th International Ornithological Congress (Uppsala, 1950), pp. 216–240.

Durant, Will

1952. The story of philosophy. New York: Pocket Books.

Duvall, Allen J.

1949. Migration of the Ring-necked Duck. Pp. 29–31 of John W. Aldrich and others, Migration of some North American waterfowl, U.S. Fish and Wildlife Service, Special Scientific Report (Wildlife) No. 1, pp. 1–49.

Dzubin, Alex

1954. An intensive study of waterfowl populations on agricultural land. Unpublished thesis, Univ. of British Columbia.

1955. Some evidences of home range in waterfowl. Trans. 20th North Amer. Wildlife Conference, pp. 278–297.

Ebbinghaus, Hermann

1913. Memory, a contribution to experimental psychology. New York: Columbia Univ. Press.

Eddington, A. S.

1930. The nature of the physical world. New York: Macmillan.

Einstein, Albert

1950. The meaning of relativity (3rd rev. ed.). Princeton, N.J.: Princeton Univ. Press.

Elder, William H.

1946. Age and sex criteria and weights of Canada Geese. J. Wildlife Management 10 (2):93–111.

————, and Nina L. Elder

1949. Role of the family in the formation of goose flocks. Wilson Bull. 61 (3):133–140.

Elton, Charles
    1927. Animal ecology. In Julian S. Huxley, ed., Textbooks of Animal Biology. New
        York: Macmillan.
Emlen, John T., Jr.
    1938. Midwinter distribution of the American Crow in New York state. Ecology
        19:264–275.
    1940. The midwinter distribution of the Crow in California. Condor 42 (6):287–294.
Ennion, Eric A. R.
    1943. The British bird. London: Oxford.
Errington, Paul L.
    1941. An eight-winter study of central Iowa bob-whites. Wilson Bull. 53 (2):85–102.
Evans, Charles D.
    1951. A study of the movements of waterfowl broods in Manitoba. Unpublished
        thesis, Univ. of Minnesota.
————, Grady Mann, and Kenneth Black
    1951. Waterfowl breeding grounds survey at Waubay, South Dakota, 1950 and
        1951, U.S. Fish and Wildlife Service, Special Scientific Report No. 13,
        pp. 159–163.
————, and Warren Nord
    1952. Progress report on pothole drainage (unpublished). River Basin Studies,
        U.S. Fish and Wildlife Service, Region 3.
Fabricius, Eric
    1951. Zur Ethologie junger Anatiden. Acta Zoologica Fennica 68.
Farley, Frank L.
    1939. Further notes on the bird-life of Churchill, Manitoba. Canadian Field-Naturalist
        48 (2):57.
Farley, John L.
    1954. Waterfowl potentials. Trans. 19th North Amer. Wildlife Conference, pp. 94–
        101.
Farner, Donald S.
    1945. The return of Robins to their birthplaces. Bird-banding 16 (3):81–99.
    1950. The annual stimulus for migration. Condor 52 (3):104–122.
Fashingbaur, Bernard A.
    1953. Waterfowl breeding ground survey in North Dakota. U.S. Fish and Wildlife
        Service, Special Scientific Report: Wildlife No. 25, pp. 183–190.
Fisher, James
    1951. The changes in the distribution of the fulmar (Fulmarus glacialis) Proc. 10th
        International Ornithological Congress (Uppsala, 1950), pp. 449–462.
————, and R. A. Hinde
    1949. The opening of milk bottles by birds. British Birds 42:347–357.
    1951. Further observation on the opening of milk bottles by birds. British Birds
        44:393–396.
Foley, Donald
    1954a. Studies on survival of three strains of Mallard ducklings in New York State.
        New York Fish and Game Journal 1 (1):73–83.
    1954b. Survival and establishment of waterfowl released as ducklings. New York Fish
        and Game Journal 1 (2):206–213.

265

Forbush, Edward Howe
    1912. Game birds, wildfowl and shore birds of Massachusetts and adjacent states.
        Massachusetts State Board of Agric.
    1925. Birds of Massachusetts and other New England states, Vol. 1. Massachusetts
        Dept. of Agric.
Ford, Edmund B.
    1949. Mendelism and evolution (5th ed.). London: Methuen.
Frisch, Karl von
    1947. The dances of the honey bee. Bull. of Animal Behavior No. 5; pp. 1–32.
    1950. Bees, their vision, chemical senses and language. Ithaca, N.Y.; Cornell Univ.
        Press.
Fuller, Robert W.
    1952. Studies in the life history and ecology of the American pintail. Quarterly
        Report Utah Cooperative Wildlife Research Unit 17 (3):36–42.
Gavin, Angus
    1947. Birds of Perry River district, Northwest Territories. Wilson Bull. 59 (4):
        195–203.
    1953. Agriculture reaches northward in Canada. Trans. 18th North Amer. Wildlife
        Conference, pp. 118–121.
Gaylord, Robert M.
    1954. Man is the limiting factor. Trans. 19th North Amer. Wildlife Conference,
        pp. 105–109.
Gerard, Ralph W.
    1953. What is memory? Scientific American 189 (3):118–126.
Geyr von Schweppenburg, H. F.
    1933. "Zwischenzug." Vogelzug 4:154.
    1948. Zur Theorie der Zugrichtung. Ardea 36:219–257.
Gibson, James J.
    1950. Perception of the visual world. Boston: Houghton.
Götz, W. H. J.
    1929. Der Vogelzug in seinen Beziehungen zur Mauser. Verh. VI. Int. Orn. Kongr.,
        p. 102.
Gollop, J. B., John J. Lynch, and William Hyska
    1952. Waterfowl breeding ground survey in Saskatchewan. U.S. Fish and Wildlife
        Service, Special Scientific Report: Wildlife No. 21, pp. 33–40.
Gordon, Donald A.
    1948. Sensitivity of the homing pigeon to the magnetic field of the earth. Science
        108 (2817):710–711.
Gregg, F. M.
    1939. Are motor accompaniments necessary to orientational perception? J. Psychology
        8:63–97.
Griffin, Donald R.
    1940. Homing experiments with Leach's Petrels. Auk 57 (1):61–74.
    1943. Homing experiments with Herring Gulls and Common Terns. Bird Banding
        14:7–33.
    1944. The sensory basis of bird navigation. Quarterly Rev. Biology 19 (1):15–31.
    1952a. Bird navigation. Biological Rev. (Cambridge) 27:359–393.

1952b. Airplane observations of homing pigeons. Bull. Museum Comparative Zoology Harvard 107 (8):411–440.

1953. Sensory physiology and the orientation of animals. Amer. Scientist 41 (2):209–281.

————, and Raymond J. Hock

1949. Airplane observations of homing birds. Ecology 30 (2):176–198.

Griffith, R. E.

1946. Nesting of Gadwall and Shoveller on the middle Atlantic coast. Auk 63 (3):436–438.

Grinnell, Joseph

1913. Note on the palustrine faunas of west-central California. Univ. California Publ. Zoology 10:191–195.

1921. The principle of rapid peering in birds. Univ. California Chron. 23:392–396.

1931. Some angles in the problem of bird navigation. Auk 48 (1):22–32.

1937. The swallows at the Life Sciences Building. Condor 39 (5):206–210.

Grohmann, Josef

1939. Modifikation oder Funktionsreifung? Zeitschrift für Tierpsychologie 2:132–144.

Gudmundsson, Finnur

1951. The effects of the recent climatic changes on the bird life of Iceland. Proc. 10th International Ornithological Congress (Uppsala, 1950), pp. 502–514.

Gulliksen, Harold

1950. Memory. In Encyclopaedia Britannica.

Hall, Leonard

1949. Missouri. In E. V. Connett, ed., Wildfowling in the Mississippi Flyway, pp. 269–289. New York: Van Nostrand.

Hamerstrom, Frances

1942. Dominance in winter flocks of Chickadees. Wilson Bull. 54 (1):32–42.

Hanson, Harold C., Murray Rogers, and Edward S. Rogers

1949. Waterfowl of the forested portions of the Canadian Pre-Cambrian shield and the Palaeozoic basin. Canadian Field-Naturalist 63:183–204.

Hanson, Harold C., and Robert H. Smith

1950. Canada Geese of the Mississippi Flyway. Illinois Natural History Survey Bull. 25, Art. 3, pp. 67–210.

Hawkins, Arthur S.

1940. A wildlife history of Faville Grove, Wisconsin. Trans. Wisconsin Acad. of Science, Arts and Letters 32:29–65.

1948. Waterfowl breeding conditions in Manitoba, 1947. U.S.D.I. Special Scientific Report No. 45, pp. 39–42.

1949. Waterfowl breeding ground survey in Manitoba, 1949. U.S. Fish and Wildlife Service, Special Scientific Report: Wildlife No. 2, pp. 53–68.

Hawkins, Arthur S., E. G. Wellein, and W. F. Crissey

1950. A waterfowl reconnaissance in the James Bay–Hudson Bay region. U.S. Fish and Wildlife Service, Special Scientific Report: Wildlife No. 8, pp. 17–22.

Heilner, Van Campen

1939. A book on duck shooting. Philadelphia: Penn Publ. Co.

Heinroth, O.

1911. Beiträge zur Biologie namentlich Ethologie und Psychologie der Anatiden. Verh. V. Int. Orn. Kongr. (Berlin, 1910).

Henderson, G. H.
   1948. Physical basis of bird navigation. Science 107 (2788):597–598.
Henshaw, H. W.
   1910. Migration of the Pacific Plover to and from the Hawaiian Islands. Auk 27 (3):
       245–252.
Hess, Gertrud.
   1951. The bird: Its life and structure (tr. from German by Phyllis Barclay-Smith).
       New York: Greenberg.
Heyerdahl, Thor
   1950. Kon-tiki, across the Pacific by raft (tr. from Norwegian by F. H. Lyon). Chicago:
       Rand McNally.
Hickey, Joseph J.
   1942. Eastern population of the Duck Hawk. Auk 59 (2):176–204.
   1943. A guide to bird watching. New York: Oxford.
   1951. Mortality records as indices of migration in the Mallard. Condor 53 (6):284–297.
   1952. Survival studies of banded birds. U.S. Fish and Wildlife Service, Special Scien-
       tific Report: Wildlife No. 15.
Hitchcock, Harold Bradford
   1950. Aerial observations of homing pigeons. Anat. Rec. 108 (3):83–84.
   1952. Airplane observations of homing pigeons. Proc. Amer. Philosophical Soc.
       96 (3):270–289.
Hjelle, Brandt V.
   1951. Waterfowl breeding ground survey in North Dakota, 1951. U. S. Fish and Wild-
       life Service, Special Scientific Report: Wildlife No. 13, pp. 147–150.
Hoar, William S.
   1953. Control and timing of fish migration. Biological Rev. (Cambridge) 28:437–452.
Hochbaum, H. Albert
   1939. Waterfowl studies at Delta, Manitoba, 1938. Trans. 4th North Amer. Wildlife
       Conference, pp. 389–394.
   1942. Sex and age determination of waterfowl by cloacal examination. Trans. 7th
       North Amer. Wildlife Conference, pp. 299–307.
   1944a. The Canvasback on a prairie marsh. Washington, D.C.: American Wildlife
       Institute.
   1944b. Strange actions of a migrating flight of Lesser Scaups. Flicker 16 (4):77–79.
   1946. Recovery potentials in North American waterfowl. Trans. 11th North Amer.
       Wildlife Conference, pp. 403–418.
   1947. The effect of concentrated hunting pressure on waterfowl breeding stock.
       Trans. 12th North Amer. Wildlife Conference, pp. 53–62.
   1948. Harvesting the waterfowl crop. Trans. 13th North Amer. Wildlife Conference,
       pp. 481–492.
Höhn, E. O.
   1947. Sexual behavior and seasonal changes in the gonads and adrenals of the
       Mallard, Proc. Zool. Soc. of London 117:281–304.
Howard, H. Eliot
   1920. Territory in bird life. London: Murray.
   1929. An introduction to the study of bird behaviour. Cambridge, England: Cam-
       bridge Univ. Press.
   1940. A waterhen's worlds. Cambridge, England: Cambridge Univ. Press.

Hudson, W. H.
 1922. On the sense of direction. Century Magazine 104:693–701.
Huxley, Aldous
 1954. A case for ESP, PK and PSI. Life 36 (2):96–108.
Huxley, Julian
 1930. Bird-watching and bird behaviour. London: Chatto.
Imhof, Thomas A.
 1953. Effect of weather on spring bird migration in northern Alabama. Wilson Bull.
  65 (3):184–195.
Ising, Gustaf
 1945. Die physikalische Möglichkeit eines tierischen Orientierungssinnes auf Basis
  der Erdrotation. Arkiv Matematik, Astronomi och Fysik 32A (18):1–23.
Jaccard, P.
 1931. Le sens de la direction et l'orientation lointain chez l'homme. Paris: Payot.
Jack, Anthony
 1953. Feathered wings. Methuen: London.
Jeans, Sir James
 1943. Physics and philosophy. New York: Macmillan.
Jones, Bradley
 1940. Aerodynamics for pilots. Civil Aeronautics Authority, Civil Aeronautics Bull. 26
  (Sept. 1940), Supt. of Documents, Washington, D.C.
Kalela, Olavi
 1954. Populationsökologische Gesichtspunkte zur Entstehung des Vogelzuges. An-
  nales Zoologici Societatis Zoologicae Botanicae Fennicae 'Vanamo' 16 (4):1–30.
Kalmbach, E. R.
 1937. Crow-waterfowl relationships. U.S.D.I. Circular No. 433.
 1943. Birds, rodents and colored lethal baits. Trans. 8th North Amer. Wildlife
  Conference, pp. 408–416.
 ———, and Don R. Coburn
 1937. Disease factors in reported cases of starvation in waterfowl. Trans. 2nd North
  Amer. Wildlife Conference, pp. 404–410.
Karplus, Martin
 1952. Bird activity in the continuous daylight of Arctic summer. Ecology 33
  (1):129–134.
Katz, David
 1953. Animals and men, (translated by Hannah Steinberg and Arthur Summerfield).
  Baltimore: Penguin Books.
Kendeigh, S. Charles
 1949. Effect of temperature and season on energy resources of the English Sparrow.
  Auk 66 (2):113–127.
Kessel, Brina
 1953. Distribution and migration of the European Starling in North America. 55
  (2):49–67.
Keve, A., and M. D. F. v. Udvardy
 1951. Increase and decrease of the breeding range of some birds in Hungary. Proc. 10th
  International Ornithological Congress (Uppsala, 1950), pp. 468–476.
Kiel, William H., Jr.
 1950. Waterfowl breeding population and production in Manitoba inventory district

No. 8. U.S. Fish and Wildlife Service, Special Scientific Report: Wildlife No. 8, pp. 52–54.

1953. Waterfowl breeding population and production in the Newdale-Erickson district of Manitoba—1953. U.S. Fish and Wildlife Service, Special Scientific Report: Wildlife No. 25, pp. 81–85.

Knorr, O. A.

1954. The effect of radar on birds. Wilson Bull. 66 (4):264.

Kortright, Francis H.

1942. The ducks, geese and swans of North America. Washington, D.C.: American Wildlife Institute.

Kramer, Gustav

1949. Über Richtungstendenzen bei der nächtlichen Zugunruhe gekäfigter Vögel. In Ornithologie als biologische Wissenschaft. Heidelberg.

1950. Orientierte Zugaktivität gekäfigter Singvögel. Naturwissenschaften 37:188.

1951. Eine neue Methode zur Erforschung der Zugorientierung und die bisher damit erzielten Ergebnisse. Proc. 10th International Ornithological Congress (Uppsala, 1950), pp. 269–280.

1952. Experiments on bird orientation. Ibis 94:265–285.

1953. Wird die Sonnenhöhe bei der Heimfindeorientierung verwertet? J. für Ornithologie 94:201–219.

———, and Ursula von Saint-Paul

1954. Das Heimkehrvermögen Gekäfigter Brieftauben. Der ornithologische Beobachter, 51 (1/2):4–12.

Lack, David

1943. The life of the Robin. London: Witherby.

1949. The significance of ecological isolation. In Genetics, Paleontology, and Evolution, pp. 299–308. Princeton, N.J.: Princeton Univ. Press.

———, and Elizabeth Lack

1949. Passerine migration through England. British Birds 42 (Oct.):320–326.

1953. Visible migration through the Pyrenees: An autumn reconnaissance. Ibis 95 (2):271–309.

Landsberg, H.

1948. Bird migration and pressure patterns. Science 108:708–709.

Lashley, K. S.

1950. In search of the engram. Symposia of Society for Experimental Biology No. 4, Physiological Mechanisms in Animal Behavior. Cambridge, England: Cambridge Univ. Press.

Laven, Hannes

1949. Vögel als Augentiere. In Ernst Mayr and Ernst Schütz, eds., Ornithologie als biologische Wissenschaft, 28 Beiträge als Festschrift zum 60. Geburtstag von Erwin Stresemann, pp. 147–152. Heidelberg: Carl Winter.

Lebret, T.

1947. Migration of the teal, Anas crecca crecca L., in Western Europe. Ardea 35:79–131.

Lehrman, Daniel S.

1953. A critique of Konrad Lorenz's theory of instinctive behavior. Quarterly Rev. of Biology 28 (4):337–363.

Leopold, Aldo
1931. Report on a game survey of the North Central States for the Sporting Arms and Ammunition Manufacturers' Institute. Madison, Wisc.: Democrat Printing Co.
1933. Game management. New York: Scribner's.
1940. Spread of the Hungarian Partridge in Wisconsin. Trans. Wisconsin Acad. of Science, Arts and Letters 32:5–28.
1949. A sand county almanac. New York: Oxford Univ. Press.
Leopold, A. Starker
1944. The nature of heritable wildness in turkeys. Condor 46 (4):133–197.
Leopold, Frederic
1951. A study of nesting Wood Ducks in Iowa. Condor 53 (5):209–220.
Lewis, Harrison F.
1937. Migrations of the American Brant (*Branta bernicla hrota*). Auk 54 (1):73–95.
1939a. Duration of colonies of the Cliff Swallow. Condor 41 (2):41–79.
1939b. Reverse migration. Auk. 56 (1):13–27.
Lincoln, Frederick C.
1934. Can waterfowl marshes be restocked with hand-reared ducks? Trans. 20th Amer. Game Conference, pp. 78–81.
1935a. The waterfowl flyways of North America. U.S.D.A. Circular No. 342.
1935b. The migration of North American birds. U.S.D.A. Circular No. 363.
1939. The individual vs. the species in migration studies. Auk 56 (3):250–254.
1943. American Pintail on Palmyra Island. Condor 45 (6):232.
1950a. Migration of birds. U.S. Fish and Wildlife Service, Circular No. 16.
1950b. Navigation in nature. Manuscript paper read at joint ION-RTCA-RTCM Meeting, New York.
Lloyd, Hoyes
1954. Mid-Atlantic migrations of Long-tailed Jaeger (*Stercorarius longicaudus* Viellot) and tern. Typed circulation draft.
Lockley, Ronald M.
1942. Shearwaters. London: Dent.
Löve, Askell, and Doris Löve
1954. Vegetation of a prairie marsh. Bull. Torrey Botanical Club 81 (1):16–34.
Lorenz, Konrad Z.
1935. Der Kumpan in der Umwelt des Vögels. J. für Ornithologie 88:137–213, 289–413.
1937. The companion in the bird's world. Auk 54 (3):245–273.
1950. The comparative method in studying innate behavior patterns. Symposia of Society for Experimental Biology No. 4, Physiological Mechanisms in Animal Behaviour. Cambridge, England: Cambridge Univ. Press.
1952. King Solomon's ring. London: Methuen.
1953. Comparative studies on the behavior of the Anatinae. Reprinted from Avicultural Magazine, London.
Low, Seth H.
1949. The migration of the Pintail. Pp. 13–18 of John W. Aldrich and others, Migration of some North American Waterfowl, U.S. Fish and Wildlife Service, Special Scientific Report (Wildlife) No. 1, pp. 1–49.

Lowenstein, Otto
  1950. Labyrinth and equilibrium. Symposia of Society for Experimental Biology No. 4, Physiological Mechanisms in Animal Behaviour. Cambridge, England: Cambridge Univ. Press.
Lowery, George H., Jr.
  1945. Trans-Gulf spring migration of birds and the coastal hiatus. Wilson Bull. 57a (2):92–121.
  1946. Evidence of trans-Gulf migration. Auk 63 (2):175–211.
  1951. A quantitative study of the nocturnal migration of birds. University of Kansas Publ. Museum Natural History (Lawrence, Kan.) 3 (2):363–472.
Ludington, C. Townsend
  1943. Smoke streams. New York: Coward-McCann.
Lynch, John
  1949. Waterfowl breeding ground survey in Saskatchewan, 1949. U.S. Fish and Wildlife Service, Special Scientific Report: Wildlife No. 2, pp. 48–52.
McCabe, Robert A.
  1947. The homing of transplanted young Wood Ducks. Wilson Bull. 59 (2):104–109.
McClanahan, Robert C.
  1940. Original and present breeding ranges of certain game birds in the United States. U.S.D.I., Bureau Biological Survey, Wildlife Leaflet BS 158, pp. 1–21.
McCreary, Otto
  1934. The shifting of the route of migrating birds due to wind. Auk 51 (2):255–256.
McIlhenny, E. A.
  1934. Twenty-two years of banding migratory wild fowl at Avery Island, Louisiana. Auk 51 (3):328–337.
Mackenzie, Locke L.
  1946. Migration of the Sooty Shearwater off the Washington coast. Auk 63 (2): 257–258.
McKinney, D. F.
  1953. Studies on the behavior of the Anatidae. Unpublished thesis, Univ. of Bristol.
Mair, W. Winston
  1954. Ducks need more than breeding grounds. Trans. 19th North Amer. Wildlife Conference, pp. 82–85.
Mann, Grady E.
  1950. Reverse fall migration. J. Wildlife Management 14 (3):360–362.
Mann, Roberts, David H. Thompson, and John Jedlicka
  1947. Report on waterfowl banding at McGinnis Slough, Orland Wildlife Refuge, for the years 1944 and 1945. Forest Preserve District of Cook County, Illinois.
Marshall, Joe T., Jr.
  1948. Ecological races of Song Sparrows in the San Francisco region. Condor 50 (5):193–215; (6):233–256.
Manwell, R. D.
  1936. The homing instinct of the Song Sparrow. Bird Banding 7:128.
Matthews, G. V. T.
  1951a. The experimental investigation of navigation in homing pigeons. J. Exper. Biol. 28:508–536.
  1951b. The sensory basis of bird navigation. J. Institute of Navigation 4:260–275.
  1952. An investigation of homing ability in two species of gulls. Ibis 94:243–264.

1953a. Navigation in the Manx Shearwater. J. Exper. Biol. 30:370–396.

1953b. The orientation of untrained pigeons: A dichotomy in the homing process. J. Exper. Biol. 30:268–276.

1955a. An investigation of the "chronometer" factor in bird navigation. J. Exper. Biol. 32 (1):39–58.

1955b. Bird navigation. Cambridge, England: Cambridge Univ. Press.

Maurain, Ch.

1926. Les propriétés magnétiques et électriques terrestres et la faculté d'orientation du Pigeon voyageur. La Nature No. 2728 (July), p. 44–45.

Mayhew, Wilbur W.

1955. Spring rainfall in relation to Mallard production in the Sacramento Valley, California. J. Wildlife Management 19 (1):36–47.

Mayr, Ernst

1937. The homing of birds. Bird-lore 39 (1):5–13.

1942. Systematics and the origin of species, from the viewpoint of a zoologist. New York: Columbia Univ. Press.

1946. History of the North American bird fauna. Wilson Bull. 58 (1):1–68.

1951. Speciation in birds. Progress Report on the years 1938–1950. Proc. 10th International Ornithological Congress (Uppsala, 1950), pp. 91–131.

1952. German experiments on orientation of migrating birds. Biological Rev. (Cambridge) 27:394–400.

————, and Wilhelm Meise

1930. Theoretisches zur Geschichte des Vogelzuges. Vogelzug 1:149–172.

Meinertzhagen, R.

1935. Ornithological results of a trip to Syria and adjacent countries in 1933. Ibis 13:110.

1954. Birds of Arabia. Edinburgh: Oliver and Boyd.

Menner, Erich

1938. Die Bedeutung des Pecten im Auge des Vogels für die Wahrnehmung von Bewegungen. Zoologische Jahrbücher Abteilung für allgemeine Zoologie und Physiologie der Tiere 58:481–538.

Miller, Alden H.

1942. Habitat selection among higher vertebrates and its relation to intraspecific variation. Amer. Naturalist 76 (762):25–35.

Miller, Loye

1940. Observations on the Black-footed Albatross. Condor 42 (5):229–238.

Moffitt, James

1937. The White-cheeked Goose in California. Condor 39 (4):149–159.

Morrison, Alva

1952. The Greater Snow Goose. Bull. Massachusetts Audubon Society 36:285–291.

Munro, J. A.

1939. Studies of waterfowl in British Columbia: Barrow's Golden-eye, American Golden-eye. Trans. Royal Canadian Institute 22:259–318.

1941. Studies of waterfowl in British Columbia: Greater Scaup Duck, Lesser Scaup Duck. Canadian J. Research 19:113–138.

1942. Studies of waterfowl in British Columbia: Bufflehead. Canadian J. Research 20:133–160.

1944. Studies of waterfowl in British Columbia: Pintail. Canadian J. Research 22: 60–86.

1949. Studies of waterfowl in British Columbia: Green-winged Teal. Canadian J. Research 27:149–178.

Murdy, Ray, and Maurice Anderson
1951. Waterfowl breeding ground survey in South Dakota, 1951. U.S. Fish and Wildlife Service, Special Scientific Report: Wildlife No. 13, pp. 151–158.

1953. Waterfowl breeding ground survey in South Dakota. U.S. Fish and Wildlife Service, Special Scientific Report: Wildlife No. 25, pp. 190:194.

Murphy, Robert Cushman
1936. Oceanic birds of South America. New York: American Museum of Natural History.

Musgrove, Jack W.
1949. Iowa. In E. V. Connett, ed., Wildfowling in the Mississippi Flyway, pp. 193–223. New York: Van Nostrand.

Natorp, O.
1932. Ruckzugbeobachtungen im Frühjar 1931. Vogelzug 3:72.

Nice, Margaret Morse
1935. Some observations on the behavior of Starlings and Grackles in relation to light. Auk 52 (1):91–92.

1937. Studies in the life history of the Song Sparrow, I. Trans. Linnaean Soc. of New York, Vol. 4.

1939. What determines the time of the Song Sparrow's awakening song? IXᵉ Congrès Ornithologique Int. (Rouen), pp. 249–255.

1943. Studies in the life history of the Song Sparrow, II. Trans. Linnaean Soc. of New York, Vol. 6.

1953. Some experiences in imprinting ducklings. Wilson Bull. 55 (1):33–37.

Nicol, J. A. C.
1945. The homing ability of the carrier pigeon, its value in warfare. Auk 62 (2): 286–298.

Odum, Howard T.
1948. The bird navigation controversy. Auk 65 (4):584–597.

Palmén, J. A.
1874. Om Foglarnes flyttningsvägar. Helsingfors: J. C. Frenckell & Son.

Palmgren, Pontus
1936. Über die Vogelfauna der Binnengewässer Ålands. Acta Zoologica Fennica, Vorgelegt am 20.

1949. On the diurnal rhythm of activity and rest in birds. Ibis 91 (4):561–576.

Paton, D. Noël
1928. Reflex postural adjustments of balance in the duck. Proc. Royal Soc. of Edinburgh (48):28–36.

Paynter, Raymond A., Jr.
1953. Autumnal migrants on the Campeche Bank. Auk 70 (3):338–349.

Person, H. S., E. Johnston Coil, and Robert T. Beall
1935. Little waters. Rural Electrification Service, Washington, D.C.

Peterson, Elmer
1952. Marsh drainage. Trans. 17th North Amer. Wildlife Conference, pp. 123–131.

Peterson, Roger Tory
 1947. A field guide to the birds (2nd rev. ed.) Boston: Houghton.
Pettingill, Olin Sewall, Jr.
 1936. The American Woodcock, *Philohela minor* (Gmelin). Memoirs Boston Society of Natural History 9 (2):167–391.
Phillips, Allan R.
 1951. Complexities of migration: A review with original data from Arizona. Wilson Bull. 63 (2):129–136.
Phillips, John C.
 1926. A natural history of the ducks, IV. New York: Houghton.
———, and Frederick C. Lincoln
 1930. American waterfowl. New York: Houghton.
Pirnie, Miles D.
 1935. Michigan waterfowl management. Lansing, Mich.: Michigan Dept. of Conservation.
 1938. Restocking of the Canada Goose successful in southern Michigan. Trans. 3rd North Amer. Wildlife Conference, pp. 624–627.
 1941. The dispersal of wild ducks from the W. K. Kellogg bird sanctuary, near Battle Creek, Michigan. Papers Michigan Acad. of Science, Arts and Letters 26: 251–259.
Poole, Earl L.
 1938. Weights and wing areas in North American birds. Auk 55 (3):511–517.
Poor, Hustace H.
 1946. Birds and radar. Auk 63 (4):631.
Preston, F. W.
 1949. The Pacific flyway of the Golden Plover. Auk 66 (1):87–88.
Promptoff, A. N.
 1930. Die geographische Variabilität des Buchfinkenschlags (*Fringilla coelebs* L.), etc. Biologisches Zentralblatt 50:479–503.
Pumphrey, R. J.
 1948. The sense organs of birds. Ibis 90 (2):171–199.
Putzig, P.
 1937. Von der Beziehung des Zugablaufs zum Inkretdrüsensystem. Vogelzug 8: 116–130.
 1938. Weitere Versuche über die Beziehungen der Keimdrüsen zum Zugverhalter. Vogelzug 9:189–200.
Queeny, Edgar M.
 1947. Prairie wings (2nd ed.). New York: Lippincott.
Rabaud, Etienne
 1928. How animals find their way about. New York: Harcourt, Brace.
Ramsay, A. O.
 1951. Familial recognition in domestic birds. Auk 68 (1):1–16.
———, and Eckhard H. Hess
 1954. A laboratory approach to the study of imprinting. Wilson Bull. 66 (3):196–206.
Reynaud, G.
 1898. The laws of orientation among animals. Smithsonian Annual Report of Board of Directors, pp. 481–498.

Robbins, Chandler S.
1949. Migration of the Redhead, Pp. 25–28 of John W. Aldrich and others, Migration of some North American waterfowl, U.S. Fish and Wildlife Service, Special Scientific Report (Wildlife) No. 1, pp. 1–49.

Roberts, Thomas S.
1932. The birds of Minnesota. Minneapolis: Univ. of Minnesota Press.

Roosevelt, Theodore
1927. Hunting adventures in the west. New York: Putnam.

Rowan, William
1926. On photoperiodism, reproductive periodicity, and the annual migrations of birds and certain fishes. Proc. Boston Soc. of Natural History 38 (6):147–189.

1929. Experiments in bird migration, I. Manipulation of the reproductive cycle: Seasonal histological changes in the gonads. Proc. Boston Soc. Natural History 39 (5):151–208.

1929. Migration in relation to barometric and temperature changes. Bull. Northeastern Bird-banding Assoc. (Bird-banding) 5 (3):85–92.

1931. The riddle of migration. Baltimore: Williams and Wilkins.

1945. Homing, migration and instinct. Science 102:210–211.

1946. Experiments in bird migration. Trans. Royal Soc. of Canada, Third Series, Section V, 40:123–135.

1947. Birds, migration of. In Encyclopaedia Britannica, Vol. 3.

Russell, E. S.
1934. The behavior of animals. London: Edward Arnold.

1937. Fish migrations. Biological Rev. (Cambridge) 12:320.

Salomonsen, Finn
1948. The distribution of birds and the recent climatic change in the North Atlantic area. Danst Ornith. Forenings Tidsskr. 42.

1951. The immigration and breeding of the Fieldfare (*Turdus pilaris* L.) in Greenland. Proc. 10th International Ornithological Congress (Uppsala, 1950), pp. 515–526.

Santschi, F.
1923. L'orientation sidérale des fourmis et quelques considérations sur leurs différentes possibilités d'orientation. Mémories de la Société Vaudoise des Sciences Naturelles, 1:137–176.

Schenk, J.
1931. Die Prognose des Frühjahrzuges der Waldschnepfe in Ungarn. Proc. 7th International Ornithological Congress.

Schiermann, G.
1939. "Stammesgenossenschaften" bei Vögeln. Ornithologische Monatsberichte 47: 1–4.

Schifferli, A.
1942. Verfrachtungversuch mit Alpenseglern (*Micropus m. melba*) solothurn-Lissabon. Der ornithologische Beobachter 39:145–150.

Schildmacher, Hans
1937. Zur Physiologie des Zugtriebes, III. Versuche künstlich verlängerter Tagesdauer. Vogelzug 8:107–114.

1938. Zur Physiologie des Zugtriebes, IV. Weitere Versuche mit künstlich veränderter Belichtungszeit. Vogelzug 9:146–152.

Schoenfeld, Clay
    1949. Good-by potholes. Field and Stream, April, pp. 35–37.
Schorger, A. W.
    1941. The Crow and the Raven in early Wisconsin. Wilson Bull. 53 (2):103–106.
    1955. The Passenger Pigeon. Madison: Univ. of Wisconsin Press.
Schüz, Ernst
    1952. Vom Vogelzug: Grundriss der Vogelzugskunde. Frankfurt a. M.
Schwartzkopff, J.
    1950. Zur Frage des "Wahrnehmens" von Ultrakurzwellen durch Zugvögel. Vogel-
        warte 15:194–196.
Scott, Peter
    1939. Wild chorus. London: Country Life.
    1951a. Key to the wildfowl of the world. Slimbridge, England: Severn Wildfowl Trust.
    1951b. Wild Geese and Eskimos. New York: Scribner's.
    1953. Comments on paper by Taylor (1953). Ibis 95 (4):641–642.
——————, and Hugh Boyd
    1951. Severn Wildfowl Trust, Third annual report, 1949–1950. London: Country Life.
    1954. The Wildfowl Trust, Sixth annual report, 1952–1953. London: Country Life.
    1955. The Wildfowl Trust, Seventh annual report, 1953–1954. London: Country Life.
Sedwitz, Walter, Irwin Alperin, and Malcolm Jacobson.
    1948. Gadwall breeding on Long Island, New York. Auk 65 (4):610–612.
Seibert, Henri C.
    1951. Light intensity and the roosting flight of herons in New Jersey. Auk 68 (1):
        63–74.
Seligmann, C. G., and S. G. Shattock
    1914. Observations made to ascertain whether any relation subsists between the sea-
        sonal assumption of the "eclipse plumage" in the Mallard (*Anas boscas*) and
        the functions of the testicle. Proc. Zoological Soc. of London, pp. 23–43.
Selous, Edmund
    1931. Thought-transference (or what?) in birds. London: Constable.
Seton, Ernest Thompson
    1910. Life-histories of northern animals. London: Constable.
Shortt, Terence M.
    1943. Correlation of bill and foot coloring with age and season in the Black Duck.
        Wilson Bull. 55 (1):2–7.
Sick, Helmut
    1939. Über die Dialektbildung beim "Regenruf" des Buchfinken. J. für Ornithologie
        87:568–592.
Siebenaler, J. B.
    1954. Notes on autumnal trans-Gulf migration of birds. Condor 56 (1):43–48.
Simmons, K. E. L.
    1951. Raptor migration in the Suez Area, autumn 1949–spring 1950. Ibis 93 (3):
        402–406.
Simms, Eric
    1952. Bird migrants. London: Cleaver-Hume.
Skinner, B. F.
    1950. Are theories of learning necessary? Psychological Rev. 57 (4):193–216.

Slepian, Joseph
1948. Physical basis of bird navigation. J. Applied Physics 19:306.
Smith, Allen G.
1951. Waterfowl breeding ground survey in Alberta, 1951. U.S. Fish and Wildlife Service, Special Scientific Report: Wildlife No. 13, pp. 28–34.
Smith, J. Donald
1946. The Canvasback in Minnesota. Auk 63(1):73–81.
Smith, J. Maynard
1953. Birds as aeroplanes. New Biology No. 14, pp. 64–81. London: Penguin Books.
Smith, Robert H., and Robert P. Allen
1948. An aerial waterfowl reconnaissance in the Far North. U.S. Fish and Wildlife Service, Special Scientific Report No. 60 pp. 5–12.
Smith, Robert H., and Everett L. Sutton
1953. Waterfowl breeding ground survey in northern Alberta, the Northwest Territories, and the Yukon. U.S. Fish and Wildlife Service, Special Scientific Report: Wildlife No. 25, pp. 7–15.
Smith, Stuart
1945. How to study birds. London: Collins.
Snow, D. W.
1953. Visible migration in the British Isles: A review. Ibis 95 (2):242–270.
Snyder, L. L.
1941. On the Hudson Bay eider. Occasional papers of the Royal Ontario Museum of Zoology No. 6, pp. 1–7.
1948. Tradition in bird life. Canadian Field-Naturalist 62 (2):75–77.
Soper, J. Dewey
1930. The Blue Goose (*Chen caerulescens* [*Linnaeus*]). Dept. Interior, Ottawa.
1942. Life history of the Blue Goose (*Chen caerulescens* [Linnaeus]). Proc. Boston Soc. of Natural History 42 (2):121–222.
1948. Canada looks at waterfowl. Trans. 13th North Amer. Wildlife Conference, pp. 52–56.
Sowls, Lyle K.
1946. The 1946 fall waterfowl flight at Delta, Manitoba. Unpublished manuscript, Delta Waterfowl Research Station.
1947a. 1947 fall waterfowl flight and shooting season at Delta, Manitoba. Unpublished manuscript, Delta Waterfowl Research Station.
1947b. New techniques for breeding ground surveys. Trans. 12th North Amer. Wildlife Conference, pp. 448–452.
1949. A preliminary report on renesting in waterfowl. Trans. 14th North Amer. Wildlife Conference, pp. 260–275.
1950. Techniques for waterfowl-nesting studies. Trans. 15th North Amer. Wildlife Conference, pp. 478–489.
1951. A study of the ecology and behavior of some surface-feeding ducks. Unpublished thesis, Univ. of Wisconsin.
1955. Prairie Ducks, a study of their behavior, ecology and management. Harrisburg: Stackpole and Heck.
Springer, Paul F., and Robert E. Stewart
1950. Gadwall nesting in Maryland. Auk 67 (2):234–235.
Stearns, Harold T.

1946. Geology of the Hawaiian Islands. Bulletin 8, Territory of Hawaii, Division of Hydrography. Distributed by U.S. Geological Survey, Honolulu, Hawaii.

Storer, John H.
1948. The flight of birds. Cranbrook Institute of Science, Bull. No. 28.

Storer, Robert W.
1952. A comparison of variation, behavior and evolution in the sea bird genera Uria and Cepphus. Univ. of California Publ. in Zoology 52 (2):121–222.

Stresemann, Erwin
1934. Aves. In W. Kükenthal and T. Krumbach, Handbuch der Zoologie, 7:2. Berlin.
1940. Zeitpunkt und Verlauf der Mauser bei einigen Entenarten, J. für Ornithologie 88:288–333.
1943. Ökologische Sippen-, Rassen- und Artunterschiede bei Vögeln. J. für Ornithologie 91:305–324.

Sullivan, Arthur
1953. Bird banding records, Libau, Manitoba. Typewritten report.

Summers, John K.
1935. Practical air navigation simply explained. London: Pitman.

Sutton, George Miksch
1932. The exploration of Southhampton Island, Hudson Bay; Part II, Zoology, Section 2, The birds of Southhampton Island. Pittsburgh: Carnegie Institute.
1934. Eskimo year. New York: Macmillan.

Sutton, Oliver G.
1949. The science of flight. New York: Penguin Books.

Svärdson, Gunnar
1949. Skruvflykt hos flyttande masar, Våar Fågelvärld 8 (1):13–33.
1953. Migration in Fenno-Scandia. Ibis 95 (2):181–211.
————, and Sigfrid Durango
1951. Spring weather and population fluctuations. Proc. 10th International Ornithological Congress (Uppsala, 1950), pp. 496–501.

Swenk, Myron
1915. The Eskimo Curlew and its disappearance. Annual report Smithsonian Institution, 1915, pp. 325–340.

Tansley, Katherine
1950. Vision. Symposia of Society for Experimental Biology No. 4, Physiological Mechanisms in Animal Behaviour. Cambridge, England: Cambridge Univ. Press.

Taverner, P. A.
1938. Birds of Canada. London: J. Murray.

Taylor, Julian
1953. A possible moult-migration of Pink-footed Geese. Ibis 95 (4):638–641.

Thompson, Ernest E.
1891. The birds of Manitoba. Proc. U.S. National Museum 13:457–643.

Thomson, A. Landsborough
1929. Birds, migration of. In Encyclopaedia Britannica, Vol. 3.
1942. Bird migration (2nd rev. ed.). London: Witherby.
1953. The study of the visible migration of birds: An introductory review. Ibis 95 (2):165–180.

Thorpe, W. H.

1944. Some problems of animal learning. Proc. Linnean Soc. of London, Session 156, Part 2, pp. 70–83.

1948. The modern concept of instinctive behavior. Bull. of Animal Behaviour 7:2–12.

1949. Recent biological evidence for methods of bird orientation. Proc. Linnean Soc. of London, Session 160, Part 2, pp. 85–94.

1950. The concepts of learning and their relation to those of instinct. Symposia of Society for Experimental Biology No. 4, Physiological Mechanisms in Animal Behaviour. Cambridge, England: Cambridge Univ. Press.

1951a. The definition of some terms used in animal behavior studies. Bull. of Animal Behaviour 9:34–40.

1951b. The learning abilities of birds. Ibis 93 (1):1–52, 252–296.

1954. The process of song-learning in the Chaffinch as studied by means of the sound spectrograph. Nature 173:465.

Tinbergen, L.
1941. Over de rol van de Hollandse duinrij bij de oriëntatie van trekkende vinken en spreeuwen. Limosa 14:1–20.

Tinbergen, Nikolaas
1939a. The behavior of the Snow Bunting in spring. Trans. Linnaean Soc. of New York 5:1–95.

1939b. On the analysis of social organization among vertebrates, with special reference to birds. Amer. Midland Naturalist 21 (1):210–234.

1942. An objectivistic study of the innate behaviour of animals. Bibliotheca biotheoretica 1:37–98.

1948. Social releasers. Wilson Bull. 60 (1):6–51.

1950. The hierarchical organization of nervous mechanisms underlying instinctive behavior. Symposia of Society for Experimental Biology No. 4, Physiological Mechanisms in Animal Behaviour, pp. 305–312. Cambridge, England: Cambridge Univ. Press.

1951. The study of instinct. Oxford: Clarendon Press.

1952. "Derived" activities; their causation, biological significance, origin, and emancipation during evolution. Quarterly Rev. of Biology 27 (1):1–32.

Trautman, Milton B.
1940. The birds of Buckeye Lake, Ohio. University of Michigan Misc. Pub., Museum of Zoology, No. 44. Ann Arbor, Mich.

Trewartha, Glenn T.
1937. An introduction to weather and climate. New York: McGraw-Hill.

United States Weather Bureau
1952. Normal weather charts for the Northern Hemisphere, Technical Paper No. 21, U.S. Dept. of Commerce, Washington, D.C.

Välikangas, J.
1933. Finnische Zugvögel aus englischen Vogeleiern. Vogelzug 4:159–166.

1951. The expansion of the Greenish Warbler in the Baltic area, especially in Finland, towards north and northwest, and its causes. Proc. 10th International Ornithological Congress (Uppsala, 1950), pp. 527–531.

Vanderplank, F. L.
1934. The effect of infra-red waves on Tawny Owls (Strix aluco). Proc. Zoological Soc. of London, pp. 505–507.

Van Riper, Walker, and E. R. Kalmbach
  1952. Homing not hindered by wing magnets. Science 115 (2995):577–578.
Varian, R. H.
  1948. Remarks on: "A preliminary study of a physical basis of bird migration." J. Applied Physics 19:306–307.
Viguier, C.
  1882. Le sens de l'orientation et ses organes. Revue philosophique de la France et de l'étranger 14:1–36.
Vogt, William
  1934. Evaluating the duck sanctuary. Trans. 20th Amer. Game Conference, pp. 267–271.
Walkinshaw, Lawrence H., and Bernard W. Baker
  1946. Notes on the birds of the Isle of Pines, Cuba. Wilson Bull. 58 (3):133–142.
Walls, G. L.
  1942. The vertebrate eye and its adaptive radiation. Cranbrook Institute of Science Bull. No. 19.
Ward, Peter.
  1953. The American Coot as a game bird. Trans. 18th North Amer. Wildlife Conference, pp. 322–327.
Waterhouse, M. J.
  1949. Rook and Jackdaw migrations observed in Germany, 1942–1945. Ibis 91 (1): 1–16.
Watson, J. B., and K. S. Lashley
  1915. An historical and experimental study of homing. Papers of Carnegie Institution of Washington, Dept. Marine Biology (Tortugas Laboratory), 7:1–60.
Wellein, Edward G., and Wesley Newcomb
  1953a. Aerial waterfowl breeding ground surveys in northern Saskatchewan and western Ontario, 1952. U.S. Fish and Wildlife Service, Special Scientific Report: Wildlife No. 25, pp. 103–107.
  1953b. Aerial waterfowl breeding ground exporations in sections of the Far North. U.S. Fish and Wildlife Service, Special Scientific Report: Wildlife No. 25, pp. 16–19.
Weller, Milton Webster
  1953a. Composition of waterfowl bag, Lake Winnipegosis, Manitoba. Manuscript report, Univ. of Missouri.
  1953b. Waterfowl bag check and flight data. Manuscript report, Univ. of Missouri.
  1954. Growth-rate and plumage development of the Redhead Duck (*Aythya americana*). Unpublished thesis, Univ. of Missouri.
Wells, Robert A.
  1954. What the states can do for waterfowl. Trans. 19th North Amer. Wildlife Conference, pp. 86–92.
Wendt, G. R.
  1951. Vestibular functions. In S. S. Stevens, ed., Handbook of experimental psychology. New York: Wiley.
Wetmore, Alexander
  1920. Observations on the habits of birds at Lake Burford, New Mexico. Auk 37:221–247, 393–412.

1921. Wild ducks and duck foods of the Bear River Marshes, Utah. U.S.D.A. Bull. No. 936.

1923. Migration records from wild ducks and other birds banded in the Salt Lake Valley, Utah. U.S.D.A., Dept. Bull. No. 1145.

1926. The migrations of birds. Cambridge, Mass.: Harvard Univ. Press.

1927. Our migrant shorebirds in southern South America. U.S.D.A., Technical Bull. No. 26.

Weyl, Hermann

1949. Philosophy of mathematics and natural science. Princeton, N.J.: Princeton Univ. Press.

White, E. F. G., and Harrison F. Lewis

1937. The Greater Snow Goose in Canada. Auk 54 (4):440–444.

Wilkinson, D. H.

1949. Some physical principles of bird orientation. Proc. Linnean Soc. of London, Session 160, Part 2, pp. 94–99.

1952. The random element in bird "navigation." J. Exper. Biol. 29 (4):532–560.

Williams, Cecil S.

1944. Migration of the Redhead from the Utah breeding grounds. Auk 61 (2):251–259.

———, and E. R. Kalmbach

1943. Migration and fate of transported juvenile waterfowl. J. Wildlife Management 7 (2):163–169.

Williams, George G.

1945. Do birds cross the Gulf of Mexico in spring? Auk 62 (1):98–111.

1947. Lowery on trans-Gulf migrations. Auk 64 (2):217–238.

1950a. Weather and spring migration. Auk 67 (1):52–65.

1950b. The nature and causes of the "Coastal Hiatus." Wilson Bull. 62 (4):175–182.

Williamson, Kenneth

1952. Migrational drift in Britain in autumn 1951. Scottish Naturalist 64:1–18.

1953. Migration into Britain from the northwest, autumn 1952. Scottish Naturalist 65:64–94.

1955. Migrational drift and the Yellow Wagtail complex. British Birds 48 (9):382–403.

Wilson, Alexander, and Charles Lucien Bonaparte

1832. American Ornithology, Vol. 1. Philadelphia: Porter and Coates.

Wister, Fanny Kemble

1955. Owen Wister's West. Atlantic Monthly 195 (5):29–35.

Witkin, H. A.

1953. Space orientation in man. Mimeographed report, American Museum of Natural History Conference on Orientation in Animals, Feb. 6–7, 1953.

Wodzicki, K., and Wojtusiak, R. J.

1934. Untersuchungen über die Orientation und Geschwindigkeit des Fluges bei Vögeln, I — Experimente an Schwalben (Hirundo rustica L.). Acta Ornithol. Mus. Zool. Polon., p. 1.

Wojtusiak, Roman J.

1949. Polish investigations on homing in birds and their orientation in space. Proc. Linnean Soc. of London, Session 160, Part 2, pp. 99–108.

Wolfson, Albert

1940. A preliminary report on some experiments on bird migration. Condor 42 (2): 93–99.

1941. Light versus activity in the regulation of the sexual cycles of birds: The role of the hypothalamus. Condor 43 (3):125–136.

1942. Regulation of spring migration in Juncos. Condor 44 (6):237–263.

1945. The role of the pituitary, fat deposition, and body weight in bird migration. Condor 47 (3):95–127.

1948. Bird migration and the concept of continental drift. Science 108 (2793):23–30.

1952. Day length, migration and breeding cycles in birds. Scientific Monthly 74 (4): 191–200.

1954. Weight and fat deposition in relation to spring migration in transient White-throated Sparrows. Auk 71 (4):413–434.

1955. Origin of the North American bird fauna: Critique and reinterpretation from the standpoint of the continental drift. Amer. Midland Naturalist 53 (2):353–380.

Woodcock, Alfred H.

1940. Observations on Herring Gull soaring. Auk 57 (2):219–224.

Woodrow, Herbert

1951. Time perception. In S. S. Stevens, ed., Handbook of experimental psychology. New York: Wiley.

Wright, Bruce S.

1954. High tide and an east Wind. Harrisburg: Stackpole and Heck.

Wynne-Edwards, V. C.

1935. On the habits and distribution of birds of the North Atlantic. Proc. Boston Soc. of Natural History 40 (4):233–346.

Yeagley, Henry L.

1947. A preliminary study of a physical basis of bird navigation. J. Applied Physics 18 (12):1035–1063.

1951. A preliminary study of a physical basis of bird navigation, II. J. Applied Physics 22 (6):746–760.

Yocom, Charles F.

1947. Observations on bird life in the Pacific Ocean off the North American shores. Condor 49 (5):204–208.

Nomenclature of Birds

THIS is the list of birds mentioned in the foregoing discussions. These fall into three categories: those observed as transients, those to which other authors have referred, and those I have studied intimately. It would be quite improper to give exact racial identification for the first two categories, and I have been as conservative as possible in the binomial listing. In the waterfowl, however, I have tried to be precise and modern, following the classification suggested by Delacour and Mayr (1945) as presented by Scott (1951), acknowledging Delacour's (1954) more recent treatment of the geese.

Throughout the text I have capitalized the common name as given in the *A.O.U. Checklist of North American Birds,* 4th edition, 1931, with only a few modifications. I have referred simply to Junco and to Flicker, rather than to Slate-colored Junco and Northern Flicker, as there has been visual evidence that not all these abundant migrants are of the same race. Nor have I held to the geographic adjectives, such as American Coot, where Coot alone seemed clear and sufficient. Every school child in Manitoba knows the Red-winged Blackbird, but only a few citizens are aware of the Giant Red-wing; hence I have held to the older name. In general, the common name has been more stable than the Latin, but even here there are some puzzles. Moffitt (1937) wrote of the White-cheeked Goose, which is the Western Canada Goose of Scott and the Vancouver Canada Goose of Delacour. Should Shoveller be spelled with two *l*'s, as by Delacour and Mayr (1945) and by the Canadian Wildlife Service, or with one *l*, as by Scott (1951) and the U.S. Fish and Wildlife Service? Shall Wigeon (for *Anas penelope*) retain its European heredity, which lacks the *d*; or when speaking of the bird as North Americans, shall we hold with the American Ornithologists' Union and call it Widgeon?

On page 239 of the text I mentioned that only one North American game duck showed subspecific variation. This may not be entirely true as things now stand. The Green-winged Teal apparently has a subspecies on the Aleutian Islands, *Anas crecca nimia,* while there may be a Pacific and an Atlantic race of the White-winged Scoter, *Melanitta fusca dixoni* and *M. f. deglandi.* Balancing these minor divisions there is the conservative revision of the Harlequin Duck, whereby the birds of the eastern and western ranges are now considered to be of one and the same race. The Black Duck is currently considered to be merely a race of *Anas fulvigula* (Delacour and Mayr, 1945; Scott, 1951). The Black Duck travels in winter as far south as the winter quarters of both the Mottled Duck and the Florida Duck, evidence, perhaps, that the isolating mechanism by which the races of *fulvigula* remain distinct may not be so simple as set forth in the text. But it does hold that most of the Black Duck population winters north of these sedentary relatives.

NORTH AMERICAN BIRDS

Common Loon .... *Gavia immer*
Eared Grebe .... *Colymbus caspicus*
Western Grebe .... *Aechmophorus occidentalis*
Black-footed Albatross .... *Diomedea nigripes*
Leach's Petrel .... *Oceanodroma leucorhoa*
White Pelican .... *Pelecanus erythrorhynchos*
Great Blue Heron .... *Ardea herodias*
American Egret .... *Casmerodius albus*
Snowy Egret .... *Leucophoyx thula*
Black-crowned Night Heron .... *Nycticorax nycticorax*
American Bittern .... *Botaurus lentiginosus*
Whistling Swan .... *Olor columbianus*
Trumpeter Swan .... *Olor buccinator*
White-fronted Goose .... *Anser albifrons frontalis*
Lesser Snow Goose (Blue Goose) .... *Anser cærulescens cærulescens**
Greater Snow Goose .... *Anser cærulescens atlanticus*
Hawaiian Goose .... *Branta sandvicensis*†
Canada Goose .... *Branta canadensis interior*
Giant Canada Goose .... *Branta canadensis maxima*
Western Canada Goose .... *Branta canadensis occidentalis*
Richardson's Goose .... *Branta canadensis hutchinsi*
Pintail .... *Anas acuta*
Green-winged Teal .... *Anas crecca carolinensis*
Mallard .... *Anas platyrhynchos platyrhynchos*
Florida Duck .... *Anas fulvigula fulvigula*
Mottled Duck .... *Anas fulvigula maculosa*
Black Duck .... *Anas fulvigula rubripes*
Gadwall .... *Anas strepera*
Baldpate (American Widgeon) .... *Mareca americana*
Blue-winged Teal .... *Anas discors*
Cinnamon Teal .... *Anas cyanoptera*
Shoveller .... *Spatula clypeata*

* Following Delacour (1954:125), the Blue Goose being merely a color-phase of this species.
† Extra-limital, not appearing on the North American list.

Canvasback ....*Aythya valisineria*
Redhead ....*Aythya americana*
Ring-necked Duck ....*Aythya collaris*
Lesser Scaup ....*Aythya affinis*
Greater Scaup ....*Aythya marila nearctica*
Wood Duck ....*Aix sponsa*
Pacific Eider ....*Somateria mollissima v-nigra*
Northern Eider ....*Somateria mollissima borealis*
American Eider ....*Somateria mollissima dresseri*
Hudson Bay Eider ....*Somateria mollissima sedentaria*§
White-winged Scoter ....*Melanitta fusca deglandi*
Harlequin Duck ....*Histrionicus histrionicus***
Old Squaw ....*Clangula hyemalis*
Barrow's Golden-eye ....*Bucephala islandica*
American Golden-eye....................................*Bucephala clangula americana*
Bufflehead ....*Bucephala albeola*
Red-breasted Merganser ....*Mergus serrator*
American Merganser ....*Mergus merganser americanus*
Ruddy Duck ....*Oxyura jamaicensis jamaicensis*
Goshawk...*Accipiter gentilis*
Sharp-shinned Hawk ....*Accipiter straitus*
Cooper's Hawk ....*Accipiter cooperii*
Red-tailed Hawk ....*Buteo jamaicensis*
American Rough-legged Hawk ....*Buteo lagopus*
Bald Eagle ....*Haliæetus leucocephalus*
Marsh Hawk ....*Circus cyaneus*
Osprey ....*Pandion haliætus*
Duck Hawk ....*Falco peregrinus*
Pigeon Hawk ....*Falco columbarius*
Sparrow Hawk ....*Falco sparverius*
Heath Hen ....*Tympanuchus cupido cupido*
Prairie Chicken ....*Tympanuchus cupido pinnatus*
Sharp-tailed Grouse ....*Pediœcetes phasianellus campestris*
Hungarian Partridge ....*Perdix perdix*
Whooping Crane ....*Grus americana*
Little Brown Crane ....*Grus canadensis canadensis*
Sandhill Crane ....*Grus canadensis tabida*
Florida Crane ....*Grus canadensis pratensis*
Cuban Sandhill Crane ....*Grus canadensis nesiotes* †
Coot ....*Fulica americana*

§ Auk 63 (3):429 (July 1946).

** "*Histrionicus histrionicus pacificus* Brooks is now considered inseparable from the eastern, nominate, form. The Harlequin Duck thus reverts to binomial status . . ." — Auk 71(3):310 (July 1954).

Golden Plover ....*Pluvialis dominica*
Black-bellied Plover ....*Squatarola squatarola*
Woodcock ....*Philohela minor*
Wilson's Snipe ....*Capella gallinago*
Eskimo Curlew ....*Numenius borealis*
Upland Plover ....*Bartramia longicauda*
Lesser Yellow-legs ....*Totanus flavipes*
Long-tailed Jaeger ....*Stercorarius longicaudus*
Franklin's Gull ....*Larus pipixcan*
Arctic Tern ....*Sterna paradisæa*
Sooty Tern ....*Sterna fuscata*
Noddy Tern ....*Anous stolidus*
Domestic Pigeon ....*Columba livia*
Passenger Pigeon ....*Ectopistes migratorius*
Carolina Paroquet ....*Conuropsis carolinensis*
Great Horned Owl ....*Bubo virginianus*
Flicker ....*Colaptes auratus*
Downy Woodpecker ....*Dendrocopus pubescens*
Arkansas Kingbird ....*Tyrannus verticalis*
Tree Swallow ....*Iridoprocne bicolor*
Barn Swallow ....*Hirundo rustica*
Cliff Swallow ....*Petrochelidon pyrrhonota*
Canada Jay ....*Perisoreus canadensis*
Blue Jay ....*Cyanocitta cristata*
Magpie ....*Pica Pica*
Raven ....*Corvus corax*
Crow ....*Corvus brachyrhynchos*
Black-capped Chickadee ....*Parus atricapillus*
Catbird ....*Dumatella carolinensis*
Robin ....*Turdus migratorius*
Starling ....*Sturnus vulgaris*
Yellow Warbler ....*Dendroica petechia*
English Sparrow ....*Passer domesticus*
Bobolink ....*Dolichonyx oryzivorus*
Western Meadowlark ....*Sturnella neglecta*
Yellow-headed Blackbird ....*Xanthocephalus xanthocephalus*
Red-winged Blackbird ....*Agelaius phoeniceus*
Baltimore Oriole ....*Icterus glabula*
Rusty Blackbird ....*Euphagus carolinus*
Brewer's Blackbird ....*Euphagus cyanocephalus*
Bronzed Grackle ....*Quiscalus quiscala*
Cowbird ....*Molothrus ater*
Evening Grosbeak ....*Hesperiphona vespertina*
Pine Siskin ....*Spinus pinus*

287

Vesper Sparrow .... *Poœcetes gramineus*
Slate-colored Junco .... *Junco hyemalis*
Oregon Junco .... *Junco oreganus*
Tree Sparrow .... *Spizella arborea*
Song Sparrow .... *Melospiza melodia*
Lapland Longspur .... *Calcarius lapponicus*
Snow Bunting .... *Plectrophenax nivalis*

EUROPEAN BIRDS

Manx Shearwater .... *Procellaria puffinus*
Common Sheld-duck .... *Tadorna tadorna*
Pink-footed Goose .... *Anser arvensis brachyrhynchus*
Wigeon (European Widgeon) .... *Anas penelope*
Sparrow Hawk .... *Accipiter nisus*
Pheasant .... *Phasianus colchicus*
Ringed Plover .... *Charadrius hiaticula*
Woodcock .... *Scolopax rusticola*
Lesser Black-backed Gull .... *Larus fuscus*
Herring Gull .... *Larus argentatus*
Collared Turtle Dove .... *Streptopelia decaocto*
Alpine Swift .... *Apus melba*
Swallow .... *Hirundo rustica*
Hooded Crow .... *Corvus cornix*
Rook .... *Corvus frugilegus*
Jackdaw .... *Corvus monedula*
Great Tit .... *Parus major*
Fieldfare .... *Turdus pilaris*
Robin .... *Erithacus rubecula*
Chaffinch .... *Fringilla coelebs*
Yellow Wagtail .... *Motacilla flava*
Red-backed Shrike .... *Lanius collurio*

Acknowledgments

T<small>HIS</small> is the fifty-first technical dissertation (and third book °) resulting from the cooperative studies of the Delta Waterfowl Research Station. The scientific program at Delta, Manitoba, was founded in 1931 by James F. Bell, of Minneapolis, who established the buildings and equipment necessary for biological research at the edge of a great breeding marsh. For the opportunity of using these materials in an ideal wild location, within an atmosphere of complete academic freedom, and for countless courtesies, I am grateful to Mr. Bell.

From 1931 to 1939 the Station was operated by Edward Ward, of Delta, who pioneered many new techniques in the captive-breeding of wild ducks. In 1938 the American Wildlife Institute joined to share sponsorship with Mr. Bell, and at this time, under the counsel of Professor Aldo Leopold, Dr. Miles D. Pirnie, and Dr. William Rowan, the plan of research by university graduate students was established. A heavy debt of gratitude is due these gentlemen.

Sponsorship was transferred to the Wildlife Management Institute in 1945; then in 1950 the North American Wildlife Foundation, with its international Board of Directors, assumed responsibility for sponsorship, the Wildlife Management Institute remaining the administrative organization. To the directors, officers, and members of these two organizations my colleagues and I at Delta are grateful for the opportunity of continuing studies under an expanding program, with improved living and working facilities. Especially helpful have been Max Mcgraw, of Chicago, President of the North American Wildlife Foundation; Colonel Arthur Sullivan, Q.C., of Winnipeg; Robert M. Gaylord, of Rockford; Glenn L. Martin, of Baltimore; W. A. Murphy, John B. Richardson, and H. E. Sellers, all of Winnipeg; and Herbert J. Symington, Q.C., and R. Howard Webster, both of Montreal.

The Station has depended heavily upon the ready counsel of the Canadian Wildlife Service and has appreciated the annual grants of permits for special studies. The Manitoba Department of Mines and Natural Resources and the Manitoba Game and Fisheries Branch have been generous with manpower, equipment, and services. The National Research Council of Canada has con-

° H. Albert Hochbaum, *The Canvasback on a Prairie Marsh*, 1944; Lyle K. Sowls, *Prairie Ducks*, 1955.

tributed funds to this and to other Delta studies. The Royal Canadian Air Force has given the Station assistance of a very specialized kind. The National Film Board of Canada, the Canadian Broadcasting Corporation, and the Manitoba Museum have supplied manpower and equipment. The U.S. Fish and Wildlife Service has worked closely with the Station since its beginning. We have benefited from the close association with Ducks Unlimited over a period of many years. The Severn Wildfowl Trust (now the Wildfowl Trust) has had a profound influence on my own studies and upon Delta operations as a whole. The Manitoba Federation of Game and Fish Associations has been a continual source of information and support. Canadian Industries Ltd. has been an enthusiastic participator in the Delta program. The New York State Conservation Department and the Wisconsin Conservation Department have been collaborators during several seasons. Borden Productions and the Moody Bible Institute have been our fellow workers. All but one of these agencies have stationed a man at Delta to carry out special projects, some for only a part of a season, others each spring for many years. Cornell University, Illinois College, and the universities of Alberta, Bristol, British Columbia, Manitoba, Minnesota, Missouri, and Wisconsin have carried out postgraduate investigations of various phases of waterfowl biology.

In addition to these organizations, every individual member working at Delta has in some way or other contributed to the development of this book. The task of making individual acknowledgments for the help and criticism that have been given so freely by so many over such a long period is therefore overwhelming. The book was started ten years ago after a series of separate discussions with James F. Bell, Dr. William Rowan, of the University of Alberta, Robert H. Smith, of the U.S. Fish and Wildlife Service, Peter Ward, of Delta, and Dr. Lyle K. Sowls. Especially important has been the generous and detailed advice of Robert L. Lillestrand, of General Mills Research Laboratories, to whom I owe a great deal for the development of the discussions on the physics and aerodynamics of flight. The original Delta investigations of Lyle Sowls on the homing behavior of waterfowl have given foundation to important sections of the book, and the keen field ability of Peter Ward has been the source of much original material. Margaret M. Nice, of the Wilson Ornithological Club, gave me the first critical review; I owe her much for this and for the help she gave me during her years at Delta. The manuscript grew from critical readings by Dr. Walter J. Breckenridge, Dr. William H. Marshall, and Dr. Dwain W. Warner, of the University of Minnesota; Dr. John E. Cushing, University of California; Dr. Ira N. Gabrielson, Wildlife Management Institute; Dr. Donald R. Griffin and Dr. Ernst Mayr, Harvard University; and E. R. Kalmbach, U.S. Fish and Wildlife Service. Dr. Rowan read the manuscript at many stages from start to finish, and I have depended heavily upon his lucid, stimulating criticisms. Dr. Frank McKinney, of Delta, helped me organize the final copy for publication. I am heavily in debt to these friends for the time they have spent and the clear and detailed guidance they have given me.

The chapters on perception and memory lean heavily on discussions with J. Ford Bell, Jr., of Minneapolis, and Dr. Robert Galambos, of Walter Reed Medical Center. J. Donald Smith, of the U.S. Fish and Wildlife Service, helped with the chapter on oceanic migration. Glenn L. Martin and G. S. Trimble, Jr., of the Glenn L. Martin Company, read the chapters on "The Aerial Environment" and "The Dimensions of Travel," presenting a number of important suggestions. Edward G. Wellein, of the U.S. Fish and Wildlife Service, also assisted me with these chapters. The original studies of blindfolded birds were made by William Carrick, of the Royal Ontario Museum. Aldo Missio, of the Royal Canadian Air Force Weather Station, Macdonald, Manitoba, advised me on the interpretation of meteorological data. The shape of the final discussion in chapters 11 and 15 was greatly influenced by the 1955 visit to Delta of Dr. G. V. T. Matthews, of the Wildfowl Trust. Dr. John E. Cushing and Peter Scott, M.B.E., D.S.C., inspired many ideas developed in the chapters on tradition. Robert M. Gaylord and Arthur S. Hawkins gave me good advice for Chapter 19. Dr. Herbert Friedmann, of the U.S. National Museum, Dr. M. D. F. Udvardy, of the University of British Columbia, and Mrs. Nice guided me to important European literature. The following persons have all given me critical readings and detailed suggestions: Bessie Schenck Bunten, Washington, D.C.; Eugene F. Bossenmaier, University of Minnesota; Dr. Warren W. Chase, University of Michigan; Dr. Nicholas E. Collias, Illinois College; Graham Cooch, J. Bernard Gollop, and Nolan G. Perret, Canadian Wildlife Service; Dr. Ian McTaggart Cowan, University of British Columbia; Dr. William H. Elder, University of Missouri; C. R. Gutermuth and James B. Trefethen, Wildlife Management Institute; Merrill C. Hammond and John C. Lynch, U.S. Fish and Wildlife Service; Dr. Eckhard H. Hess, University of Chicago; Dr. J. J. Hickey, University of Wisconsin; A. G. Lawrence, *Winnipeg Free Press*; G. W. Malaher, Manitoba Game and Fisheries Branch; H. W. Murdy, South Dakota Department of Game, Fish and Parks; Dr. H. T. Odum, Yale University; Father P. M. Plunkett and Father C. C. Ryan, St. Paul's College, Winnipeg; Carl D. Shoemaker, National Wildlife Federation, and Walker Van Riper, Colorado Museum of Natural History. But I must not carry this list further, for there are many more who have helped, these having been mentioned in the text or thanked personally.

I thank Doris E. Franklin and Jane McCarthy, of the University of Minnesota Press, for the warm and sympathetic manner in which they have shaped the book from manuscript and drawings. Aileen Burton, Pat Martin, and Doris Weller typed parts of the many manuscripts. Beverly Dillon, Brenda McKinney, and Dorothy Richardson, together with Dr. Fred Cadham, helped me with the proof. I am indebted to members of the Station staff, especially Norman Godfrey, Nan

Mulder, Ray Burton, and Les Garnham, and their families. The members of the Hutchinson, Loucks, and MacDonald families, together with numerous other friends in the Village of Delta, have been always helpful. Many sportsmen and farmers in the city and rural municipality of Portage la Prairie, in Winnipeg, and throughout the province have been a continual source of information about the waterfowl of Manitoba.

Finally, I am ever grateful to my wife Joan and to my children, who, together with my parents and members of the Ward family, have encouraged me toward the completion of this book. Nor, in spring, summer, and fall, could I have learned half so much about the waterfowl of the Delta Marsh without good old faithful Tim, a Black Labrador Retriever.

Index of Authorities

Subject Index